THE NORTH-EAST OF SCOTLAND

A survey prepared for the Aberdeen
Meeting of the British Association
for the Advancement of Science, 1963

PUBLISHED BY THE LOCAL COMMITTEE

THE CENTRAL PRESS, ABERDEEN

1963

Printed on paper made in
Aberdeenshire

PRINTED IN GREAT BRITAIN BY
THE CENTRAL PRESS (ABERDEEN) LTD.

PREFACE

WHILE this handbook has been prepared to assist British Association members on the occasion of the Meeting in Aberdeen in 1963 it is also hoped that it will be of interest to local residents and others as an account of North-East Scotland. The preparation has been aided by the willing co-operation of many people. Most of the burden of map compilation and drawing was undertaken by Mrs. M. J. F. Barnett of the Geography Department. We are indebted to the Controller of H.M. Stationery Office for permission to publish Figure 1 based on an official map, and to Thomas Nelson & Sons Ltd. for the use of the map on which Figure 11 was based.

Further recent publications which are of interest to visitors and students of the North-East are *Forests of North East Scotland* (Edited by H. L. Edlin (H.M.S.O., 1963)) and the Aberdeen number of the *Scottish Geographical Magazine* issued by the Royal Scottish Geographical Society on the occasion of this British Association meeting.

Enquiries as to the supply of further copies of this volume should be directed to the Geography Department at the University of Aberdeen.

Editorial work has been greatly eased by Dr. Charles H. Gimingham editing and proofing the physical science sections, and Mr. Joseph H. Smith the sections on agriculture, forestry and fisheries and Dr. W. P. D. Wightman the concluding sections from page 209 onwards. Miss Margaret A. Stephen assisted with proof-reading.

Finally, but not least, the task of publication was made easier by the guidance and skill of Dr. John N. Milne of the Central Press, Aberdeen, and the cartographical firm of John Bartholomew & Son Ltd., of Edinburgh.

A. C. O'DELL.
J. MACKINTOSH.

CONTENTS

	PAGE
PREFACE	V

THE SETTING 1
Andrew C. O'Dell, M.Sc., F.R.S.E., Professor of Geography.

THE GEOLOGY AND STRUCTURE 3
William E. Fraser, M.A., B.Sc., Ph.D., F.G.S., Department of Geology.
Fig. 1. Geological map (based on 1:625,000 map with the sanction of the Controller of H.M. Stationery Office and the Director of the Geological Survey (Scotland)); p. 4.

GEOMORPHOLOGY 16
Kenneth Walton, M.A., Ph.D., Department of Geography.
Fig. 2. Physiographic diagram, p. 18.
Fig. 3. Aspects of the geomorphology, p. 19.
Fig. 4. Morphology of the low dune fringed coasts north of Aberdeen, p. 26.
Fig. 5. Coastal features near Loch of Strathbeg, p. 27

CLIMATE 33
Kenneth Walton, M.A., Ph.D., Department of Geography.
Fig. 6. Procession of temperature at Dyce, 1961, p. 34.

SOILS 38
Robert Glentworth, B.S.A., Ph.D., Soil Survey of Scotland, Macaulay Institute.
Fig. 7. Soil map, p. 42.

FLORA 46
J. Grant Rogers, B.Sc., The Nature Conservancy.

FAUNA 54
George M. Dunnet, B.Sc., Ph.D., Department of Natural History, and Adam Watson, B.Sc., Ph.D., Nature Conservancy Unit of Grouse and Moorland Ecology.

THE REGION BEFORE 1700 70
W. Douglas Simpson, C.B.E., M.A., D.Litt., LL.D., F.S.A., F.S.A.Scot., University Library.
Fig. 8. Standing stones, p. 73.
Fig. 9. Vitrified, Gallic and other Forts, p. 74.
Fig. 10. Pictish symbol stones, p. 78.
Fig. 11. Castle sites (by permission of Thomas Nelson & Sons, Ltd.), p. 80.

PAGE

REGIONAL SETTLEMENT 87
Kenneth Walton, M.A., Ph.D., Department of Geography.
Fig. 12. Settlement pattern from survey of William Roy, 1747-55, p. 89.
Fig. 13. Settlement pattern from the atlas of James Thomson, 1828, p. 90.
Fig. 14. Selected planned settlements of the North-East, p. 95.

FISHING VILLAGES, 1750-1880 100
Malcolm Gray, M.A., Department of Political Economy.

AGRICULTURE 107
John R. Raeburn, B.Sc.Agr., M.S., Ph.D., M.A., F.R.S.E., Strathcona-
Fordyce Professor of Agriculture.

FORESTRY 118
William M. McNeill, M.B.E., T.D., M.A., M.S., Dip.For., Department
of Forestry.
Fig. 15. State forests, native pine woods and research stations, p. 121.

FISHERIES 129
Bennet B. Rae, M.A., B.Sc., Ph.D., F.R.S.E., Marine Laboratory, Torry.
Fig. 16. Methods of fishing used in the North-East, p. 130.
Fig. 17. The fishing industry, p. 132.

INDUSTRIES AND COMMERCE 140
Henry Hamilton, M.A., D.Litt., Jaffray Professor of Political Economy.
Fig. 18. Distilleries, p. 153.
Fig. 19. Granite outcrops and quarries (open and closed), p. 159.
Fig. 20. The granite industry of Aberdeen city.
Fig. 21. Passenger transport facilities, summer 1962, p. 186.

POPULATION CHANGES 193
Andrew C. O'Dell, M.Sc., F.R.S.E., Professor of Geography.
Fig. 22. Graph of population changes, 1755-1961, p. 194.
Fig. 23. Parish population change, 1931-51, p. 194.
Fig. 24. Percentage change of population of urban areas, 1931-51, p. 196.

LOCAL DIALECTS 196
David D. Murison, B.A., M.A., Department of English.
Fig. 25. Dialect districts, p. 200.

LOCAL GOVERNMENT IN SCOTLAND 203
J. C. Rennie, B.L., Town Clerk, City of Aberdeen.
Fig. 26. Changes in the boundaries of Aberdeen City, 1871-1952, p. 205.

PAGE

SCHOOLS 209
J. Mackintosh, M.A., formerly Principal Teacher of History, Robert
Gordon's College.
Figs. 27-29. School rolls in 1874, 1901 and 1962, pp. 210-11.

ABERDEEN UNIVERSITY 215
W. Douglas Simpson, C.B.E., M.A., D.Litt., LL.D., F.S.A., F.S.A.Scot.,
University Library.

RESEARCH INSTITUTES 221
William P. D. Wightman, M.Sc., Ph.D., F.R.S.E., Department of History
and Philosophy of Science.

TECHNICAL EDUCATION 226
J. R. Clark, M.A., B.Sc., Ed.B., Director of Education, City of Aberdeen.

ABERDEEN COLLEGE OF EDUCATION 231
John L. Hardie, M.A., Ed.B., F.E.I.S., formerly Principal, College of
Education, Aberdeen.

LOCAL SCIENTIFIC SOCIETIES 233
Henry J. H. Drummond, M.A., University Library.

THE MUSEUMS 235
Charles Carter, M.Sc., Director, Aberdeen Art Gallery and Museums.

THE HIGHLAND FOLK MUSEUM AT KINGUSSIE 238
George Davidson, Senior Research Fellow in Scottish Arts and Crafts.

SCIENTISTS OF THE REGION 240
William P. D. Wightman, M.Sc., Ph.D., F.R.S.E., Department of History
and Philosophy of Science.

INDEX 253

THE SETTING

THE knuckle of North-East Scotland projecting from the Grampians and with a long coast to the North Sea has a distinctive character of its own. In its various aspects there is a unique combination of qualities which gives the North-East a sense of entity equivalent to that of a French *pays*.

The area generally taken as the North-East is that of the counties of Aberdeenshire, Banffshire and Kincardineshire but for the purposes of this volume Moray and Nairnshire are often included although they tend to look to Inverness or Perth for their regional capital. Kincardineshire is not completely of the North-East because the southern part turns towards Angus and Dundee.

It is not satisfactory to take as the region the area which looks to Aberdeen as its regional capital because, for example, the Orkneys and the Shetland Islands are within the sphere of influence of the city as regards newspaper publishing and hospital services and are part of the area supplying students to the university. Transport links by land, sea and air do much to extend the sphere of influence eccentrically to the north and northwest as compared with the south and southwest.

Land transport links are modified by relief and the limitation to the south is largely due to the barrier effect of the Grampians which reach the coast immediately south of Aberdeen. It is true that the eastern sector of these is lower but even so the Mounth roads are sharply graded, railways were unable to cross and so there is a funnelling of routeways across the low plateau surface of north Kincardineshire to the crossing of the Dee near its mouth. The ancient bridges of Dee and Balgownie have long brought travellers and trade into the city of Aberdeen. There is no such barrier towards Moray and road and rail traffic can readily pass from Aberdeen to this rich, dry lowland zone.

Aberdeen is the largest agglomeration of population north of the Forth and, although size is not a particularly valuable criterion, with its industrial, commercial and professional activities the city has an influence relatively far more important than there would be with a city of the same population in the Midlands of England. Part of this importance is due to geographical factors and part to historical. Since the geographical features are being presented more fully in the special Aberdeen number of the *Scottish Geographical Magazine* to be issued on the occasion of this British Association meeting they are only presented in outline in this volume.

The city of Aberdeen grew up as twin-towns with the ecclesiastical town near the mouth of the Don and the port and commercial town near the mouth of the Dee. Despite, or more probably because of, the hard conditions of the

1

North-East, men worked hard and made a success of their studies or their business. If they migrated to warmer climes then the rigid schooling they had received in formative years could come to their aid in gathering fame or fortune in the easier south. The record of emigrants from the North-East as soldiers, doctors, merchants and scholars is an impressive one and surely can be attributed as much to earlier environment as to ethnic characteristics. The late Professor James Ritchie said that the Aberdonian had ' a bent for minute, detailed work; for accuracy in small things '—a characteristic commonly found in the North-East and surely an excellent foundation for science as well as other walks of life.

One historical event which still moulds the character of the North-East was the founding of the University by Bishop Elphinstone in 1495. This, conjoined in 1860 with Marischal College (founded in 1593), gave a chance of education to a poorly endowed region. The University today is moving from its long-held position as a regional university to one drawing on an ever-increasing proportion of its students from south of the Border. Its increasing size is bringing many changes including that of becoming a leading employer in the town. Some traditional industries are tending to die but if the University by 1975 has 4,500 students in residence then it will be a major economic factor in the well-being of the city. It is to be hoped that the long existing good feeling between Town and Gown will be maintained with these new circumstances.

The first head of a Department of Geography in the University was John McFarlane and he wrote vividly of the position of Aberdeen in the *Scientific Survey of Aberdeen and District* presented to the British Association at its meeting in 1934 :

'A visitor to Aberdeen, taken to Rubislaw Quarry on the western margin of the city and shown the surrounding country from the height of a small eminence there, might at first be surprised to learn that, if he were to proceed due west from where he stood, it would be necessary for him to cross North America, Asia, and part of Europe before he came to or passed to the south of, a town as large as that which lay at his feet. Only when he reached the shores of the Baltic would he find Leningrad, Stockholm, and a few other towns lying in or beyond the latitude of Aberdeen, and equalling or surpassing it in importance.'

The situation has somewhat changed in over a quarter of a century. Settlements have been growing in the northern regions of Asia and of North America, north of the latitude of Aberdeen. Aberdeen is the most northerly university city in Britain and so to many folk is regarded as a northern outpost.

This, the largest urban unit north of the Forth, prides itself on the welcome offered to visitors, epitomised on civic occasions by the toast, ' Bon Accord —happy to meet, sorry to part, happy to meet again.'

THE GEOLOGY AND STRUCTURE

This article incorporates excerpts from an article, by the same author, on the ' Physical Features and Geology of North-East Scotland ' printed in the Forestry Commission Guide to the Forests of North-East Scotland. These excerpts and the geological map of North-East Scotland are reproduced by courtesy of the Forestry Commission.

Geology

THE main features of the geology of North-East Scotland are indicated in Figure 1. The geological succession and the main geological events in the area can be summarised as follows:

Quaternary. *Recent* rock screes, river alluvium, bog-peat, raised beach deposits and coastal sand dunes.

Pleistocene boulder clays, with fluvio-glacial sands and gravels, covering practically the entire area.

Tertiary. Practically unrepresented except for ? *Pliocene* gravels, found very occasionally at 350 ft. to 400 ft. in the Buchan area of Aberdeenshire.

Mesozoic. Practically unrepresented.

Upper Palaeozoic. *Permo-Triassic* desert sandstones around Lossiemouth.

Permo-Carboniferous movements, slight in North-East Scotland.

Upper Old Red Sandstone around Elgin and near Dundee.

Middle Old Red Sandstone in patches north of River Dee.

Lower Old Red Sandstone and associated *Volcanic Rocks* in area southeast of the Highland Boundary fault.

Intrusion of *Basic Igneous Rocks* and *Granites* in the highland area: the former mainly confined to area north of River Don; the latter far more widespread, but with their main development near the valley of the River Dee.

Main *Caledonian Orogeny*, when the Scottish Highlands were uplifted as a major mountain chain.

Lower Palaeozoic. *Downtonian*, in the Stonehaven area, resting unconformably on Cambro-Ordovician *Highland Border Series*, the latter occurring in a very narrow intermittent strip along the line of the Highland Boundary fault.

Pre-Cambrian. *Metamorphic Schists and Gneisses*, mainly of the *Dalradian Series*, but including, towards the extreme west, members of the *Central Highland Granulites*. These rocks are mainly former sediments, laid down in geosynclinal troughs probably during Pre-Cambrian times, but they also include associated igneous rocks, often basic in character. After extensive metamorphism, this succession was uplifted into a mountain chain during the Caledonian Orogeny.

The *Metamorphic Schists and Gneisses* are former geosynclinal sediments and associated contemporaneous igneous rocks, all of which have been metamorphosed to form a great variety of rock-types. Two main series are represented: the *Central Highland Granulites*, to the west of the area under consideration, and the *Dalradian* rocks, which occupy the majority of the highland area (Read and MacGregor, 1948). The former are typically pale

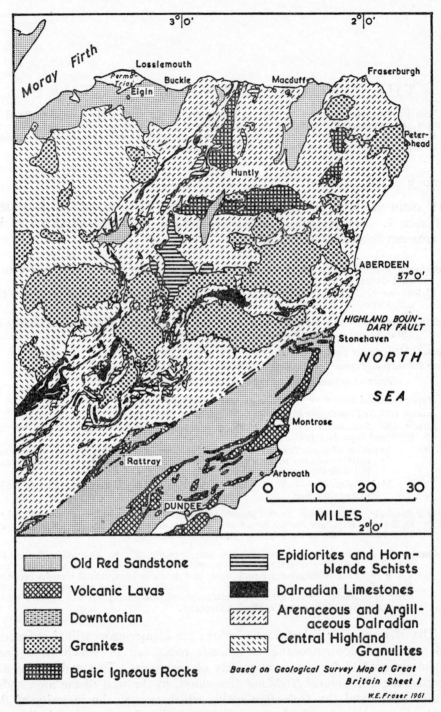

Old Red Sandstone
Volcanic Lavas
Downtonian
Granites
Basic Igneous Rocks
Epidiorites and Horn-blende Schists
Dalradian Limestones
Arenaceous and Argill-aceous Dalradian
Central Highland Granulites

Based on Geological Survey Map of Great Britain Sheet I

W.E. Fraser 1961

Fig. 1. Based on Crown Copyright Geological Survey map, by permission of the Controller of H.M. Stationery Office.

grey in colour and can be broken readily into flaggy slabs along micaceous divisional planes. The latter consist mainly of grey or rusty-grey micaceous schists and gneisses but also include divers other rock-types: pale quartzites, grey or grey-brown clay-slates, silvery phyllites, grey knotted phyllites, rusty garnetiferous schists and gneisses, black graphite schists, and greyish-white limestones, the latter frequently interleaved with darker impure bands.

The age of these former sediments is generally accepted as Pre-Cambrian (Giletti, Moorbath and Lambert, 1961) and no direct evidence to the contrary has yet been recorded. Portions of the Dalradian are, however, sometimes assigned to the Lower Palaeozoic on the basis of correlations either with the Highland Border Series (Anderson, 1947), across the Highland Boundary fault, or with the metamorphosed Palaeozoic rocks of Scandinavia (Holtedahl, 1952; Kolderup, 1935; Kvale, 1953), across the North Sea. Within the area of Dalradian rocks, on the other hand, correlations with the Perthshire succession (Read and MacGregor, 1948) become increasingly tentative as one moves northwards, for lack of exposures makes it very difficult to follow any horizon across the ground. North of Deeside, the standard Dalradian section is that of the Banffshire coast, where Read (1936) has recognised two major divisions, the Keith and the Banff, separated by the discordant Boyne Line. These divisions have been further subdivided into lithological groups, some of which have been traced inland in a general way (Read, 1955).

Various grades of regional metamorphism are developed. The lowest grades are found immediately north of the Highland Boundary fault and in a belt stretching southwards from Macduff towards the Glens of Foudland; the highest grades occur along Deeside, along a belt near the western margin of the Dalradian, i.e. in the Keith division, and in a belt running northwards from Ellon. Northwards from the Highland Border, progressive metamorphism may be marked by the successive appearance of the minerals chlorite, biotite, garnet, staurolite, kyanite, and sillimanite (Barrow, 1893, 1912; Harry, 1958; Phemister, Fraser, and Williamson, 1960); the low grade clay-slates of the belt from Macduff to the Glens of Foudland are followed to the west, south, and east by higher grade phyllites with knots or crystals of andalusite.

In the belts of highest metamorphism, migmatites are frequently developed (Barrow, 1892, 1893, 1912; Read, 1927, 1952; Harry, 1958; Phemister, Fraser, and Williamson, 1960). The rocks include veined schists and gneisses, lit-par-lit gneisses, granitic gneisses, agmatites, streaky xenolithic gneissose granites, and nebulitic granites. Some of these rocks have been sufficiently mobile to intrude the surrounding rocks. Under such movements, fluxion mixing took place to such an extent that, although the rock is still demonstrably hetero-geneous, its constituent members may be so streaked out in the direction of flow that their former relationships can no longer be deduced. The finest development of such migmatites is near Aberdeen, where the distinction between 'older' granites of the migmatite belt and 'younger' intrusive granites is sometimes very difficult to apply.

The most resistant metamorphic rocks are the quartzites, which frequently form high ground (e.g. Bin of Cullen, Durn Hill, and Mormond Hill). In areas of more diverse geology, the ridges are often ribbed and reinforced by quartz-rich bands. During deformation, the quartzites acted as competent members, so the minor structures that they display are less intricate than those shown by both the argillaceous and the calcareous rocks. These quartzite structures can nevertheless be extremely complex: on occasion the rocks are rodded (e.g. Cullen—Portsoy) or rolled into larger cigar-shaped mullions; in practically every case, the original detrital grains have been recrystallised to give an interlocking mosaic of sutured grains.

The least resistant rocks are the limestones, which are usually so poorly exposed that their outcrops have frequently to be deduced from the vegetation. The best exposures of limestone occur towards the western margin of the Dalradian in flat-lying belts at considerable elevations (e.g. near Braemar). In steep belts, the rock is usually etched out by drainage channels; it is nowhere sufficiently extensive to form large swallow holes. The limestone is now worked as a source of agricultural lime at a few large quarries; in the days of slower transport, small-scale quarrying was more extensive, so that some of the smallest occurrences have been worked out completely, especially in those areas where the rock is rare and the soils are acid.

The argillaceous rocks, formerly muds but now affected by various degrees of metamorphism, are also comparatively soft, especially where metamorphism has been slight (e.g. to the south of Macduff); they become tougher, however, when converted to knotted phyllites (as in the Correen Hills) or hornfelses (as at Knockandy and Tap o' Noth).

During the main deformation to which the area was subjected, the argillaceous beds and, to an even greater extent, the calcareous beds behaved in a plastic manner, especially when sandwiched between more competent formations. Both these categories of rock may occur in lenticular, highly crenulated masses at the apices of folds, having been squeezed completely out of the limbs of the folds where pressures were greater (e.g. Lion's Face, Braemar, and east of the mouth of the Boyne Burn, between Portsoy and Whitehills); alternatively, the possibility that such rocks may occasionally have been injected along faults and thrusts still remains open. Under such movements, thin intercalated competent members were sometimes broken up to form tectonic xenoliths in more plastic limestone or schist (e.g. Glen Clunie, near Braemar). Such tendencies are particularly strong in the western portion of the Dalradian, where limestones are most abundant and where some of the argillaceous rocks contain graphite which makes them even more incompetent than usual.

The *Epidiorites and Hornblende Schists* (Read, 1923b; Wiseman, 1934) represent older basic igneous rocks or material that was originally partly igneous, partly sedimentary. Their response to weathering is very variable: sometimes they degenerate rapidly to incoherent rubble, especially when they contain large quantities of felspar; at other times they form strong massive sombre outcrops or even large hills (e.g. Morven). During deformation, many of these rocks remained tough and competent, even at high temperatures. Under extreme metamorphism associated with movement, slabs of hornblende schist were sometimes broken up to form tectonic xenoliths in migmatite complexes but, even under these circumstances, the rock seems to have remained tough and compact, with its mineralogy more or less unaffected.

The *Highland Border Series* is confined to a narrow intensely compressed belt on the downthrow side of the Highland Boundary fault. Two members have been recognised (Barrow, 1901): the 'Green Rocks' consist of sheared basic igneous rock, conspicuously green in colour, with rare black mudstones and red jasper; the 'Margie' beds consist of grits and sandstones with shales and limestones. On the basis of a basal conglomerate containing fragments of Green Rocks, the Margie beds were assigned to the upper portion of the series. The finding of Cambrian fossils near Callander in rocks regarded as the equivalents of the North Esk Margie beds has, however, thrown some doubts on the relative ages of the two main members of the series (Pringle, 1942). Complications due to the proximity of the Highland Boundary fault make it difficult to resolve these doubts and, since the palaeontological evidence is in any case rather fragmentary, it seems best to ascribe the series as a whole to the Cambro-Ordovician.

The *Downtonian*, nearly 3,000 ft. thick, is confined to a small area near Stonehaven. The main rock is sandstone, with conglomerate, shales, and some volcanic tuffs and agglomerates (Campbell, 1913). North of Stonehaven, the beds can be seen to rest unconformably on the Highland Border Series, the plane of unconformity being more or less vertical and somewhat imbricated because of its proximity to the Highland Boundary fault.

The *Caledonian Orogeny*, at the end of Silurian times, was the culmination of a series of movements which, in the Highlands especially, must have had an extremely protracted history. Although the whole of Britain was affected, the mountains that evolved have been called the 'Caledonides' since it is in Scotland that the most complex structures can best be studied. In the Highlands, the movements were accompanied or closely followed by large-scale intrusions of igneous rocks, mainly granites; in North-East Scotland, basic rocks were also intruded. The structure of the area is discussed later. At this stage it is merely necessary to state that, as a result of the movements, the Highlands became a major mountain chain (the Caledonian Mountains) and the Southern Uplands were also uplifted; between these two areas, a continental intermontane basin, the Midland Valley of Scotland, was developed.

Basic Intrusive Igneous Rocks, dark or very dark in colour, are mainly confined to the portion of the area north of the River Don, where they constitute an important petrographic province. Many of them weather rapidly, so they frequently form low ground (e.g. the east-west valley through Insch). Seven basic masses, ranging from seven square miles to almost 100 square miles in area, have been described (Watt, 1914; Read, 1921, 1923a and b, 1924, 1931, 1935; Read and MacGregor, 1948; Read, Sadashivaiah, and Hag, 1961; Whittle, 1936; Stewart, 1947; Sadashivaiah, 1950, 1954a and b). These rocks are slightly later than the main Caledonian movements; they are also contemporaneous with or slightly earlier than the newer granites and, like the latter, earlier than the Old Red Sandstone sediments in which they occur as boulders.

The main rock-type is hyperite, with two pyroxenes, but, depending on the relative abundance of monoclinic or orthorhombic pyroxene, the rocks are generally referred to as gabbro or norite; true gabbros and norites also occur. The more basic and ultrabasic rocks may develop small-scale rhythmic banding (Shackleton, 1948; Stewart, 1947; Stewart and Johnson, 1960). More acid rocks, subordinate in amount and normally younger than the basic rocks, occur either as stringers, veins, or patches within the masses or as isolated outcrops in their immediate vicinity.

The general mode of occurrence is roughly concordant and sheet-like; the general grouping is U-shaped so that, from the map, one is tempted to regard the masses as part of a complex sheet in a north-pitching, broadly synclinal structure. Contact metamorphism may be extensive or practically absent, suggesting that some contacts may be mechanical. Sometimes a marginal zone of contaminated rock full of xenoliths is developed; xenoliths are also locally abundant within the masses. Contamination is marked by the development of cordierite and garnet; also by more abundant development of orthopyroxene.

In addition to the main basic masses, various smaller outcrops of serpentine, most of them too small to be shown on the map, occur towards the western margin of the Dalradian area. These may form quite prominent hills (e.g. the Coyles of Muick). Many of these smaller occurrences show signs of having been involved in strong movements, so they are considered older than the rocks of the larger masses.

Granite occurs in large masses in the Cairngorms and around Lochnagar, Hill o' Fare, and Mount Keen; in smaller masses at Bennachie, Peterhead, Strichen, and Ben Rinnes. Structurally, these masses are very varied: often transgressive, sometimes apparently concordant; their exact shapes are often difficult to specify but examples of stocks, bosses, batholiths, and sheets occur, in addition to highly irregular masses. Contacts are often sharp, with contact metamorphism that may or may not be extensive (MacGregor, 1928; Hutchison, 1933); alternatively, and especially in areas where older granites are also present, they may be less definite, with associated assimilation, injection, and metasomatism. Compared with the older granites of the migmatite areas, the younger granites show far fewer signs of having been involved in strong movements. As already stated, they are regarded as roughly contemporaneous with the main masses of basic rocks.

The proportion of alkali felspar to plagioclase is variable, so that true granites, adamellites, and granodiorites are all represented. Some complexes also include diorites or still more basic rocks (Deer, 1938, 1950, 1953), the latter being generally represented in the area as a whole by streaks or xenoliths rich in hornblende or biotite. The colour of the rocks is mainly pink but sometimes grey (Bisset, 1931); near Aberdeen, both pink and grey granites can sometimes be worked in a single quarry, the two types being coarsely interfingered as a result of partial mixing by fluxion.

Compared with the surrounding metamorphic rocks, the granites are more compact and resistant to weathering, so they produce the highest ground in the area. Rectangular jointing, exploited by the weather, is responsible for the spectacular 'tors' near the summits of Ben Avon, Bennachie, etc. Although the rocks are mechanically anisotrophic, foliation and lineation are not normally conspicuous and the complete structural pattern described by Balk (1937) and Cloos (1946) has not yet been found. In wet weather, however, a distinct fluxion foliation frequently becomes apparent on well-dressed blocks of younger granite.

Granite provides the material for one of the main industries of Aberdeen, but only a few of the many original quarries are still in active operation. The latter do, however, include Rubislaw Quarry (465 ft.), probably the deepest of its kind in the world; Kemnay Quarry (480 ft.) is no longer active. Apart from its value as a building stone, granite is much used for monumental work; polished slabs of the rock are also used for facing buildings in industrial areas in order to cut down maintenance costs. Some of the spoil-heaps of the older quarries are now being re-worked as a source of aggregate for concrete blocks.

The *Lower Old Red Sandstone*, confined to the area south-east of the Highland Boundary fault, consists of a spectacular series of conglomerates which is followed upwards by much finer-grained rocks. A thick group of lavas occurs about the middle of the succession. The aggregate thickness is 18,000 ft. The sediments, representing the erosional debris of the former Caledonian Mountains, were laid down as a gigantic piedmont alluvial fan. The conglomerates in the lowest group (Campbell, 1913) are particularly coarse, with well-rounded boulders up to several feet in diameter. At the time of their deposition, therefore, the relief in the adjoining mountains must have been particularly strong and the transporting streams very powerful. As one ascends the succession, the sediments become less coarse and the uppermost group consists of shales, marls, flagstones, and sandstones. The Lower Old Red Sandstone thus records the main denudation of the Caledonian Mountains.

The lavas, mainly basalts and andesites, often show signs of contemporaneous weathering and erosion, with the eroded fissures filled with later sediment; this suggests that deposition in any one locality was a very sporadic affair. Weathering of the rocks produces a distinctively red soil. The lavas are more resistant than the sediments and are responsible for most of the higher ground in the lowland area; their main development is in the Sidlaw Hills.

The *Middle Old Red Sandstone*, confined to the area north of the River Dee, occurs only in small patches—outliers of the main mass which is developed in the Moray Firth area, Caithness, Orkney, and Shetland. The sediments were laid down unconformably on an irregular, eroded surface of crystalline rocks, so denudation of the Caledonian Mountains must have been well advanced before their deposition began. This suggests that the rocks are distinctly younger than the Lower Old Red Sandstone of the Midland Valley. More definite indications of their age are, however, provided by occasional fish remains (Traquair, 1894, 1904, 1906, 1896), especially those of the Gardenstown area (Prestwich, 1837). The Rhynie occurrence is notable for the Rhynie chert (Mackie, 1914), in which the microscopic details of various primitive plants have been perfectly preserved (Kidston and Lang, 1917, 1920, 1921).

The main rocks are coarse sandstones with associated conglomerates, the pebbles in the latter being far smaller and often far more angular than those in the Lower Old Red Sandstone conglomerates. The sediments are therefore intermediate in type between the very coarse Midland Valley succession and the much finer Middle Old Red Sandstone flagstones of Caithness. Compared with the surrounding rocks, the sandstone is soft and easily eroded (hence, for example, the north-south valley through Rhynie), but it can also form fairly prominent hills (e.g. Hill of Fisherie and Windyheads Hill). In the higher areas of sandstone the streams form very deep gullies; the rock can also produce spectacular coastal scenery (e.g. east and west of Pennan).

To the south of the area, near Arbroath and Dundee, *Upper Old Red Sandstone* rests unconformably on Lower, with the Middle Old Red Sandstone missing. Immediately west of the area, near Elgin (Mackie, 1897), Middle Old Red Sandstone is succeeded unconformably by Upper (Traquair, 1897), which is followed in turn by *Permo-Triassic* sandstones (Watson and Hickling, 1914). The latter, of desert type, sometimes contain wind-rounded grains and faceted pebbles; they may also contain reptilian footprints and remains.

The gap in the succession, following the deposition of the Permo-Trias, extends over practically the entire Mesozoic and Tertiary eras, for the next formation comprises only a few patches of gravel, possibly *Pliocene* in age, in the Buchan district of Aberdeenshire (Flett and Read, 1921). In spite of their restricted development, these gravels are of great interest, for they occur at 350 ft.— 400 ft. above sea-level and suggest a submergence of the land by this amount towards the end of Tertiary times. In conjunction with the evidence of the *Pleistocene* and *Recent* deposits (described in the section on Geomorphology), and especially with the evidence indicating overdeepening of many river valleys, they suggest that, in the comparatively recent geological past, movements of the land relative to the sea may have had an amplitude of the order of many hundreds of feet.

Structure

The Highland Boundary fault, running southwestwards from Stonehaven, divides the area into two distinct parts: a highland area of predominantly crystalline rocks to the northwest, and a lowland area of Palaeozoic sediments with associated lava flows to the southeast. The actual fault-plane may be filled with dolomite, or iron-stained chert, or, further southwest, with serpentine. The fault is steep and can sometimes be seen to be inclined towards the northwest (e.g. north of Stonehaven); sometimes a complex fault-zone is developed (e.g. in the River North Esk and towards the southwest). The amount of downthrow is not known, but it must be equal to or greater than the total thickness of the sediments on the downthrow side, i.e. 20,000 ft.

Southeast of the Highland Boundary fault, the main structure is the Strathmore or Howe o' the Mearns syncline (Campbell, 1913). This syncline is asymmetrical, with its steep northwest limb wedged against the scarp of the fault. The gentle southeast limb shows the finest development of the lavas which, stretching southwestwards from the general vicinity of Montrose, form the backbone of the Sidlaw Hills. The axis of the syncline runs northeast —southwest and pitches to the southwest.

Northwest of the Highland Boundary fault, structures are extremely complex, even by orogenic standards, for the rocks have been subjected to more than one type of movement. The main grain of the rocks, parallel to the original axis of the mountain chain, is northeast—southwest, but cross-folding has produced a series of additional flexures whose dimensions range from the order of several miles down to microscopic. In the Schiehallion area (Bailey and McCallien, 1937; Rast, 1958), and for many miles further north, three consecutive sets of axes can be identified: northeast—southwest; north-west—southeast; and east—west. Similarly complex, though not necessarily strictly analogous, situations have been described from a variety of areas (McIntyre, 1950; Sutton and Watson, 1956; Johnson and Stewart, 1960; Phemister, Fraser, and Williamson, 1960; Johnson, 1962).

It transpires that the history of movement and metamorphism is prolonged and complex and that, insofar as each major event tends to obliterate the evidence for earlier events, the elucidation of this history may take a very long time. The main inhibiting factor in such investigations is the isolated nature and, therefore, the small scale of the available evidence. It is often

difficult to correlate the microscopic evidence of a rock slice with the macro-
scopic evidence of the sample from which the slice has been cut; it is still
more difficult to correlate this microscopic evidence with that of the outcrop
from which the sample has been obtained. Structures of a type that can be
seen on a single outcrop tend to be more useful, for they may and quite
frequently do correlate with mappable structures whose dimensions are of
the order of one or two hundred yards. In the absence of continuous outcrops,
however, large-scale and regional structures are very difficult to deduce, still
more difficult to vindicate, and virtually impossible to demonstrate. In spite of
this, a few major structures have been advocated, though with varying degrees
of confidence.

The most obvious major structure is the east—west Deeside anticline, with
an extensive axial flat belt occupied by the lower valley of the River Dee.
West of the flat belt, the axis extends towards the Cairngorm Mountains and
is probably responsible for the major flexure in the tentative Dalradian/
Central Highland Granulite boundary shown on the Geological Survey map
of Scotland. Assuming this boundary to be even approximately correct, the
flexure indicates that its regional dip must be towards the east. The axis of
the anticline is marked by high-grade regional metamorphism, by extensive
development of migmatites and older granites, and by the strongest concentration of younger intrusive granites in Scotland. The anticlinal flexuring
movements would seem therefore to have facilitated or even to have promoted
the upward migration both of granitising fluids and of magmatic granites.

The occurrence of Middle Old Red Sandstone outliers north of the River
Dee and their absence further south suggests that the Deeside axis may also
have exercised some control over the deposition of the sediment or, alternatively, that it may be partly responsible for their preservation. In either case,
a prolonged history of movement in the vicinity of the axis is implied. The
later stages of this movement may, however, have been more of the nature
of a monoclinal flexure; they may even have involved faulting with downthrow
to the north.

Along the Banffshire coast, meticulous mapping has established the
existence of the complex Boyndie syncline (Read, 1936; Sutton and Watson,
1955, 1956). Further inland, the U-shaped distribution of andalusite schists
suggests that this syncline pitches northwards and that it may therefore have
been cross-folded about an east—west axis. This seems to strengthen the
proposition, based both on general grounds and on small-scale evidence, that
the northnortheast—southsouthwest Boyndie syncline is an earlier structure
than the east—west Deeside anticline. The U-shaped distribution of the main
basic igneous masses and their broad general concordance with the main belt
of andalusite schists suggests a fundamental connection with the Boyndie
syncline. Thus, whereas the main granites of North-East Scotland seem to

be genetically associated with actual or suggested anticlinal axes, the main basic intrusions are associated with a major syncline.

East of the Boyndie syncline, the Buchan anticline (Read and Farquhar, 1956) is a very reasonable possibility which is further strengthened by the coincidence of the anticline with a belt of high metamorphism and migmatisation. West of the Boyndie syncline, a similar anticline could equally reasonably be postulated in the general vicinity of the Keith division of the Dalradian or of the tentative Dalradian/Central Highland Granulite boundary.

The concept of the Banff nappe (Read, 1955) has been put forward as a general interpretation of the distribution and stratigraphical order of the rocks of North-East Scotland. Before it can be completely vindicated, however, it will be necessary to establish where it came from and why it moved. The arguments in favour of the Banff nappe are not yet to this extent conclusive and many of them could be met by promoting the Boyndie syncline to the status of a geosyncline and by accepting the possibility of nappe structures rooted in or derived from this geosyncline.

Smaller-scale structures in North-East Scotland can only be established in a desultory manner when and where evidence permits. Nappe-type structures occur near Braemar (Barrow, 1904; Bailey, 1928). A Huntly—Tarves antiform, similar to but of a much lower order of magnitude than the Deeside anticline, has been suggested (Johnson and Stewart, 1960). The Boyne Line (Read, 1936) has been extrapolated for many miles (Read, 1955). North of Collieston, Read (1956) has established the eastward movement of an east-dipping set of nappe-type structures; near the Highland Boundary fault, Shackleton (1958) has suggested a similar but steeper set of downward-facing structures. Up to date, no one has had the temerity to correlate Read's Collieston structures with Shackleton's downward-facing structures or to consider the implications of such a correlation on the possible southerly extension of the Buchan anticline. Possibly for the same reason, no one has yet attempted a stage-by-stage reconstruction of events in the immediate vicinity of the Highland Boundary fault.

SELECTED REFERENCES

ANDERSON, J. G. C., 'The Geology of the Highland Border: Stonehaven to Arran.' *Trans. Roy. Soc. Edin.*, **61** (1947), 497.

BAILEY, E. B., 'Schist Geology: Braemar, Glen Clunie, and Glen Shee.' *Trans. Roy. Soc. Edin.*, **55** (1928), 737.

—— and McCALLIEN, W. J., 'Perthshire Tectonics—Schichallion to Glen Lyon.' *Trans. Roy. Soc. Edin.*, **59** (1937), 79.

BALK, R., 'Structural behaviour of igneous rocks.' *Mem. Geol. Soc. Amer.* (1937), No. 5.

BARROW, G., 'On certain gneisses with round-grained oligoclase and their relation to pegmatites.' *Geol. Mag.* (1892), 64.

—— 'On an intrusion of muscovite-biotite gneiss in the South-eastern Highlands of Scotland, and its accompanying metamorphism.' *Q.J.G.S.*, **49** (1893), 330.

—— 'On the occurrence of Silurian (?) rocks in Forfarshire and Kincardineshire along the eastern border of the Highlands.' *Q.J.G.S.*, **57** (1901), 328.

—— 'Moine gneisses of the east Central Highlands and their position in the Highland sequence.' *Q.J.G.S.*, **60** (1904), 400.

BARROW, G., 'On the geology of Lower Deeside and the Southern Highland border.' *Proc. Geol. Assoc.*, **23** (1912), 274.

BISSET, C. B., 'Contribution to the study of some granites near Aberdeen.' *Trans. Edin. Geol. Soc.*, **13** (1931), 72.

CAMPBELL, R., 'The geology of South-eastern Kincardineshire.' *Trans. Roy. Soc. Edin.*, **48** (1913), 923.

CLOOS, E., 'Lineation.' *Mem. Geol. Soc. Amer.* (1946), No. 18.

DEER, W. A., 'The diorites and associated rocks of the Glen Tilt complex, Perthshire.' I.—'The granites and intermediate hybrid rocks.' *Geol. Mag.* (1938), 174. II.—'Diorites and appinites.' *Geol. Mag.* (1950), 181. III.—'Hornblende and hornblendite.' *Geol. Mag.* (1953), 137.

FLETT, J. S. and READ, H. H., 'Tertiary gravels of the Buchan District of Aberdeenshire.' *Geol. Mag.* (1921), 215.

GILETTI, B. J., MOORBATH, S. and LAMBERT, R. S. T. J., 'A geochronological study of the metamorphic complexes of the Scottish Highlands.' *Q.J.G.S.*, **117** (1961), 233.

HARRY, W. T., 'A re-examination of Barrow's older granites and metamorphic zones in Glen Clova, Angus.' *Trans. Roy. Soc. Edin.*, **63** (1958), 393.

HOLTEDAHL, O., 'The structural history of Norway and its relation to Great Britain.' *Q.J.G.S.*, **108** (1952), 65.

HUTCHISON, A. G.. 'The metamorphism of the Deeside Limestone, Aberdeenshire.' *Trans. Roy. Soc. Edin.*, **57** (1933), 557.

JOHNSON, M. R. W. and STEWART, F. H., 'On Dalradian structures in North-East Scotland.' *Trans. Edin. Geol. Soc.*, **18** (1960), 94.

JOHNSON, M. R. W.,' Relations of movement and metamorphism in the Dalradians of Banffshire.' *Trans. Edin. Geol. Soc.*, **19** (1962), 29.

KIDSTON, R. and LANG, W. H., 'On Old Red Sandstone plants showing structure from the Rhynie chert bed, Aberdeenshire.' *Trans. Roy. Soc. Edin.*, **51** (1917), 761; **52** (1920), 603, 643; **52** (1921), 831.

KOLDERUP, C. F., Address on the 'geology of the Scottish Highlands and of Western Norway.' *Trans. Geol. Soc. Edin.*, **13** (1935), 217.

KVALE, A., 'Linear structures and their relation to movement in the Caledonides of Scandinavia and Scotland.' *Q.J.G.S.*, **109** (1953), 51.

MacGREGOR, A. G., 'Metamorphism around the Lochnagar granite, Aberdeenshire.' *Rep. Brit. Assoc.*, Glasgow (1928), 553.

McINTYRE, D. B., 'The tectonics of the area between Grantown and Tomintoul (mid-Strathspey).' *Q.J.G.S.*, **107** (1951), 1.

MACKIE, W., 'The sands and sandstones of Eastern Moray.' *Trans. Edin. Geol. Soc.*, **7** (1897), 148.

—— 'The rock series of Craigbeg and Ord Hill, Rhynie, Aberdeenshire.' *Trans. Edin. Geol. Soc.*, **10** (1914), 205.

PHEMISTER, T. C., FRASER, W. E. and WILLIAMSON, D. H., 'Dalradian metamorphism and structure—Stonehaven to Aberdeen.' *Rep. 21st Internat. Geol. Congr.* (1960), Pt. 13, 352.

PRESTWICH, J., 'On the structure of the neighbourhood of Gamrie, Banffshire, particularly on the deposit containing ichthyolites.' *Trans. Geol. Soc.*, **5** (1837), 139.

PRINGLE, J., 'The relationship of the Green Conglomerate to the Margie Grits in the North Esk, near Edzell; and on the probable age of the Margie Limestone.' *Trans. Geol. Soc. Glasgow,* **20** (1942), 136.

RAST, N., 'Metamorphic history of the Schichallion complex, Perthshire.' *Trans. Roy. Soc. Edin.,* **63** (1958), 413.

READ, H. H., The contaminated gabbro of Easter Saphook, near Oldmeldrum in Aberdeenshire.' *Geol. Mag.* (1921), 177.

—— 'The petrology of the Arnage district in Aberdeenshire: a study of assimilation.' *Q.J.G.S.*, **79** (1923a), 446.

—— 'The geology of Banff, Huntly, and Turriff.' *Mem. Geol. Surv. Scotland* (1923b).

—— 'On certain xenoliths associated with the contaminated rocks of the Huntly mass, Aberdeenshire.' *Geol. Mag.* (1924), 433.

—— 'The igneous and metamorphic history of Cromar, Deeside, Aberdeenshire.' *Trans. Roy. Soc. Edin.,* **55** (1927), 317.

—— 'On corundum—spinel xenoliths in the gabbro of Haddo House, Aberdeenshire.' *Geol. Mag.* (1931), 446.

—— 'The gabbros and associated xenolithic complexes of the Haddo House district, Aberdeenshire.' *Q.J.G.S.*, **91** (1935), 591.

—— 'The stratigraphical order of the Dalradian rocks of the Banffshire coast.' *Geol. Mag.* (1936), 468.

READ, H. H., 'Metamorphism and migmatisation in the Ythan valley, Aberdeenshire.' *Trans. Edin. Geol. Soc.*, **15** (1952), 265.
—— 'The Banff nappe.' *Proc. Geol. Assoc.*, **66** (1955), 1.
—— and FARQUHAR, O. C., 'The Buchan anticline of the Banff nappe of Dalradian rocks in North-East Scotland.' *Q.J.G.S.*, **112** (1956), 131.
—— and MACGREGOR, A. G., 'The Grampian Highlands.' *Regional Geology*, 1948.
—— SADASHIVAIAH, M. S., and HAG, B. T., 'Differentiation in the olivine-gabbro at the Insch mass, Aberdeenshire.' *Proc. Geol. Assoc.*, **72** (1961), 391.
SADASHIVAIAH, M. S., 'Olivine-bearing and other basic hornfelses around the Insch igneous mass, Aberdeenshire.' *Geol. Mag.* (1950), 121.
—— 'The form of the eastern end of the Insch igneous mass, Aberdeenshire.' *Geol. Mag.* (1954a), 137.
—— 'The granite-diorite complex of the Insch igneous mass, Aberdeenshire.' *Geol. Mag.* (1954b), 286.
SHACKLETON, R. M., 'Overturned rhythmic banding in the Huntly gabbro of Aberdeenshire.' *Geol. Mag.* (1948), 358.
—— 'Downward-facing structures of the Highland Border.' *Q.J.G.S.*, **113** (1958), 361.
STEWART, F. H., 'The gabbroic complex of Belhelvie in Aberdeenshire.' *Q.J.G.S.*, **102** (1947), 465.
—— and JOHNSON, M. R. W., 'The structural problem of the younger gabbros of North-East Scotland.' *Trans. Edin. Geol. Soc.*, **18** (1960), 104.
SUTTON, J. and WATSON, J., 'The deposition of the Upper Dalradian rocks of the Banffshire coast.' *Proc. Geol. Assoc.*, **66** (1955), 101.
—— 'The Boyndie Syncline of the Dalradian of the Banffshire coast.' *Q.J.G.S.*, **112** (1956), 103.
TRAQUAIR, R. H., 'A monograph of the fishes of the Old Red Sandstone of Britain.' *Monograph Palaeont. Soc.*, Pt. II, No. 1 (1894), No. 2 (1904), No. 3 (1906).
—— 'The extinct vertebrate animals of the Moray Firth area.' in J. A. Harvie-Brown and T. E. Buckley's *Vertebrate Fauna of the Moray Basin*, **2** (Edinburgh, 1896).
—— 'Additional notes on the fossil fishes of the Upper Old Red Sandstone of the Moray Firth area.' *Proc. Roy. Phys. Soc. Edin.*, **13** (1897), 376.
WATSON, D. M. S. and HICKLING, G., 'On the Triassic and Permian Rocks of Moray.' *Geol. Mag.* (1914), 399.
WATT, W. R., 'The geology of the country around Huntly (Aberdeenshire). *Q.J.G.S.*, **70** (1914), 266.
WHITTLE, G., 'The eastern end of the Insch igneous mass, Aberdeenshire. *Proc. Liverpool Geol. Soc.*, **17** (1936), 64.
WISEMAN, J. D. H., 'The Central and South-west Highland epidiorites, etc.' *Q.J.G.S.*, **90** (1934), 354.

GEOMORPHOLOGY

BETWEEN the Old Red Sandstone lowlands of Moray and Strathmore, the knuckle' of the North-East projects into the North Sea as a complex of lowland and upland plateaux drained by the Dee, Don, Ythan, Ugie, Deveron and Spey, which have their sources in the highland rim in the west and south. Elements of highland and lowland scenery are interdigitated as straths and glens cut back into the hill masses producing a variegated relief, which is further diversified by the contrasts in the effect of glaciation. In general, the highlands bear witness to the power of glacial erosion with minor depositional features in the valleys whereas the lowlands are covered, for the most part, with a thin mantle of glacial drift and outwash, deposited at different stages by glaciers from the Moray Firth, from Strathmore and from Deeside. Since there is little variation in structure between highland and lowland areas, except in the Old Red Sandstone districts, variations in the major relief must be sought in the erosional history and in the variations in character and degree of process which have operated in the two districts. The coastline, with alternate grandiose, intricately sculptured cliffs and broad sweeps of low dune-fringed coasts, bears witness to the late- and post-glacial changes in sea level, with which were associated the deposition of extensive shingle ridges in the Moray Firth and North Sea coastlands (Fig. 2).

For the most part the relief is developed on closely folded Moine and Dalradian metamorphic rocks which are aligned northnortheast—southsouthwest following the Caledonian trend. Their continuity is broken by extensive intrusions of acid and basic igneous rocks, granite and gabbro covering the widest areas, and by outcrops of Old Red Sandstone, preserved by downfaulting as in the Cabrach or Strathbogie. The Highland Boundary Fault, which reaches the sea at Garron Point, Stonehaven, separates the crystalline rocks of the Highlands from the Old Red Sandstone of Strathmore with its sediments and lavas displayed to perfection in the cliffs south of Stonehaven. In the northwest, the Old Red Sandstone of Moray rests upon the worn-down edges of the Highland schists without marked tectonic break. Here, too, are found the most recent sandstones of the district in the coastal ridge between Lossiemouth and Burghead. This Permian or Triassic sandstone was used for the chapel of King's College. Of great interest are the presumed Pliocene gravels of Buchan, composed of rounded quartzite pebbles and flints with Cretaceous fossils, since they appear to rest on a platform about 400 ft. O.D., with which is associated marked breaks of slope in many parts of the region.

Fracturing has helped to determine the lineaments of relief on both large and small scales. The complicated Highland Boundary Fault, however, does not always coincide with the fault-line scarp of the Highland edge and some of the important hill masses (such as Strathfinella Hill), which produce the marked topographic break between Strathmore and the Highlands, are formed of Old Red Sandstone. The straightness of the Moray Firth coast, cutting across the strike of the rocks at almost a right angle, suggests some tectonic influence which might also be invoked for the alignment and general straightness of the east coast of Kincardineshire and Aberdeenshire. Faults in the Highlands have been important in determining the direction of rivers, such as the continuation of the Glen Tilt fault across Upper Deeside, which is followed by the meltwater channel of Clais Fhearnaig, a section of the river Quoich and the headwaters of the Gairn. Faults bound the western sides of the Old Red Sandstone outcrops in the Cabrach and Strathbogie, while the intricacy of the cliff outlines is in part the result of shattering and in part the result of minor intrusive dykes which have proved less resistant under marine attack than the country rock.

The metamorphic series offer considerable lithologic variation which locally has determined the relief. The quartz-schists and quartzites interfolded with less resistant black schists and phyllites, as in the hills of Banffshire, have produced, under the influence of strike stream erosion, ridges and valleys with the quartzite forming the high ground; occasionally, the quartzites form isolated hills such as the conspicuous Mormond Hill in northeast Aberdeenshire, which rises above the general level of the 400 ft. platform. The larger intrusions of granite are found in both highland and lowland situations. The highest plateaux of the Cairngorms such as Ben Macdhui (4,296 ft.) and Lochnagar (3,768 ft.) are cut across granite, yet granite also forms the basement of the 400 ft. surface west of Aberdeen, which is surmounted by the granite Hill of Fare (1,502 ft.) and the Tyrebagger (823 ft.) and Brimmond Hills (870 ft.). The great lowland of western Aberdeenshire is, however, clearly the result of differential erosion of the Insch gabbro intrusion between the slates of the Foudland Hills in the north and the granite and metamorphic complex of the Bennachie-Correen Hills range in the south. While, therefore, rock type has made a contribution to the landforms, it is apparent that the complex basement has behaved under erosion almost as though it were homogeneous. Only in the Old Red Sandstone districts is there a clear relationship between structure and scenery on a large scale. For the elucidation of relief problems one must seek guidance from the drainage network and the remnants of erosion surfaces which suggested to Bremner[1] and Linton[2] the superimposition of a west—east drainage system from a sedimentary cover on to the crystalline basement beneath. The remnants of the former drainage lines are evident in high-level valleys in both high and lowland areas (see for instance the drainage line along the interfluve between Dee and Don from the Howe of Cromar to the Hill of Fare).

2

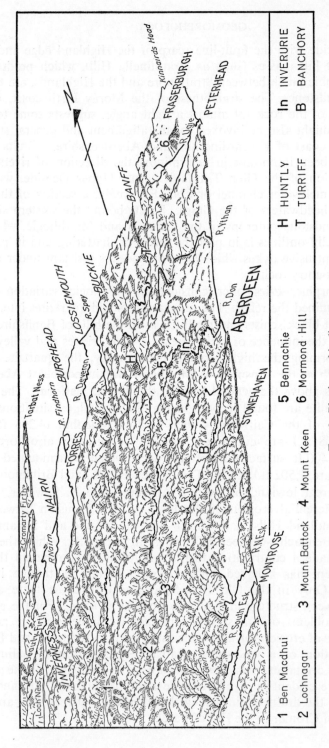

Fig. 2. Physiographic diagram.

1 Ben Macdhui   3 Mount Battock   5 Bennachie   H HUNTLY   In INVERURIE

2 Lochnagar   4 Mount Keen   6 Mormond Hill   T TURRIFF   B BANCHORY

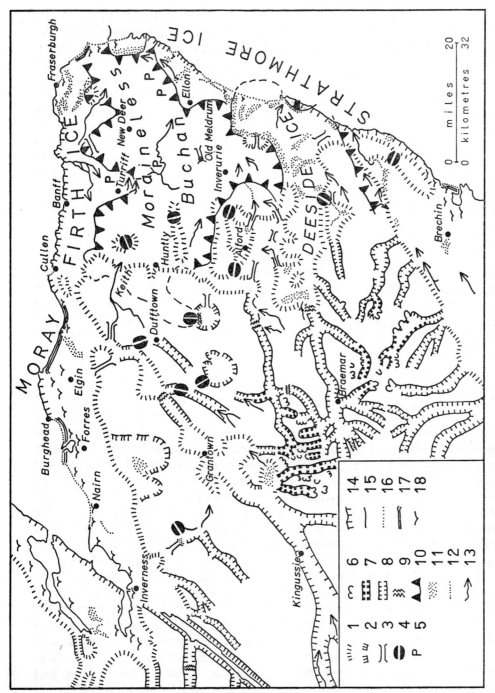

Fig. 3. Aspects of the geomorphology. 1 Margin of Uplands, 2 Margin of Upland basins, 3 Wind gaps, 4 Water gaps, 5 Pliocene gravels, 6 Corries, 7 Glacial troughs, 8 Glaciated Valleys, 9 Valley moraines, 10 Ice margins, 11 Kames, 12 Eskers, 13 Meltwater channels, 14 Cliff coasts, 15 Low coasts, 16 Dune fringed low coasts, 17 Shingle ridges, 18 Conspicuous raised beaches.

Apart from the obvious change in process which resulted from the glaciations and the sub-arctic climates of the unglaciated districts, there are also the significant phenomena of deep weathering found in many parts of the region. The rotting of the rock on such a scale can only have taken place under warmer and more humid climatic conditions than the present day and it is tempting to relate the inselberg-like outlines of Mount Battock and Mount Keen on the 'Mounth' (the extension of the Grampians towards the sea between Aberdeen and Stonehaven) and the formation of the tors of the Cairngorms and Bennachie to such conditions. It might be that the landscape was evolving in Tertiary/early Pleistocene times under warm, seasonally arid conditions and inselberg-pediment profiles have been suggested to explain the characteristic of slopes in both highland and lowland zones. If the quartzites were almost immune to the effects of chemical weathering, they were under attack in the sub-arctic climates which obtained at the close of the Ice Age.[3] Glaciation appears to have been slight over the greater part of the lowland region and, as has been pointed out by Synge[4] and Charlesworth,[5] part of Buchan may not have been glaciated, which would account for the survival of the Pliocene gravels. The ground was, however, exposed to severe periglacial processes which, for instance, produced by solifluction smooth slopes incorporating drift and the mantle rock provided by the chemical weathering. This soliflucted layer is generally about two feet thick but deeper at the base of slopes and thinner on the ridges. Frost wedges are found in sections exposed in fluvio-glacial materials or in raised beach deposits capping cliffs, as at the Bay of Nigg; the pebbles in the upper layers of the Tertiary gravels of Buchan show superb examples of erection and till-fabric analysis has revealed the down-slope orientation of soliflucted material. In the highland areas wide expanses of frost-shattered rock are arranged as sheets on the high-level plateaux or as stone-banked lobes seen on the slopes of Lochnagar. It is apparent that periglacial processes still operate, but with lesser intensity, above about 2,000 ft. and it has been shown that a slight fall of average annual temperature (about 0·5°F., 0·3°C.) would produce a permanent snowline on Ben Macdhui. Finally, the catastrophic nature of fluvial processes in the area deserves consideration since great floods are common on the rivers in both highland and lowland zones which have produced striking changes in river channels and valley side slopes.

Long continued erosion with respect to varying base-levels has produced a succession of erosion surfaces which increase in elevation away from the sea. Although the drift mantle is thin in the lowlands, which permits the identification of rock-cut platforms, it is possible that geophysical exploration will reveal drift-plugged valleys such as those visible in the cliffs near Muchalls south of Aberdeen. The higher surfaces are probably the work of rivers draining the highland block but below about 1,100 ft. the position and characteristics of the platforms suggest that they may be of marine origin.

The lowest surface at about 200—250 ft. is developed along the major valleys as near Dyce on lower Donside, and as a coastal platform on both North Sea and Moray Firth coasts as between the Ythan estuary and Peterhead or between Banff and Buckie. It is gently undulating with drift and fluvio-glacial deposits controlling the detailed relief. In it are incised the lower reaches of the principal rivers such as the Don and the Ythan, both of which have gorge sections within short distances of the sea. Much more extensive is the Buchan Platform with an upper limit of about 400 ft. and frequently backed by a slope which, although degraded, suggests a former cliff line. It is developed over wide areas as a coastal platform as between Aberdeen and Stonehaven and in northeast Aberdeenshire near New Pitsligo with the resistant quartzite Hill of Mormond rising abruptly above it. On this surface rest the controversial Pliocene gravels of Buchan, which are found especially on the interfluve between the Ythan and Ugie drainage as on the Windy Hills of Fyvie. This platform extends inland as a broad strath along the Ythan, and forms the Culter Basin of lower Deeside, which has a clearly defined rim with the base about 400 ft. O.D.; further up Deeside it forms the floors of the basins of Lumphanan, Torphins and part of Cromar and it is prominent in the eastern section of the Garioch Lowland, where it appears to be graded to the wind gap at Old Meldrum which opens out on to an extensive remnant of the coastal platform at the same level. It is the most prominent and important relief element in lowlands. At 500—750 ft. occur benches in the valleys of the Isla and Deveron and notably on the north side of the Feugh Basin, where they are continued as a wind gap to the east of the Feugh's northerly bend to join the Dee at Banchory. High-level meanders on the east side of Strathbogie are cut into the Hills of Foudland and their northern extension at about the same level. Between about 850 and 1,000 ft. benches are prominent in the valleys of the North Esk, Dee and Don (Fleet's Grampian valley benches[6]), and notably on the former drainage line between the Howe of Cromar and the Culter Basin along the north side of the Hill of Fare. These smaller remnants are dwarfed by the extensive development of the 1,000 ft. surface which is such an important element of landscape in the Highlands as a whole. It appears in the region as flats on the Highland edge overlooking Strathmore and as a prominent level on the north side of the Hills of Foudland traversed by the main road between Aberdeen and Huntly. Further to the north and west the plateau of Aultmore between the Isla and the coast has extensive stretches of gentle slope at the same elevation; it is present on the northern flanks of the Monadhliath Mountains west of the Spey and appears to perfection on Dava Moor drained by the Findhorn and its tributaries.

Above 1,000 ft. the levels determined by Fleet in his cartographic analysis of the Grampian Highlands are well represented in upper Deeside. The Grampian Lower Surface extends beyond the confines of the Highlands into the uplands of western Aberdeenshire where it is represented in the hills surrounding the Alford Basin and in the ridge which forms the watershed between the Dee and Don drainage north of the Howe of Cromar. At the upper level of 2,000 ft. it appears as Bremner's High Plateau of the Southeast Highlands,[7] where one can walk for miles on the Mounth and rarely descend below the general level except where the surface is breached by the deep glacial troughs oriented towards Strathmore. Above lies the Grampian Main Surface with an upper limit of about 3,000 ft., which in turn is dominated by the Grampian summits which Linton believes represent the surface on which were laid the deposits of the Cenomanian Sea (the cover on which the proto-drainage flowed before superimposition on to the highland crystalline rocks beneath). Much more work will need to be done before the story of landscape evolution in Tertiary times may be told.

The Tertiary landforms were considerably modified by the glaciations of the Quaternary but, since the region lies on the drier eastern side of Scotland, erosion by rivers and glaciers was less than in the western Highlands, which accounts for the survival of such extensive remnants of the old plateaux. Nevertheless, considerable modifications of the pre-glacial landscape have resulted with development of corries which scallop the edges of the high surfaces, the breaching of watersheds by ice, the formation of fine glacial troughs (as in Glen Clova and Glen Avon) and numerous examples of meltwater drainage with channels cut in rock across spurs and on the valley sides. The retreat phenomena in the valleys impress by their fresh appearance and by the extent of the deposits of fluvio-glacial material connected with stagnant ice masses. It is on the lowlands, however, that we must seek the evidence which indicates the chronology and extent of the glaciations (Fig. 3).

The North-East has been well served by the ranks of glacial geomorphologists. Jamieson,[8] Bremner,[9] Scott Simpson[10] and Synge,[4] have studied and sifted the evidence so that it is possible to detail events with a fair degree of accuracy. Jamieson distinguished four main ice movements and, although modifications of his ideas and nomenclature have been made, they still form the basis of modern work. The oldest is represented by a clayey till which contains fragments of marine shells; it occurs at numerous localities in Aberdeenshire and Kincardineshire, and its situation and included shell fragments suggest that it was dredged from the floor of the North Sea. Although no Scandinavian boulders have as yet been discovered in this till, it is clear that the ice came from Scandinavia—the *Scandinavian Glaciation*. An expansion of local Highland ice in an easterly direction then followed which, meeting Scandinavian Ice in the North Sea, appears to have split into a north and south flowing stream, the point of bifurcation perhaps in the area where the Pliocene gravels survive. This *Greater Highland Glaciation* is regarded by Synge as the equivalent of the Alpine Riss Glaciation. During the third glacial phase (Würm) ice from the Firths of Forth and Tay fanned out northwards along the coast of Kincardine and Aberdeenshire, joined by the confluent glaciers of Strathmore, as a result of Scandinavian ice in the North Sea blocking its route in an easterly direction. This Strathmore Glacier whose terminal moraine is recognisable near St. Fergus near Peterhead laid down the characteristic red till which covers the coastal fringe of eastern Aberdeenshire and with it are associated the most striking marginal channels and lake clay deposits of the district. Simultaneously, ice fanned out along the Moray Firth from centres of dispersion in the North-west Highlands sending lobes into the lower reaches of the valleys on the Moray Firth Lowlands such as the Findhorn and the Spey, and covering the northerly coastlands of Banffshire and Aberdeenshire (*Strathmore-Moray Firth Glaciation*).

Since the Moray Firth, Deeside and Strathmore Ice did not coalesce during this third phase of glaciation, a considerable portion of Buchan was subjected to intense periglacial weathering as were sections of the Mounth plateaux. Soliflucted slopes are found beneath shattered rock summits on the ridges; everywhere the slopes are smooth and the ridges rounded. Compared with the freshness of the glacial landforms elsewhere, the landscape is quite distinctive with no fresh till overlying the frost-shattered or chemically-weathered bedrock. One must assume that 'Moraineless Buchan' has not been glaciated since a period when the climate was warmer than that of the present day, which would mean at least since the last Interglacial. If this area was not actually subject to ice action, nevertheless it carried large quantities of meltwater as along the margins of the Strathmore Ice north of Ellon, which was joined by meltwater from the Moray Firth lobe coming down the Ythan valley. The North Ugie also discharged meltwater from the Moray Firth glacier towards the coast north of Peterhead.

After the wastage of the Strathmore-Moray Firth glaciers, a further extension of the Grampian and Northwest Highland ice cap caused the Deeside glacier to advance as far as Aberdeen and the Moray Firth glacier to the line of the Spey, where were deposited the very prominent moraines on the west bank of the Spey between Fochabers and Lhanbryde. It was this *Aberdeen or Perth Re-advance* which left the extensive moraine and fluvio-glacial relief on which the city of Aberdeen is built. The road between King's and Marischal Colleges runs along the kames which mark a stage in the retreat of the ice from its maximum extent. To the north of the Bridge of Don near Balmedie the Fife Hills appear to be terminal moraines deposited beneath the sea as confluent delta fans.[8] The sand and gravel mounds which form the site of Aberdeen, such as the Broad Hill, Woolmanhill, Ferryhill, are part of this morainic complex. (The chronology of the Strathmore glaciation and Aberdeen Re-advance phases in the district has been worked out from the excellent section exposed at the Bay of Nigg to the south of the promontory of Girdleness.) To the west of Aberdeen, the Deeside ice at its maximum extent lapped against the eastern slopes of the Brimmond and Tyrebagger Hills with prominent kames on the col through which passes the main road between Aberdeen and Inverurie. Spillways carrying meltwater into the ice-free basin of Clinterty to the west are cut deeply into the western slopes of these hills. Retreat stages of the Aberdeen Re-advance are visible at various points in the Dee valley, such as the arc of moraine at Peterculter where the Dee loops north to seek a way through, and at Durris a few miles upstream.

The wastage of this ice was followed by another cold phase when the Deeside Ice advanced once more but this time only as far as Dinnet, where the Dee emerges from the Highlands proper (*Dinnet Re-advance*). Here there is a wide spread of kames and eskers with huge kettle holes occupying the site of the mass of dead ice which was detached from the main glacier as the retreat began. In this area of Loch Davan and Loch Kinord may be found one of the finest examples of dead-ice topography in the Highlands similar to that of Glenmore on Speyside or Dava Moor on the Findhorn. With it is associated the meltwater channel of the Vat Burn and the famous ' pot hole ' which is probably unique in Britain. In the northeast of this basin of Cromar another important series of channels marks an earlier stage in the escape of meltwater from the Deeside ice and leads into Donside. Higher up the valleys, such as in Glen Derry, fresh loops of moraine mark the final stages of the ice from the region.

The imprint of the glacial process in North-East Scotland is quite clear and variations in the character of the till derived from different ice sheets has produced significant, although sometimes subtle, variations in land utilisation and economy. One may contrast the richness of the red Strathmore drift with the stony grey till of the Deeside Ice in the vicinity of Aberdeen; the difference in the character of Deeside and Donside is the result of the abundance of fluvio glacial material in the former—

> ' The River Dee for fish and tree,
> The River Don for horn and corn.'

The massive consumption dykes of the surface west of Aberdeen, where the soil is full of granite fragments, contrast with the fences and small dykes of the old lake floors or with ' Moraineless Buchan ' or with the area overlain by Strathmore till along the coast. The rejuvenation and diversion of river courses were important in the early location of the textile and paper industries on lower Donside. The production of dry and wet areas, the former by the deposition of easily drained sands and gravels, and the latter by impeding drainage on the already gentle slopes of the old erosion surfaces, affected population distribution. The dry areas attracted settlement while the wet patches were, for long, negative areas for agriculture and population.

Scenic contrasts are not confined only to highland and lowland districts. The coastline offers a wide variety of erosional and depositional forms made the more attractive and complicated by their development in relation to varying sea levels. The fine cliff scenery cut in crystalline rocks or Old Red Sandstone, and the sweeping bays bounded by marram fringed dunes or shingle ridges combine to give the succession of high and low coasts which characterise the coastal scenery (Fig. 3).

The cliff coasts vary in form with the lithology so that the more massive granite and the Old Red Sandstone cliffs have a wall-like appearance with less intricacy of outline than cliffs cut in the metamorphic rocks, which tend to be intricately sculptured with inlets or 'yawns' cutting back deeply into the land. There is, for instance, an interesting variation in the cliff outline north of the Highland Boundary Fault at Stonehaven where, as the metamorphism becomes more intense towards the north, so the cliff outline becomes more varied. The effect of marine erosion in the weaker rocks is well demonstrated in the deep 'yawns', partially plugged with boulder clay, cut along dolerite dykes between Stonehaven and Aberdeen. Fine natural arches occur both in the Old Red Sandstone, as at Catterline south of Stonehaven, and in the metamorphic rocks, such as the famous Bow Fiddle at Portknockie in Banffshire, where an arch has been cut in a stack formed of the Cullen quartzite. At the Bullers o' Buchan, between Cruden Bay and Peterhead, a blow hole on the cliff top has become enlarged to give a dramatic demonstration of the efficiency of marine erosion. Stacks formed in relation to modern and earlier sea levels are prominent on many parts of the coast; particularly fine examples in Old Red Sandstone are found on the low raised beach at Cullen and in the Permo-Triassic sandstone at Covesea on the promontory between Lossiemouth and Burghead.

The cliffs in profile usually have a slope-over-wall appearance with the slope formed in the capping of till left by the Strathmore or Moray Firth glaciers. The till frequently rests on an uplifted abrasion platform, which may be seen at Stonehaven harbour rising gently to about 80 ft. above sea level at its inner edge. Wave-cut notches above the level of modern wave attack are found along some sections of the cliff coasts but abrasion platforms related to modern sea level are very discontinuous. The best examples are found in the south near Gourdon and Johnshaven but further north along the coast of Kincardineshire the cliffs plunge steeply into the sea and the 20 fathoms line runs very close to the coast, except where abraded sections of headlands, such as Dunnottar and Garron Point, cause a shallowing of the water.

The low coasts formed in response to the changes in sea level since late-glacial times offer many interesting features. As may be seen in Figure 4 they are formed of several elements. Prominent is the fossil cliff of the ' 25 foot ' or Littorina beach which extends for several miles north of Aberdeen to the Ythan estuary and is prominent at Cruden Bay and between St. Fergus and Peterhead. Most of the small bays on the Moray First coast, east of the Spey, are fringed with sections of this beach which forms the site of many fishing settlements. To seaward the flat is often covered by small grey dunes behind the main dune ridges with numerous blow-outs. Small streams, incised in the edge of the fossil cliff, turn sharply south before recurving north through the dune ridge to enter the sea. The origin of the 'boathook' bends is still obscure but since they all possess the same characteristics one must assume that they are the result of the same processes in which the

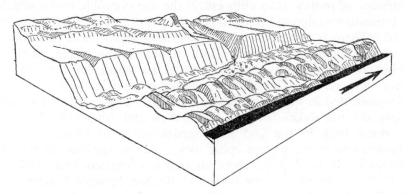

FIG. 4. Morphology of the low dune fringed coasts north of Aberdeen.

northward movement of sand along the coast by wave and wind action has deflected the outlets. The reason for the southerly component of the bend must perhaps be related to a different direction of longshore drift at an earlier period. The dune coasts are well developed also at Cruden Bay and north of Peterhead, but the finest stretch of dunes occurs north of the Ythan on the peninsula of Forvie. Here, between two main sub-parallel dune belts, resting on shingle ridges developed in relation to higher sea levels, great parabolic dunes are spread at intervals from the tip of the peninsula to the surface of the 100 ft. beach near Collieston. The movement of the sand spread gradually over the Errol Estate, with perhaps occasionally more catastrophic movements, which eventually overwhelmed the agricultural land, ridges of which are still to be seen on the Ythan side of the peninsula, and buried the medieval landscape to which the remains of the church at Forvie bear silent witness. Further south earlier traces of human settlement dated to the late Bronze—early Iron Age were disclosed by the movement of the sand.[11]

Near Rattray Head between Peterhead and Fraserburgh, the southward extension of great shingle spits offers a parallel to the peninsula of Forvie. Shingle eroded from the boulder clay cliffs near Lonmay accumulated across the mouth of a shallow inlet at the time of the '25 ft.' or Littorina Sea and later the tidal lagoon so formed persisted with lowering sea level until the modern era when the inlet was blocked by sand (about the beginning of the eighteenth century) which converted the lagoon into the freshwater Loch of Strathbeg.[12] The latest movement of sand appears to be in a northerly direction (Fig. 5). The finest development of shingle ridges and beaches is, however, to be found on the Moray Firth extending westwards from the cliffs at Buckie across the mouth of the Spey to the sandstone cliffs at Lossiemouth, while ridges extending westwards from Burghead tied the promontory which had persisted as an island in late- and post-glacial times to the coast near Forres. The stages in the extinction of the former strait and

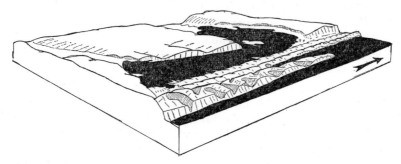

FIG. 5. Coastal features near the loch of Strathbeg.

its partial survival in the Loch of Spynie have been carefully mapped and explained by Ogilvie.[13] That the westward movement of shingle continues is shown by the deflection of the mouth of the Spey which is undermining the settlement of Kingston. The westward movement of material along the coast is also clearly seen at the mouth of the Deveron, where material brought by the river has been deflected to the west and caused severe silting of the harbour at Banff.

Relief Regions

The elevation and dissection of the erosion surfaces detailed earlier gives rise to a simple division into Highland, Upland and Lowland Regions which may be seen represented in Figure 2.

The Highlands

Culminating in the boulder-strewn summit plateau of Ben Macdhui (4,296 ft.) the high dissected tablelands of the Grampians and the Banffshire Hills form a sparsely populated rim to the lowland areas. The division between these two zones of highland is roughly along the watershed between the Don and Deveron drainage systems.

As a result of dissection by the Dee and Don the Highland plateaux of the Grampians have an east—west trend although the underlying structure is aligned from southsouthwest to northnortheast. The highest levels, the granite masses of the Cairngorms and Lochnagar, rise well above the general level of the tableland and have been deeply dissected by rivers, glaciers and corrie erosion. Rock-strewn summits and precipitous corries rise above the glaciated valleys to give magnificent scenery rendered more conspicuous by the fact, for instance, that Lochnagar is almost 2,000 ft. higher than the lower plateaux.

These lower plateaux, although deeply trenched by valleys, are still clearly recognisable. The ridges are formed mainly of resistant quartzite while the valleys have often been incised in less resistant materials such as the crystalline limestone. The shape and depth of these strike valleys such as Glen Ey, Glen Clunie and Glen Muick, has been altered by intense glaciation which lowered the watersheds and produced the fine, through valley of the Lairig Ghru from upper Deeside to Speyside. Towards the east the Highland plateaux on the south of the Dee become lower and finally merge into the Kincardineshire Plateau, the extension of the Buchan Platform south of Aberdeen. The Mounth retains the tableland characteristics of gently sloping surfaces dissected by deep glaciated valleys and is surmounted by the prominent residuals of Mount Battock and Mount Keen.

North of the watershed between Don and Deveron the Highland zone has a somewhat different aspect. The highest surface is absent and much of the remainder is far more dissected than its Grampian counterpart. The remnants of the surfaces are represented by strike ridges and valleys determined by the outcrops of quartzites and less resistant schists, phyllites and crystalline limestone. One of the best examples of the quartzite ridges is that to the west of the Upper Deveron overlooking the upland basin of the Cabrach on the east. This high basin represents an outlier of Old Red Sandstone down-faulted against the metamorphic rocks to the west. Other tectonic influences are seen in the straight trench-like hollow extending from Dufftown to Rothes and beyond the Spey. This belt of weakness has been excavated by the Fiddich and now forms an important routeway across the grain of the country.

The valleys in both Grampian and Banffshire Hills offer fine examples of glacial erosion and deposition. End moraines are found in most of the tributary glens of the Dee and Don such as Glen Derry and Glen Clunie and in the valleys of the North and South Esk draining to Strathmore. Fringing the valleys, kame terraces frequently occur as, for instance, on Deeside to the east of Crathie between Rinabaich and Coilacriech, where they rise to 100 ft. above the present flood plain. The coarse gravel with bands of sand and clay is often used for settlement sites as are the alluvial fans formed at the junction of tributaries with the main stream. In this region, where cultivable land is at a premium, the alluvial sections of the valley floor are of great importance and both Dee and Don have extensive alluvial deposits, which are also found in Glen Ey, Glen Lui and Glen Derry. The most westerly section of the cul-de-sac of Upper Deeside is a wide alluvial flat related to the rock barrier through which the Dee has cut the striking small-scale gorge at the Linn of Dee, below which another alluvial flat extends to Braemar. Marginal channels for meltwater drainage are found in many sections of the area but the most striking is the great rock-cut gorge near the Cairn o' Mounth which carried meltwater from the Deeside Ice into Strathmore.

The Western Uplands

Intermediate between the Highlands and Lowlands are the Western Uplands situated in the middle courses of the Dee and Don and having a northern outlier in the Foudland Hills. They form an elongated box-shaped area whose major axis is east to west and are the remnants of erosion surfaces now ranging between 1,000 and 1,700 ft. above sea level. They have been dissected into uplands surrounding the well marked basin of Alford, in which extensive alluvial and glacial deposits contrast strongly with the thin drift covering the schists, gneisses and granites of the uplands.

The range to the north of the Don extends from the Correen Hills to Bennachie. The glaciated and solifluction smoothed hillslopes are often covered with drift to about 900 ft. above sea level while the summits are strewn with weathered debris. The granite mass of Bennachie (1,733 ft.) has some fine tors while the summit and flanks of the hills are, in many places, covered with loose sandy debris as a result of the decomposition of the abundant felspars. South of the Don another hill range extends from the Highlands in the west to Corrennie Forest where it bifurcates, one ridge running north to form the Green Hill, while the south branch terminates in the heather clad Hill of Fare, a flat-topped granite tableland. Extensive deposits of peat, used in the past for fuel, are found on the more gently sloping surfaces.

Through these uplands flows the Don, whose characteristics of close gorge and open reach have been investigated by Bremner.[14] It enters and leaves the Alford basin by gorges while other major breaks in the uplands rim include the gap at Tillyfourie, an old water gap modified by meltwater, which now forms the main route into the basin for both road and railway. The northern part of the basin is a large triangular area of terraced alluvium, along the north side of which the Don is incised in a gently winding course. On both north and south sides of the basin there is much evidence of the stages of downcutting with bevelled spurs and frequent river capture while marginal channels seam the hill slopes.

Beyond the Correen Hill—Bennachie range to the north, and separated from it by the intervening lowland of the Garioch, lie the Foudland Hills developed on slates and other metamorphic rocks with summit levels at about 1,500 ft. The Foudland Hills are flanked on the north by the 1,000 ft.

platform and on the south by remnants of benches about 800 ft. O.D. This hill mass has many features in common with the rest of the Western Uplands —gently sloping summit surfaces terminating in steeper slopes, the whole, above the limit of cultivation, covered with heather or peat according to situation.

The Lowlands

From the bold relief of the higher plateaux, the aspect of the country changes to one of weak relief at lower level with, locally, steep slopes. The major part of the lowlands is the Buchan Plateau which extends beyond the area of the ancient territorial unit to embrace the lowlands of Banffshire and some sections of northern Kincardineshire. Inland it extends along the Dee and Don Valleys to abut against the Western Uplands, and forms the greater portion of the Insch and Garioch lowland. Only rarely does the surface exceed 500 ft. above sea level except in the west and north, and the greater part consists of the 250 and 400 ft. erosion surfaces. Drained by the Dee, Don, Ythan, Ugie, Deveron and Isla rivers the landscape consists of the main valleys which open into broader basins and rise by steps to the higher interfluves such as that which extends from Stirling Hill, near Peterhead, southwest to include the Hill of Dudwick (572 ft.), the Hills of Skelmuir (435 ft.) and Skilmafilly (578 ft.) before bending north in the Windy, Deer and Waggle Hills. The Pliocene gravels rest at about 400 ft. O.D. on this interfluve. Quartzite is a frequent but not exclusive ridge former in the lowlands, as in the highlands, and is responsible for the prominent residuals such as Mormond Hill in Aberdeenshire and the Bin of Cullen in Banffshire. The relief is far from monotonous. The succession of broad ridges with accordant summits gives way frequently to enclosed basins whose evolution may be traced in the marginal benches and wind gaps at corresponding levels. The monotony lies in the lack of trees and the uniformity of agricultural activities.

The imprint of glaciation on this area is very marked and the major glacial landforms are shown in Figure 3. Prominent are the belts of kames which mark the extensions of the Strathmore, Moray Firth and Deeside Ice and the meltwater channels associated with these ice sheets. Meltwater for instance produced the through valley of the Ythan from the North Sea to the Moray Firth coasts in which the drainage is now separated by an almost imperceptible watershed north of Fyvie. It also caused the severe dissection of the Old Red Sandstone near Troup Head to give some of the most strikingly youthful scenery of the region near Gardenstown and Pennan. Such channels breach the cliffs between Stonehaven and Aberdeen and further increase the complexity of origin. Other important channels margin the western edge of the Strathmore Ice northeast of Ellon and break through the interfluve into the Ugie basin west of Peterhead.

The northwestern and southeastern extremities of the region are lowlands of a different character, the result of the underlying structure of Old Red Sandstone. The northeastern section of Strathmore (the Howe of the Mearns), developed on a synclinal structure of sandstones, conglomerates and marls, is overlooked by the coastal ridge of contemporaneous Old Red Sandstone lavas and the crystalline edge of the Grampians. The central depression is drained by the Bervie Water, which breaches the volcanic coastal ridge to reach the sea at Inverbervie, and by the Luther Water, tributary to the North Esk. Belts of kame moraines are prominent on the lowland floor with old lake depressions and meltwater channels. The latter are aligned both parallel and oblique to the Highland Edge. That which breaches the watershed to reach the sea at Stonehaven is very prominent and gives access for the main railway line. With these channels are associated outwash fans and deltas. Outwash material (on which are built The Burn and the village of Edzell at the mouth of the Esk) covers a large area.

In the northwest lie the fertile lands of Moray, whose southern margin abuts against the Monadhliath Mountains, from which come the rivers Spey, Lossie and Findhorn. These rivers traverse the lowland developed on the Middle and Upper Old Red Sandstone rocks which are frequently masked by till from the Moray Firth glacier and by the magnificent terminal moraine of that ice sheet, corresponding to the Aberdeen Re-advance, just to the west of the Spey. The Permo-Triassic Sandstone outcrops in the coastal ridge from Burghead to Lossiemouth but it has been considerably modified by the declining sea levels of late- and post-glacial times which washed over the glacial deposits and left a series of erosional and depositional features which have few parallels in the British Isles. The cliff coast of the New Red Sandstone ridge contrasts strongly with the low emergent coast of shingle ridges to the east and west while the Laich of Moray, the former strait between island and mainland, still retains a marshy floor and improperly drained lake, the Loch of Spynie, in the central section. Of all the lowland areas Moray shows the most marked individuality and to cross the Spey is almost to cross into another world.

For References see page 36.

CLIMATE

In an area which varies in altitude from sea level to over 4,000 ft. with numerous variations in exposure and shelter it is impossible to generalise about the climate although there are certain common factors which apply. Sheltered from the moist westerly winds by its situation on the lee side of the country the rainfall is much less than in the west and varies from about 60 ins. (1,524 mm.) per annum in the highest areas of the Cairngorms to about 25 ins. (635 mm.) in the coastal areas of the Moray Firth and in a narrow coastal strip between Peterhead and Fraserburgh. To the north and east, however, the country is much exposed so that cold winds in the winter bring a great deal of snow, on an average 30 to 35 days each year, but there is, of course, variation in the length of snow lie according to altitude. Snow patches on Ben Macdhui and Braeriach persist almost the whole year round and it is this long duration of snow cover in the sub-arctic high Cairngorms which has made the district increasingly important for winter sports, encouraged by the provision of ski tows and a chair lift with suitable access road. In 1962 it was possible to find unbroken ski runs on the north side of the Cairngorms in June, and roads such as the Devil's Elbow and the Lecht Road to Tomintoul are frequently blocked during the winter and have even been closed in June. Exposure to easterly winds also brings a modification of the climate of the North Sea coastal strip in the spring and early summer when sea mist or ' haar ' drifts over the land and penetrates more deeply along the river valleys. The coastal zone is then characterised by a chill clamminess while inland, at Banchory, the sun may shine from clear blue skies. Being sheltered from the main effects of such winds, the Moray Firth Coasts have a much lower incidence of fog, which accounts for the large number of airfields which were built on the raised beaches during the war; two of these have survived near Lossiemouth and Forres.

With increasing distance from the sea, the climate becomes more extreme and is heightened by the basin-like nature of much of the inland relief. The greatest temperature variations are probably experienced in hollows such as the Alford Basin or the basin of Monymusk on Donside, where cold air draining down the slopes converts them into frost hollows. Variations in aspect and exposure produce important human responses such as the building of the principal suburbs of Aberdeen on the north bank of the Dee at Cults, Bieldside and Culter, while the string of villages such as Banchory and Aboyne often with large numbers of retired persons living therein is not paralleled on the south side of the Dee valley, which lies in the cold shadow of the Mounth. Shelter from the winds which sweep unmolested over the lowlands is also an important feature of human distributions and contributes to the generally treeless aspect of the Buchan area except where Forestry Commission Plantations offer some variation in the west.

The considerable altitudinal range of the city of Aberdeen produces striking variations in its micro-climates especially in the winter months. Post-war housing development has taken place on terraces in the Dee valley at about 150 ft. (46 m.) above sea level (Kaimhill, Garthdee and Kincorth) which correspond in altitude to the late nineteenth century and inter-war housing development of the western districts such as Mannofield. Kaimhill and Garthdee on the north side of the river have the advantage of a favourable southern aspect and shelter from the north winds (cf. the suburban development on the north side of the Dee valley as far as Milltimber) whereas Kincorth both faces and is exposed to the north. Since it is along the valleys that the 'haar' penetrates, these new housing developments tend to have slightly greater mist incidence in the spring and early summer than the older residential districts in the rest of the city. In winter cold air drainage down the Dee and its valley slide slopes tends to produce mist and frost conditions in such districts as Kaimhill, Garthdee and Kincorth.

The most striking variations are probably found in the housing schemes of Northfield, Mastrick and Cummings Park on the 400 ft. (122 m.) plateau to which the roads climb straight and steeply from the lower town whose average elevation is about 100 ft. (30 m.). Snow falls more frequently and lies longer in these new housing areas and the incidence of frost is considerably higher than near sea level with effects on public transport and other road users. Conversely sunshine amounts and temperatures in the spring and summer tend to be higher than in the immediate coastal fringe and valleys where the sea mist lowers temperatures and hides the sun.

Observations made under calm cloudless conditions in the winter of 1947-48 demonstrated the existence of a 'heat island' in the city of Aberdeen which was sufficiently strong to overcome the katabatic inversion of temperature produced by the drainage of cold air from the arc of plateau surface. The interference offered to the cold air drainage by buildings was indicated by katabatic inversion pockets where cold air draining down the main roads was trapped by buildings as the streets became narrower permitting the temperature to build up in the protected area. Here the preponderance of dark roofs and roads which act as heat retainers and absorbers caused temperatures to be as much as 5°F. (2·8°C.) above the outer districts of the city at comparable altitudes. Low lying zones within the city such as the depressions traversed by Westburn Road and Cromwell Road exhibit cold air pockets while the ridges in between have higher temperatures.[15]

The diurnal temperature range at Dyce (Aberdeen Airport), a few miles to the northwest of the city, illustrates for the year 1961 some of the characteristics of temperature for the city of Aberdeen. The bowl-like situation of

3

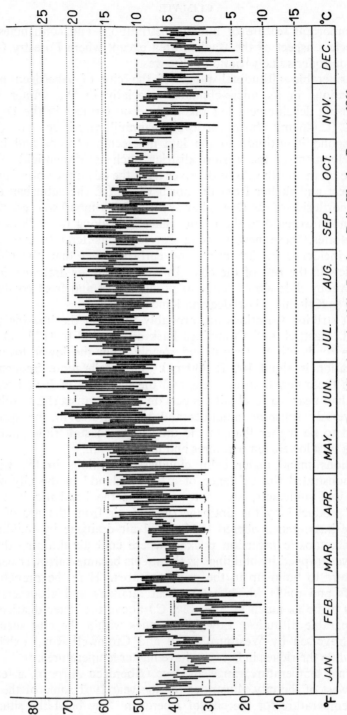

Fig. 6. The procession of temperature at Dyce (Aberdeen) in 1961. Based on Daily Weather Reports, 1961.

the airport with the high ground of Tyrebagger Hill on the west and the valley slopes on the east tends to produce colder night temperatures through katabatic inversion than in the city; in the summer, the inland situation prevents temperatures being lowered by the ' haar ' under all but the most extreme cases of ' haar ' development.

Although not to be taken as representing average conditions the temperature pattern shown in Figure 6 is interesting. On only one occasion in the year did the maximum day temperature reach over 75°F. (24°C.) falling to under 50°F. (10°C.) at night; from late May to the beginning of September the temperature rose to over 70°F. (21°C.) on only 11 occasions while the lowest maximum temperature recorded was 50°F. (10°C.) during the same period. On six occasions the minimum temperature recorded in the summer months was about 35°F. (1·6°C.).

Winter temperatures showed maxima of about 50°F. (10°C.) while maximum temperatures in the short spring (April) were similar to those in September but with higher ranges and minima sometimes below 32°F. (0°C.). The lowest daytime temperatures, experienced in the middle of February, scarcely rose above freezing point. Frost liability persisted until the end of April and recommenced at the end of the first week in November.

The salient features of the regional variations in climate within the general framework already discussed may be conveniently summarised as follows :

The Mountains, High Valleys and Basins

If one compares the temperatures of coastal and inland stations such as Banff and Glenlivet or Aberdeen and Braemar it will be seen that the differences are greater in winter than in summer. The average January temperature at Braemar is 33·9°F. (1°C.), at Aberdeen 38·7°F. (3·75°C.); the corresponding figures for July are 55·6°F. (13°C.) and 57·6°F. (14·1°C.). At Banff in 1957 the average temperatures were in January 41·1°F. (5°C.), and at Glenlivet 36·4°F. (2·5°C.); while in July the values were 55·9°F. (13·3°C.) and 53·1°F. (11·6°C.) respectively. The length of the growing season is correspondingly shorter and the incidence of frost, greater both at higher elevations and away from the sea, is intensified by basin situations. The frost season also begins earlier and finishes later. At higher elevations still wind speeds become greater, as was shown in the analysis of wind speeds for Ben Macdhui and Glen Derry in Upper Deeside. Velocities at the summit for the summer months averaged 13·2 m.p.h. while down in the valley the velocity was only 5·7 m.p.h. There is more cloud cover and less sunshine at the higher elevations than at the lower inland stations and a great deal more snow.

The Eastern Lowlands

These districts may best be described as possessing a maritime climate with continental tendencies although numerous variations are introduced by local micro-climates especially on the margins of the Western Uplands. The average annual temperature range increases inland but is roughly from 38° to 58°F. (3·3°-14·4°C.). The average extreme temperatures give, perhaps, a better physiological view:

	Average mean maximum hottest month		*Average mean minimum coldest month*		*Average extreme range*	
	°F.	°C.	°F.	°C.	°F.	°C.
Aberdeen	62·8	17·0	28·6	−2·0	34·2	1·25
Crathes	66·3	19·0	30·1	−1·0	36·2	2·3

The rainfall varies from about 40 ins. (916 mm.) on the west as in Strathbogie to less than 30 ins. (762 mm.) in the eastern coastal strip. The snowfall amount is high and although the coastal roads between Aberdeen and Stonehaven or Aberdeen and Peterhead are frequently blocked, the snow does not lie so long as in the inland higher districts.

The Moray Firth Lowlands are generally similar to the other lowland districts but with some important variations. They have a lower rainfall and lower cloud amount with a higher percentage of possible sunshine. Sheltered by high land in the west and south they escape the moist air, which brings rain to the more open districts, and the sea mist of the North Sea coasts. The low humidity and rainfall, however, bring problems of moisture for crop growth and there is an interesting development of irrigation on many farms in the area. The light soil may also be picked up by the wind and frequently covers the roads, sometimes to depths of nearly an inch. As in Strathmore, where the drift is also principally derived from the sandstone rocks, a long dry summer could lead to semi-dust-bowl conditions. The low rainfall has, however, long made this an important cereal growing area in Scotland and the climate is being increasingly exploited not only for military airfields but also for the development of the coastal tourist industry where it is referred to as the ' Riviera of the North '.

SELECTED REFERENCES

1. BREMNER, A., 'The origin of the Scottish River System.' *S.G.M.*, **58** (1942), 15-20, 54-9, 99-103.
2. LINTON, D. L., 'Problems of Scottish Scenery.' *S.G.M.*, **67** (1951), 65-85.
3. GALLOWAY, R. W., 'Solifluction in Scotland.' *S.G.M.*, **77** (1961), 75-87.
4. SYNGE, F. M., 'The glaciation of North-east Scotland.' *S.G.M.*, **92** (1956), 129-43.
5. CHARLESWORTH, J. K., 'The late-glacial history of the Highlands and Islands of Scotland.' *Trans. Roy. Soc. Edin.*, **62**, Pt. III, No. 19 (1955), 769-828.

6. FLEET, H., 'Erosion Surfaces in the Grampian Highlands of Scotland.' In *Rapport de la Commission pour la Cartographie des Surfaces d'Applanissment Tertiaires*, Int. Geog. Union, Paris (1938).

7. BREMNER, A., 'A geographical study of the high plateau of the Southeast Highlands.' *S.G.M.*, **35** (1919), 331-51.

8. JAMIESON, T. F., e.g., 'The glacial period in Aberdeenshire and the Southern border of the Moray Firth.' *Quart. Journ. Geol. Soc.*, **62** (1906), 13-39.

9. BREMNER, A., e.g., 'Problems in the glacial geology of Northeast Scotland.' *Trans. Edin. Geol. Soc.*, **10** (1916), 334-47.

10. SIMPSON, S., 'A re-interpretation of the Drifts of Northeast Scotland.' *Trans. Edin. Geol. Soc.*, **16** (1955).

11. KIRK, W., 'Prehistoric Sites at the Sands of Forvie, Aberdeenshire.' *Aberdeen University Review*, **35** (1953), 150-71.

12. WALTON, K., 'Rattray, a study in coastal evolution.' *S.G.M.*, **72** (1956), 85-96.

13. OGILVIE, A. G., 'Physiography of the Moray Firth Coast.' *Trans. Roy. Soc. Edin.*, **53** (1923), 377-404.

14. BREMNER, A., 'The physical geology of the Don Basin.' *Aberdeen University Studies*, **83** (Aberdeen, 1921).

15. TOWNSHEND, G. K., 'Some micro-climatical aspects of the Aberdeen area.' *S.G.M.*, **64** (1948), 66-70.

SOILS

THE region here referred to as North-East Scotland includes the counties of Banff, Aberdeen and Kincardine. It covers some 3,000 square miles, about one-tenth of the land area of Scotland, and in it almost one-quarter of the arable acreage of Scotland is located.

Climatic Background

The North-East region is a wedge-shaped promontory open to the winds which sweep off the sea from north, east and south at relatively low temperatures and with high humidity. The mountain barrier to the west and southwest does, however, protect the area from the high rainfall associated with the southwesterly winds of the Atlantic depressions. The region is sometimes described as ' bleak,' partly because of the lack of shelter, but the climate is rated as moderately dry; except in local areas of higher ground the average annual rainfall, although generally more than 30 ins. (76 cm.), is less than 35 ins. (88 cm.). January is the coldest month of the year, with an average day maximum of 43°F. (6·1°C.), and the warmest months are July and August with 62°F. (16·6°C.).

At the higher elevations and in the partially landlocked valleys the winter climate is more severe and frost is more frequent, harder and more persistent than over the open plains of Buchan, but in spring and through summer to late September, the maximum day temperatures exceed those of the plains. Around Aberdeen the conventional ' growing season ', when the mean daily temperature exceeds 42°F. (5·5°C.), is 241 days; inland, it is 222 days at Craibstone (300 ft., 91·1 m.) and 207 at Logie Coldstone (608 ft., 185 m.). More than half the rainfall falls in the last 6 months of the year. The rainfall distribution has two implications for agriculture : germination and quick growth are assisted by the dry spells which tend to occur in spring (reflected in the low April average), and harvesting is often delayed or prolonged by the lack of drying winds in September.

Geological Background

North of the Highland Boundary Fault are found rocks of Precambrian age—the Highland Schists. These ancient rocks are thought to have been originally marine sediments, sands, silts, clays and calcareous muds, since metamorphosed to varying degree. Two divisions of these rocks are recognised in the North-East—the Banff Division of low grade metamorphism, with argillaceous schists, slates and spotted-schist such as andalusite-schist, and the Keith Division of strongly metamorphosed rocks such as quartzite, quartz-schist and mica-schist. Large sills of igneous rock of Old Red Sandstone age have been intruded into the Highland Schists. These intrusions vary in extent from one square mile to several hundred square miles, and in composition they vary from granite to basic and ultra-basic igneous rock. In Aberdeenshire the Highland Schists underlie a denuded peneplain which forms a gently sloping incline from west to east. It is thought that at one time more recent geological formations covered the whole of the North-East, but these have long since been eroded off and now only faulted-in remnants of Middle Old Red Sandstone age remain, such as in the Bogie Valley and about Kildrummy and in the Gamrie-Turriff outlier.

South of the Highland Boundary Fault in Kincardineshire, rocks of the Old Red Sandstone formation underlie the whole area. Three broad divisions of these rocks can be made as affecting the composition of the parent material of soils. Alongside the fault line arenaceous (sandstone) rocks occur, giving rise to soils of moderately coarse texture (sandy loams). Through the Howe o' the Mearns, in the centre portion of the county, bright red mudstones or marl rocks give rise to fertile loam or clay loam textured soils, while on the coastal side, occupying the Garvock Hills, conglomerate and interbedded contemporaneous lava rocks give rise to stony clay loam soils.

Glaciation background

The whole of the region has been glaciated. Ice movements across the area emanated from ice-caps in the mountains to the northwest and southwest, and the presence of the Scandinavian ice-sheet off the eastern coast affected the direction of movement. Evidence points to three glacial periods, with an interglacial period between the first and second. The first movement passed across Banffshire and Aberdeenshire from northwest to southeast, depositing a black Jurassic clay which originated in Brora, Sutherlandshire, and possibly in the bed of the Moray Firth. This deposit, which can be seen in the Whitehills Brick and Tile Works and the Boyndie Limestone Quarry, Banffshire, has been observed as far south as Anderson Drive, Aberdeen. It forms the basal boulder clay since overlain by more recent deposits.

Marine silts and clays, referred to by Read (1923) as the coastal deposits were laid down in the interglacial period between the first and second iceages, and small areas are located about Sandend, Banffshire, and elsewhere along the Moray Firth coast.

The direction of the ice movement in the second ice-age was from southeast to north; this is thought by glaciologists to have been responsible for the transportation of the red drift, known as the Strathmore drift, from south of the Highland Boundary Fault to the eastern sea-board of Aberdeenshire. Soil survey evidence supports the view that it was pushed in from the east by Scandinavian ice from the bed of the North Sea. The deposit covers an area of 70 square miles, extending from the neighbourhood of Balmedie to St. Fergus. Some eighteen square miles of this drift is a lacustrine deposit of banded silt and clay which occurs at Balmedie, north of Ellon, and north of Cruden Bay, indicating that glacial lakes were impounded between the land ice and the Scandinavian ice-sheet. The remainder of the drift is glacial till. The northerly movement is clearly shown by the glacial striae in Kincardineshire.

The third ice movement came from the west and northwest, and moved east and southeast along the valleys. It was less extensive than either the first or the second glacial period, and failed to remove the Strathmore drift in Aberdeenshire where in many places third ice-age drift overlies the western margin of the Strathmore drift. An area in northeast Buchan is considered by Charlesworth (1956) to have remained free of third ice-age drift. Hummocky mounds of retreat moraines are a feature of the mouths of Highland glens, particularly in Kincardineshire, and spreads of outwash gravel are also common. A considerable amount of surface water sorting of the second ice-age till by third ice-age meltwater has been observed in soils surveys of Kincardineshire and Angus.

All the rivers in the North-East have high level terraces of fluvioglacial gravel deposited by meltwaters at the end of glacial times.

Soils

Soil may be defined as a natural body, containing mineral and organic matter, which occurs on the earth's surface and which supports life. It consists not of top soil only but of all the layers exposed when a pit is dug. In Britain soils are often 3 to 4 ft. deep. The character of the soil in any one place is the result of the interaction of climate, parent material, relief, vegetation, time, and the influence of man. These factors operate gradually and continuously, and the variation in their influence is reflected in the morphological properties of soil. Over a rolling landscape the soil cover forms a continuum. In classifying and mapping soils the continuum is separated into units known as soil series. Soil series are distinguished as conforming to various genetic soil groups, i.e. groups of soils having certain kinds, and a given sequence, of layers or horizons. In Scotland the individual units mapped, the soil series, are grouped into a larger unit, the soil association. This is defined as a group of soil series developed on parent materials of similar lithological origin. Within an association, series differ mainly in their degree of natural drainage or hydrologic condition and this is assessed by the consideration of morphological features such as structure and particularly colour and mottling.

In North-East Scotland a common pattern is to find soils with free drainage occupying the flanks of the hills, imperfectly drained soils the gentler contours on the lower slopes, poorly drained soils the foot slopes, and very poorly drained soils the depressions and bottom lands. Clayey texture, irregularities in slope, and proximity of bed rock can modify this hydrologic sequence. Soils representative of the four drainage classes are found in many of the associations in the North-East. In southwest Scotland, however, where clayey parent materials abound and rainfall may exceed 50 ins., 127 cm., it is usual to find poorly drained soils on slopes which in the North-East would normally give rise to freely drained soils.

Altitude, together with the accompanying change in climate, precipitation, temperature, and wind velocity, affects the energy relationships in plant growth and hence the vegetative cover and the soils developed. Above 2,500 ft., 762 m., where there may be only 90 frost-free days, alpine humus soils supporting a low growing mossy vegetation have shallow profiles developed mostly on physically weathered shattered rock. The name ' alpine humus soil ' and the soil names which follow are names of genetic soil groups, the main purpose of which is to relate differences in soil properties to causal environmental factors.

In the region between 2,500 ft., 762 m. and 1,000 ft., 305 m. high rainfall, low temperature and mainly quartz-rich parent materials encourage moorland vegetation, and conditions favour the accumulation of organic matter. Hill peat up to 8 ft., $2\frac{1}{2}$ m. thick and peat podzol soils develop. Peat podzol soils contain a thin layer rich in iron, known as an iron pan; water and roots cannot penetrate this pan, and when it is continuous the horizons above become periodically waterlogged and the organic surface soil builds up sufficiently to form hill peat. Many of the Forestry Commission plantations are established on peat podzols, but planting is preceded by ploughing in order to disrupt partially the pan and free the drainage.

Except in isolated instances cultivation seldom exceeds the 1,000 ft., 305 m. contour and generally stops at 800 ft., 244 m. In addition to the more favourable climate of the lowland region, parent materials there are often more base-rich and of finer texture because of the softer rock of the parent material. A wider range of genetic soil groups occur, including peat podzols and hill peat on strongly acid parent materials.

Acid brown forest soils occur on naturally well-drained sites which formerly supported a birch-hazel or an *Agrostis-Festuca* vegetation; these have a mull surface with well defined sub-surface horizons. On similarly well-drained sites which formerly carried dry heath and open Scots pine woodland, iron podzol soils are more extensive. These soils have a raw humus surface, a quartz-rich sub-surface horizon, and beneath this a thick iron-rich horizon. Over that part of Kincardineshire underlain by Old Red Sandstone, acid brown forest soils with imperfect drainage are common. These have loam surface horizons and clay loam sub-surface horizons, and have been equated with the grey brown podzolic soils of the U.S.A. Associated with the acid brown forest soils on the poorly drained positions are moderately acid ground water gley

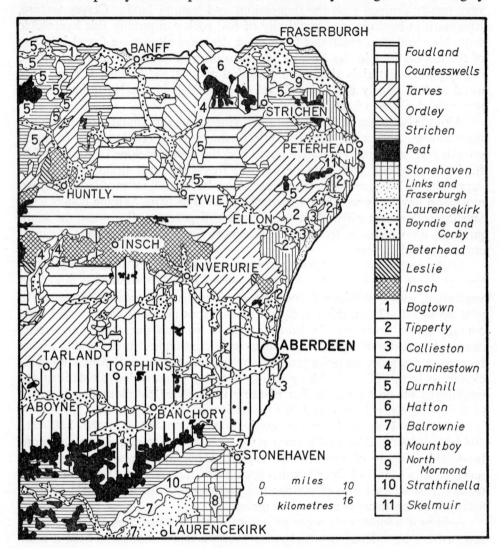

FIG. 7. Soil map.

soils. The poorly drained soil associated with the iron podzol is an acid ground water gley. Surface water gley soils, in which the effect of poor drainage is confined to the top 2 ft. or so, are found on clayey textured parent materials. The distinction between ground water and surface water gleys is of importance in drainage practice as it affects the depth of placing tile drains. In the concave depressions peaty gley soils and basin peat occur.

Anthropogenic or man-made soils, which have an unusually deep top soil and which are found around old settlements can be related to the former 'infield' land of the prefertilizer era; soils of this type have been described by Walton[4] and Glentworth[2] and are still some of the most highly productive soils in the North-East.

The Soil Associations

A sketch map showing the distribution of most of the soil associations is given in Figure 7, and covers the published maps of Sheets 76 (Inverurie), 77 (Aberdeen), 86 (Huntly), 96 (Banff), 87/97 (Peterhead/Fraserburgh) and also Sheet 66/67 (Banchory/Stonehaven), for which the soil map will shortly be published. The key gives the association name and indicates the lithological nature of the parent material.

Most of the associations are developed on glacial drifts on either till or fluvio-glacial deposits, but an area of flint and quartzite cobbles in a white, clayey matrix over the Corse of Balloch and an area of quartzite cobbles and silver sand at Woodhead of Fyvie are thought to be of preglacial origin. Both these areas are covered by hill peat and peat podzol soils.

The major associations in the region are the Countesswells, developed on granitic till, the Foudland, on slaty till, the Insch, on basic-igneous till, and the Tarves, on till derived from a mixture of acid and basic igneous rocks. Also extensive are several associations derived from rocks of the Old Red Sandstone formation. The Peterhead Association on clay textured red till and the Tipperty Association on red lacustrine silts and clays form part of the Strathmore drift along the eastern seaboard of Aberdeenshire. In Kincardineshire till derived from Old Red Sandstone arenaceous rocks is distinguished as the Strathfinella Association, a till derived from Old Red Sandstone red marl as the Laurencekirk Association and a till derived from Old Red Sandstone conglomerate and lava as the Stonehaven Association.

Frequently a soil association conforms to a particular land form unit, while the individual series can often be related to a change in slope. In soil mapping, however, there is no short-cut to digging small inspection holes in order to observe the sequence of horizons, colour, texture, depth, etc.

Some Properties of the Associations

The *Durnhill Association,* developed on till derived from quartzite, often appears on isolated hills, e.g. the Bin of Cullen, Sillyearn Hill and Mormond Hill. The rock is resistant to weathering and extremely low in nutrients resulting in strongly leached soils such as peat podzols with a poor type of vegetation. Agriculturally, and from the grazing and forestry standpoint, the Durnhill Association forms some of the poorest land in the region.

On the other hand, the *Insch Association* developed on till derived from basic igneous rocks, has an inherently high degree of fertility. The rock is richer in calcium, phosphorus and iron than granite or slate, and certain trace constituents which are of importance to plant and animal growth are also present in higher amounts. The Insch soils are thought to have supported a broad-leaved deciduous woodland. In the well-drained position the acid brown forest soils have a loam texture and a remarkably well-developed crumb structure. Relics of stone-age man are frequently recorded on the 6-inch Ordnance Survey maps for this area, giving some indication of the fertility and long occupation of the Insch Valley. Deep ' infield ' soils have been extensively found about the villages and farm ' toons ' in this area. Even in the Cabrach district, where this association occurs at an altitude of 1,200 ft., the soils are only weakly podzolised. Some 40 per cent. of the association is made up of poorly drained soils.

The *Foundland Association,* on till derived from argillaceous schist, is characterised by broadly rolling hills with smooth slopes. About 90 per cent. of the area covered by the association is occupied by naturally freely-drained soils, and the hill summits and upper slopes are deficient in well water. The texture of the soils is a fine sandy loam to a silt loam. Below 1,000 ft., 305 m., virtually the whole area of the association is cultivated. Fields are of regular shape and are divided by wire fences. The higher land (i.e. 1,000 ft.) with iron podzol and peat podzol soils, has been extensively planted as, for instance, in Clashindarroch Forest where there are no boulders to interfere with ploughing.

Except for one or two areas of gently rolling relief, particularly north and south of the Dee around Aberdeen, the *Countesswells Association* on granite till is largely undulating to hilly. Fields are divided by stone walls (dykes) built from boulders cleared from the fields, and over many farms many fast boulders remain in the fields. Rock outcrops are comparatively frequent, and many blocks of rough pasture and of woodland are on land too bouldery for arable use. The texture of a large part of the association is a stony coarse sandy loam. Many small burns coming off higher ground provide adequate field water supplies. The well drained soils are podzols or peat podzols and the poorly drained soils are acid ground water gleys.

In Kincardineshire the highly fertile land about Laurencekirk forms the *Laurencekirk Association.* The favourable topography and the inherent fertility of these soils makes them some of the best in Scotland.

Conclusion

Chemical analytical work on the soils of North-East Scotland has brought to light many regularly occurring trends in the distribution of chemical constituents (both major and minor nutrients) in the many soil series distinguished, and experimental field trials laid down on these soil types have conclusively proved the necessity of considering soil type in making fertility investigations and fertiliser recommendations.

The comparatively high level of present-day farm management in this region tends to counteract the limitations imposed by the often inherently poor quality soil.

SELECTED REFERENCES

1. CHARLESWORTH, J. K., 'The Late Glacial History of the highlands and islands of Scotland.' *Trans. Roy. Soc. Edin.*, **62** (1956), Pt. 3, No. 19.
2. GLENTWORTH, R., 'The soils of the country round Banff, Huntly and Turriff (lower Banffshire and north-west Aberdeenshire). (Sheets 86 and 96.)' *Mem. Soil. Surv. Scot.*, 1954, Edinburgh: H.M.S.O.
3. READ, H. H., 'The geology of the country round Banff, Huntly and Turriff. (Explanation of Sheets 86 and 96.)' *Mem. Geol. Surv. Scot.*, 1923, Edinburgh: H.M.S.O.
4. WALTON, K., 'The distribution of population in Aberdeenshire, 1696.' *S.G.M.*, **66** (1950), 17-26.

FLORA

THERE is very little evidence of botanical activity in North-East Scotland until about the middle of the 18th century, but it is noteworthy that, in 1603, Dr. James Cargill (c. 1565-1616)[1] a physician in Aberdeen, sent specimens of plants to his friend Caspar Bauhin at Basel. In his *Prodromus theatri botanici* (1620) Bauhin recorded the plants sent to him by Cargill and it is of special interest that among these plants was *Trientalis europaea*, thus described for the first time from a specimen gathered in the Aberdeen region. Dr. David Skene (d. 1771), who corresponded with Linnaeus, refers in his manuscripts (c. 1765-1770) to many plants of the North-East, while James Brodie of Brodie (1744-1824) and James Beattie (d. 1810), Professor of Natural History at Aberdeen, were outstandingly active as field botanists, making valuable contributions to our knowledge of the Scottish Flora. There were, however, no publications devoted to the plants of any part of the region until 1836 when there appeared Alexander Murray's *Northern Flora*, Part 1, and George Dickie's *Flora Aberdonensis*. Dr. Murray's *Northern Flora* gives descriptions, with notes on distribution, of about a third of the flowering plants then known to occur in north and east Scotland but this important pioneer work could not be completed because of the author's death in 1838. The Rev. George Gordon's *Collectanea to the Flora of Moray* was published in 1839 and P. H. Macgillivray's *Flora of Aberdeen* in 1853. Then in 1855 came William Macgillivray's unrivalled *Natural History of Deeside and Braemar* presenting, in beautiful prose, the author's intimate and deep knowledge of the geology, zoology and botany of the Dee valley; and just five years later, in 1860, George Dickie's well-known and invaluable *Botanists' Guide to the Counties of Aberdeen, Banff and Kincardine*, covering all groups of plants and with copious references to the records of numerous local botanists. It is noteworthy that previous to 1860 several species new to the British Flora had been discovered in the region. These include (apart from *Trientalis europaea* mentioned above) *Alopecurus alpinus*, *Carex lachenalii*, *C. norvegica*, *C. rupestris*, *C. vaginata*, *Cicerbita alpina*, *Cystopteris dickieana*, *Linnaea borealis*, *Luzula arcuata* and *Moneses uniflora*.

While Professor Macgillivray's *Natural History* and Professor Dickie's *Botanists' Guide* have never been superseded, several important publications adding substantially to our knowledge of the North-East belong to the present century. W. H. Trail's *Flora of Buchan* (1902) and W. G. Craib's *Flora of Banffshire* (1912) indicate the occurrence or absence of species in each of the parishes in Buchan and Banffshire respectively and add very considerably to the records given in Dickie's ' Guide '. Trail's *Flora of the City Parish of*

46

Aberdeen was published in the Trail Memorial Volume of 1923 and, with its Introduction, presents a very comprehensive historical account of the flora of Aberdeen.

The *Flora of Moray*, edited by James J. Burgess, appeared in 1935 giving the records made by many Morayshire botanists and referring concisely to the occurrence of species in each of the parishes of the County. During very recent years, the intensive voluntary work of field botanists recording for the Distribution Maps Scheme, under the auspices of the Botanical Society of the British Isles, has greatly increased our knowledge concerning the local occurrence of plants throughout North-East Scotland and these new records have been incorporated in the monumental *Atlas of the British Flora* (1962). From the ecological point of view, there are very valuable general and detailed references to the upland vegetation of the North-East region in *Plant Communities of the Scottish Highlands* (Monographs of the Nature Conservancy, No. 1, H.M.S.O., 1962) by Drs. D. N. McVean and D. A. Ratcliffe.

The Nature and Distribution of the Flora

The flora of the region (embracing the counties of Kincardine, Aberdeen, Banff and Moray) includes some 920 species of vascular plants, native or well naturalised, ranging altitudinally in their various associations, from sea-level to the highest land on the Cairngorms (Ben Macdhui, 4,296 ft.).

Along the sea-coast, extending to over 150 miles, the plant habitats include rocks of diverse structure (both basic and acid igneous rocks, gneisses, schists, slates and sandstones); extensive areas of blown sand, salt marshes and a few tidal river mouths. Several coastal areas are of outstanding botanical interest, especially the St. Cyrus Nature Reserve, Kincardineshire, the Sands of Forvie Nature Reserve, Aberdeenshire and the famous Culbin Sands in Moray, where, although there has been very intensive afforestation, the most important plant associations with their rare or very local species persist.[2] At St. Cyrus, the Nature Reserve occupies some 227 acres from the mouth of the North Esk to the Woodston Burn and embraces a sandy foreshore, with rocks at the north end, a line of dunes, a salt marsh, dune pasture, and cliffs (up to about 200 ft. in height) which are well covered with vegetation. This coastal area has a peculiarly rich flora because of its dry sunny climate and its remarkably fertile cliffs of andesite. For the cliffs alone, 177 species of flowering plants have been recorded including several which are very scarce in the North-East, e.g. *Astragalus glycyphyllos, Campanula glomerata, Carlina vulgaris, Dianthus deltoides, Echium vulgare, Epilobium hirsutum, Eupatorium cannabinum, Hyoscyamus niger, Origanum vulgare, Silene nutans, Trifolium scabrum, T. striatum* and *Viola hirta*. Extremely thorough ecological studies of the various plant associations at St. Cyrus have been carried out by the staff and students of the Botany Department of Aberdeen University and the results published.[3]

The Sands of Forvie Nature Reserve of 1,774 acres, lying between the estuary of the River Ythan and the village of Collieston, has its chief botanical interests in the complex series of plant communities of its very extensive system of dunes and dune hollows (some containing small lochs). The Reserve, which has formed a very important area for studies in both plant and animal ecology, includes over 190 species of vascular plants among which are many of rare and local occurrence in the region generally, such as the following, found among the dunes: *Anagallis tenella, Botrychium lunaria, Carex maritima, Centaurium littorale, Dactylorchis incarnata, Equisetum variegatum, Listera ovata, Ophioglossum vulgatum, Parnassia palustris, Pyrola minor, Radiola linoides, Salix pentandra, Saxifraga tridactylites, Teesdalia nudicaulis* and *Valerianella locusta*. On the coastal rocks towards the north end of the Reserve are *Artemisia maritima, Asplenium marinum, Ligusticum scoticum* and *Spergularia media*. On the shingle of a few bays along the Moray Firth *Mertensia maritima* is often prominent. *Saxifraga oppositifolia* and *Sedum rosea* occur very locally on the north coasts of Aberdeenshire and Banffshire; and at the base of the sea-cliffs of Dalradian slate in a bay in Banffshire, there is a long-established colony of *Saxifraga hypnoides*. The very local *Cystopteris dickieana* persists securely in its station on the Kincardineshire coast; and in the same parish is *Juncus filiformis*.

Inland, over the well-cultivated lowlands, the sheltered river valleys and older woods are generally rich in wild plants and most of the rarer species such as *Paris quadrifolia, Linnaea borealis, Moneses uniflora* and *Corallorhiza trifida* remain in at least some of their old stations in spite of damage by felling operations. The oak woodland on the south side of the Dee at Dinnet, Aberdeenshire, has been carefully preserved and is of particular interest.

The very extensive woods by the Findhorn, some miles south of Forres, have been justly extolled because of their remarkably luxuriant and species-rich flora,[4] especially where the limestone has been exposed.

While many of the lowland lochs have greatly receded or been almost eliminated because of drainage and other operations, some amply retain their characteristic aquatic and marsh vegetation referred to in the local floras.

On the uplands and lower slopes of the mountains, where cultivation is scanty or absent, heather moors (with frequent boggy areas) and wild woodlands (mostly of Birch and Scots Pine) become generally prominent; but there are, of course, very considerable local variations in the vegetation depending on geological conditions. Of peculiar interest are the areas of serpentine on Upper Donside and Upper Deeside: also the areas of limestone near Inchrory, Banffshire, and near Braemar, Aberdeenshire. Juniper occurs conspicuously in several upland woods and on hillsides, the Birch-Juniper wood on the north slopes of Morrone, Braemar, being the finest woodland of its kind in the region. *Calluna vulgaris* is dominant over large areas.

Some of the most extensive and splendid Scots Pine woods in Scotland persist on Deeside (especially those of Glen Tanar, Balmoral and Mar) and near Grantown-on-Spey in Moray. Among the characteristic plants of these woods *Goodyera repens, Listera cordata, Pyrola media* and *Trientalis europaea* are often frequent, while *Linnaea borealis* is very local and rather elusive when not in flower.

The rare and curious fern, *Asplenium septentrionale,* still occurs on shaded rocks in the Dee Valley between Ballater and Braemar, and *Equisetum x trachyodon* remains well-established by the Dee west of Banchory, where it was discovered more than a hundred years ago.

As regards the mountain flora of the region, the areas of chief interest— well-known to generations of field botanists—are in West Aberdeenshire, notably Lochnagar, Creag an Dail Bheag, the head of Glen Callater and the Cairngorms[5] (including a large part of the Cairngorms Nature Reserve). In the writer's experience, nearly all the many species of vascular plants for which these areas have been renowned persist in their particular habitats, some (e.g. *Cicerbita alpina, Saxifraga cespitosa*) being rarely seen in their remote fastnesses except by intrepid climbers.

Geographical Relationships of the Flora

On considering the species of flowering plants of North-East Scotland in relation to their general distribution in the British Isles it is clear that nearly all the plants which are relatively more common in or characteristic of this region can be referred to four of the sixteen geographical elements or groups of plants distinguished by Professor J. R. Matthews in his *Origin and Distribution of the British Flora* (1955). These elements or groups of geographically related species are represented as follows:

Continental Northern Element

The species of this group, as regards Europe, are mainly distributed in central and northern regions. About ninety-seven British species are within this group, of which fifty-nine occur in the North-East: *Alchemilla glabra, A. vestita, Angelica sylvestris, Astragalus danicus, Betula pubescens, Carex curta, C. diandra, C. dioica, C. disticha, C. echinata, C. lasiocarpa, C. pulicaris, Chrysosplenium alternifolium, Circaea intermedia, Cirsium hetero- phyllum, Coeloglossum viride, Corallorhiza trifida, Crepis paludosa, Drosera anglica, D. rotundifolia, Eleocharis multicaulis, E. pauciflorus, Eriophorum angustifolium, E. latifolium, E. vaginatum, Galium boreale, G. uliginosum, Gentianella amarella, G. campestris, Hammarbya paludosa, Hypericum hirsutum, Littorella uniflora, Melampyrum sylvaticum, Menyanthes trifoliata, Meum athamanticum, Moneses uniflora, Oxycoccus palustris, Parnassia palustris, Pinguicula vulgaris, Pinus sylvestris, Potamogeton filiformis, P. obtusifolius, P. praelongus, Potentilla palustris, Pyrola media, P. rotundifolia, Orthilia secunda, Sagina nodosa, Salix aurita, S. nigricans, S. pentandra, Sedum villosum, Sparganium augustifolium, Trichophorum caespitosum, Utricularia intermedia, U. minor, Vaccinium myrtillus, Vicia sylvatica, Viola palustris.*

As with *Moneses uniflora*, there have been extremely few records of *Hammarbya paludosa* (so easily overlooked!) in the North-East, but this species definitely persists (1962), however locally, near Braemar up to about 1,400 ft. *Melampyrum sylvaticum* occurs up to about 2,000 ft. in the same district.

Northern Montane Element

This group includes species of northern Europe and of the hilly regions of central Europe. Fifteen of the thirty British species are found in our region: *Antennaria dioica, Carex pauciflora, Goodyera repens, Juncus alpinus, J. filiformis, Leucorchis albida, Linnaea borealis, Listera cordata, Nuphar pumila, Rubus saxatilis, Salix phylicifolia, Saxifraga hypnoides, Subularia aquatica, Trientalis europaea, Trollius europaeus.*

The plants of this group do not usually range so high on our mountains as do the plants of the Arctic-Alpine Element, but *Trientalis europaea* reached an elevation of 3,500 ft. on Lochnagar and *Trollius europaeus* is well established at 3,700 ft. by the waterfall descending from the Wells of Dee on Braeriach.

Arctic-Subarctic Element

These plants are distinctly northern in distribution, ranging into the arctic and subarctic regions but absent from the mountains of central Europe. Of the twenty-seven British species represented, nineteen belong to the North-East:

Alopecurus alpinus, Carex aquatilis, C. rariflora, C. saxatilis, Cerastium arcticum, Cochlearia micacea, Cornus suecica, Deschampsia alpina, Draba norvegica, Erigeron borealis, Ligusticum scoticum, Luzula arcuata, Mertensia maritima, Poa flexuosa, Rhinanthus borealis, Rubus chamaemorus, Salix lanata, Saxifraga cespitosa, S. rivularis.

Regarding the two very rare saxifrages mentioned above, *S. caespitosa,* has at least two stations on the Eastern Cairngorms where it flowers profusely, and *S. rivularis* occurs in fairly accessible places in the great Eastern Corrie of Lochnagar and on the Central Cairngorms where it ranges from about 2,700 ft. up to about 4,000 ft.—but is very local.

The very handsome and rare willow *Salix lanata* is not found anywhere in eastern Scotland north of the Dee but occurs very sparsely on a few crags near the southern boundary of Aberdeenshire—just within the region covered by this survey.

Luzula arcuata, although widespread and locally frequent on the highest Cairngorms (up to the summit of Ben Macdhui at 4,296 ft.), is rare in the Scottish Highlands generally while *Poa flexuosa*, of Lochnagar and Cairn Toul, is an extremely local species. *Alopecurus alpinus* (Lochnagar, Glen Callater, Glas Maol (north side), and the Cairngorms) is of special interest in being the only species of this group not found in Scandinavia.

Arctic-Alpine Element

This consists of species mainly of arctic or subarctic regions and on high mountains further south, but characteristically absent from the intervening lowlands. Fifty-seven of the seventy-five species of this group occur within the North-East region:

Alchemilla alpina, A. filicaulis, A. glomerulans, Arctostaphylos uva-ursi, Astragalus alpinus, Betula nana, Cardaminopsis petraea, Carex atrata, C. bigelowii, C. capillaris, C. lachenalii, C. maritima, C. norvegica, C. rupestris, C. vaginata, Cerastium alpinum, C. cerastioides, Cicerbita alpina, Draba incana, Dryas octopetala, Empetrum hermaphroditum, E. nigrum, Epilobium alsinifolium, E. anagallidifolium, Gnaphalium norvegicum, G. supinum, Juncus castaneus, J. trifidus, J. triglumis, Loiseleuria procumbens, Luzula spicata, Minuartia verna, Oxyria digyna, Phleum commutatum, Poa alpina, P. glauca, Polygonum viviparum, Potentilla crantzii, Sagina saginoides, Salix herbacea, S. lapponum, S. myrsinites, S. reticulata, Saussurea alpina, Saxifraga aizoides, S. nivalis, S. oppositifolia, S. stellaris, Sedum rosea, Sibbaldia procumbens, Silene acaulis, Thalictrum alpinum, Tofieldia pusilla, Vaccinium uliginosum, V. vitis-idaea, Veronica alpina, V. fruticans.

Apart from being generally rather rare or local, many of the Arctic Alpine species mentioned above are among the most attractive of our native plants. One of these is *Astragalus alpinus*, which has the most northerly of its three British stations on a hillside of great ecological interest in the Forest of Invercauld, where a small belt of lime-rich rocks supports (in addition to the *Astragalus*) *Dryas octopetala, Carex atrata, C. rupestris, Cerastium arcticum, Poa alpina* and several other rare mountain species very local in North-East Scotland.

SCIENTIFIC AND COMMON NAMES OF SPECIES MENTIONED

Alchemilla alpina—Alpine Lady's Mantle
— *filicaulis*—Lady's Mantle
— *glabra*—Lady's Mantle
— *glomerulans*—Lady's Mantle
— *vestita*—Lady's Mantle
Alopecurus alpinus—Alpine Foxtail
Anagallis tenella—Bog Pimpernel
Angelica sylvestris—Wild Angelica
Antennaria dioica—Mountain Everlasting or Cat's-foot
Arctostaphylos uva-ursi—Bearberry
Artemisia maritima—Sea Wormwood
Asplenium marinum—Sea Spleenwort
— *septentrionale*—Forked Spleenwort
Astragalus alpinus—Alpine Milk-vetch
— *danicus*—Purple Milk-vetch
— *glycyphyllos*—Sweet Milk-vetch
Betula nana—Dwarf Birch
— *pubescens*—Downy Birch
Botrychium lunaria—Moonwort
Calluna vulgaris—Ling or Common Heather
Campanula glomerata—Clustered Bellflower
Cardaminopsis petraea—Northern Rock-cress
Carex aquatilis—Straight-leaved Sedge
— *atrata*—Black Sedge
— *bigelowii*—Stiff Sedge
— *capillaris*—Hair Sedge
— *curta*—White Sedge
— *diandra*—Lesser Fox Sedge
— *dioica*—Separate-headed Sedge
— *disticha*—Brown Sedge
— *echinata*—Star Sedge
— *lachenalii*—Mountain Oval Sedge
— *lasiocarpa*—Slender Sedge
— *maritima*—Curved Sedge
— *norvegica*—Close-headed Alpine Sedge
— *pauciflora*—Few-flowered Sedge
— *pulicaris*—Flea Sedge
— *rariflora*—Loose-flowered Sedge
— *rupestris*—Rock Sedge
— *saxatilis*—Russet Sedge
— *vaginata*—Sheathing Sedge
Carlina vulgaris—Carline Thistle
Centaurium littorale — Narrow-leaved Centaury
Cerastium alpinum—Alpine Mouse-ear Chickweed
— *arcticum*—Arctic Mouse-ear Chickweed
— *cerastoides*—Starwort Mouse-ear Chickweed
Chrysosplenium alternifolium — Alternate-leaved Golden Saxifrage
Cicerbita alpina—Alpine Sow-thistle
Circæa intermedia—Intermediate Enchanter's Nightshade
Cirsium heterophyllum—Melancholy Thistle
Cochlearia micacea—Small Alpine Scurvy-grass
Cæloglossum viride—Frog Orchid
Corallorhiza trifida—Coral-root
Cornus suecica—Dwarf Cornel

Crepis paludosa—Marsh Hawk's-beard
Cystopteris dickieana—Dickie's Bladder-fern
Dactylorchis incarnata—Early Marsh Orchid
Deschampsia alpina—Alpine Hair-grass
Dianthus deltoides—Maiden Pink
Draba incana—Hoary Whitlow Grass
— *norvegica*—Rock Whitlow Grass
Drosera anglica—Great Sundew
— *rotundifolia*—Round-leaved Sundew
Dryas octopetala—Mountain Avens
Echium vulgare—Viper's Bugloss
Eleocharis multicaulis — Many-stemmed Spike-rush
— *pauciflorus*—Few-flowered Spike-rush
Empetrum hermaphroditum — Mountain Crowberry
— *nigrum*—Common Crowberry
Epilobium alsinifolium—Chickweed Willow-herb
— *anagallidifolium*—Alpine Willow-herb
— *hirsutum*—Great Willow-herb
Equisetum variegatum — Variegated Horse-tail
— *x trachyodon*—Rough-toothed Horsetail
Erigeron borealis—Alpine Fleabane
Eriophorum angustifolium — Narrow-leaved Cotton-grass
— *latifolium*—Broad-leaved Cotton-grass
— *vaginatum*—Hare's-tail Cotton-grass
Eupatorium cannabinum—Hemp Agrimony
Galium boreale—Northern Bedstraw
— *uliginosum*—Rough Marsh Bedstraw
Gentianella amarella—Felwort
— *campestris*—Field Gentian
Gnaphalium norvegicum — Highland Cudweed
— *supinum*—Dwarf Cudweed
Goodyera repens—Creeping Lady's Tresses
Hammarbya paludosa—Bog Orchid
Hyoscyamus niger—Henbane
Hypericum hirsutum—Hairy St. John's Wort
Juncus alpinus—Alpine Jointed Rush
— *castaneus*—Chestnut Rush
— *filiformis*—Thread Rush
— *trifidus*—Trifid Rush
— *triglumis*—Three-flowered Rush
Leucorchis albida—Small White Orchid
Ligusticum scoticum—Lovage
Linnæa borealis—Linnæa
Listera cordata—Lesser Twayblade
— *ovata*—Twayblade
Littorella uniflora—Shore-weed
Loiseleuria procumbens—Trailing Azalea
Luzula arcuata—Curved Woodrush
— *spicata*—Spiked Mountain Woodrush
Melampyrum sylvaticum—Wood Cow-wheat
Menyanthes trifoliata—Bog Bean
Mertensia maritima—Oyster Plant
Meum athamanticum—Spignel
Minuartia verna—Vernal Sandwort
Moneses uniflora — Single-flowered Wintergreen

Nuphar pumila—Least Yellow Water-lily
Ophioglossum vulgatum—Adder's Tongue
Origanum vulgare—Marjoram
Orthilia secunda—Serrated Wintergreen
Oxycoccus palustris—Small Cranberry
Oxyria digyna—Mountain Sorrel
Paris quadrifolia—Herb Paris
Parnassia palustris—Grass of Parnassus
Phleum commutatum—Alpine Timothy Grass
Pinguicula vulgaris—Common Butterwort
Pinus sylvestris—Scots Pine
Poa alpina—Alpine Meadow Grass
— *flexuosa*—Wavy Meadow Grass
— *glauca* — Glaucous Mountain Meadow Grass
Polygonum viviparum—Viviparous Bistort
Potamogeton filiformis—Slender-leaved Pondweed
— *obtusifolius*—Grassy Pondweed
— *prælongus*—Long-stalked Pondweed
Potentilla crantzii—Alpine Cinquefoil
— *palustris*—Marsh Cinquefoil
Pyrola media—Intermediate Wintergreen
— *minor*—Common Wintergreen
— *rotundifolia*—Round-leaved Wintergreen
Radiola linoides—All-seed
Rhinanthus borealis — Northern Yellow Rattle
Rubus chamæmorus — Averans or Cloudberry
— *saxatilis*—Stone Bramble
Sagina nodosa—Knotted Pearlwort
— *saginoides*—Alpine Pearlwort
Salix aurita—Eared Willow
— *herbacea*—Least Willow
— *lanata*—Woolly Willow
— *lapponum*—Downy Willow
— *myrsinites*—Whortle-leaved Willow
— *nigricans*—Dark-leaved Willow
— *pentandra*—Bay-leaved Willow
— *phylicifolia*—Tea-leaved Willow
— *reticulata*—Netted Willow

Saussurea alpina—Alpine Saussurea
Saxifraga aizoides—Yellow Mountain Saxifrage
— *cespitosa*—Tufted Saxifrage
— *hypnoides*—Mossy Saxifrage
— *nivalis*—Alpine Clustered Saxifrage
— *oppositifolia*—Purple Saxifrage
— *rivularis*—Brook Saxifrage
— *stellaris*—Starry Saxifrage
— *tridactylites*—Rue-leaved Saxifrage
Sedum rosea—Rose-root
— *villosum*—Hairy Stonecrop
Sibbaldia procumbens—Procumbent Sibbaldia
Silene acaulis—Moss Campion
— *nutans*—Drooping Catchfly
Sparganium angustifolium — Floating Burreed
Spergularia media—Greater Sea Spurrey
Subularia aquatica—Awlwort
Teesdalia nudicaulis—Shepherd's Cress
Thalictrum alpinum—Alpine Meadow Rue
Tofieldia pusilla—Scottish Asphodel
Trichophorum cæspitosum—Deer-grass
Trientalis europæa — Chickweed Wintergreen
Trifolium scabrum—Rough Trefoil
— *striatum*— Soft Trefoil
Trollius europæus—Globe Flower
Utricularia intermedia — Intermediate Bladderwort
— *minor*—Lesser Bladderwort
Vaccinium myrtillus—Blaeberry
— *uliginosum*—Bog Whortleberry
— *vitis-idæa*—Cowberry or (in N.E. Scotland) Cranberry
Valerianella locusta—Corn Salad
Veronica alpina—Alpine Speedwell
— *fruticans*—Rock Speedwell
Vicia sylvatica—Wood Vetch
Viola hirta—Hairy Violet
— *palustris*—Marsh Violet

SELECTED REFERENCES

1. Cf. CAMERON, J. K., *Aberdeen University Review*, xxxviii, **2** (1959), 148-151 and RAVEN, C. E., *English Naturalists from Neckham to Ray* (1947), 237.
2. Cf. WEBSTER, M. McC., Rep. of B.S.B.I. meeting in Moray. *B.S.B.I. Prov.* **1** (1954-55), 246-248.
3. Cf. ROBERTSON, E. T. and GIMINGHAM, C. H., 'Contributions to the Maritime Ecology of St. Cyrus, Kincardineshire.' Part I. 'The Cliffs': and Part II. 'The Sand-dunes.' *Trans. Bot. Soc. Edin.*, **35** (1951), 370-414; and GIMINGHAM, C. H., Part III. 'The Salt-Marsh.' Ibid., **36** (1955), 137-64.
4. Cf. MacGREGOR, ALEX, 'Flora of the North East.' *British Assn. Rep.*, 1934, 33.
5. Cf. ROGER, J. GRANT, 'Flowering Plants of the Cairngorms.' *Cairngorm Cl. J.*, **17**, No. 90 (1956), 57.

FAUNA

THE counties included in this survey contain an extremely wide range of habitats and a correspondingly varied fauna. They extend into the largest area of land above 3,000 ft. in Britain: land that is so inaccessible and has so severe a climate that it has remained unaffected by man. Apart from a very few stray sheep, not even domestic livestock have been able to graze there, and it remains the largest purely natural community in the country. From this elevation one moves down through deer forest and grouse moor with progressively greater signs of human interference, through scattered remnants of the old Caledonian forests, now not quite natural in many places, to the rich agricultural area, where, centuries ago, natural communities were swept away almost completely to make way for intensive arable agriculture. Many rivers flow through this region, down to a very varied coastline of fine sandy beaches alternating with cliffs of granite, red sandstone and conglomerate. Towns and villages are numerous with Aberdeen the only large urban area, and these need not be considered separately.

Each of these kinds of country has its characteristic fauna, rarely purely natural, but usually a blend of naturally occurring and introduced species living in greatly modified habitats. We propose to treat the North-East fauna under these major biological communities.

Mountains

The Cairngorm range reaches 4,296 ft. above sea level and is the largest group of high mountains in Scotland. The extensive high-level plateaux have an arctic-alpine vegetation, and plants become so scarce over 4,000 ft. that the surface of the ground is mostly boulders and gravel. On all the high mountains the past glaciations carved out steep rocky corries with piled scree underneath, and a few have small lochs at the bottom. The numerous steep granite cliffs rise to between 600 and 1,000 ft. in many corries and provide the biggest range of snow and ice climbing routes in the country. A few snow patches lie till August (one patch has melted only twice this century), and there are occasional frosts and snowfalls even in midsummer. These mountain-tops closely resemble the stony tundras of the high arctic.

Many of the animal species belong to the arctic. They were early post-glacial colonists and occur in Britain now only as relics on the alpine zone of mountains. However, typically lowland or moorland species also occur. The invertebrates have to spend much of their time under stones or well into the soil to avoid the strong winds and freezing temperatures. For the same reason many of the insects are flightless and many of the spiders do not build webs. There are many species of small weevils including the arctic species *Otiorrhynchus arcticus*. The arctic sawfly *Amauronematus abnormis*, with flightless females, has been found only on Braeriach. The common arctic dung-beetle *Aphodius lapponum* is also abundant in the Cairngorms. High ground near Braemar provides the only known British stations for the mountain burnet, an arctic species of moth. The broad-bordered white underwing and the black mountain moth are locally abundant in the zone between 2,500 and 4,000 ft., the former especially frequenting the blooms of the mountain azalea. Craneflies and smaller numbers of other Diptera such as green-bottles, bibionids and empids are the commonest flying insects of the high tops on warm summer days. Spiders and carabid ground beetles are common; water beetles of the genus *Agabus,* and corixids occur in the pools, and stone-flies are abundant in the highest streams.

Brown trout have been caught at 3,050 ft. in Loch Etchachan, the highest record for Scotland. Frogs spawn up to 3,000 ft. but occur only rarely higher up.

Ptarmigan, which turn white in winter, are the commonest birds, reaching a density of 10 birds per 100 acres and sometimes getting into flocks of hundreds; they feed on the sparse heathy vegetation throughout the year. A few pairs of snow buntings nest on the highest plateaux and corries. The dotterel is another arctic-alpine bird living in summer on the mossy and grassy plateaux along with some golden plovers and one or two pairs of dunlin. A small number of insectivorous birds, such as wheatears and meadow pipits, also breed up to the tops of the mountains in summer. Ring ouzels live in summer in the sheltered corries and dippers occur all the year on the streams, sometimes being seen at the source of the Dee at 4,000 ft. The golden eagle has nests up to 3,000 ft. and often hunts over the highest tops.

Many birds such as wild geese, ducks, Scandinavian thrushes, and swallows migrate over the mountains, especially through the conspicuous passes. A good indicator of the arctic nature of these mountains was the snowy owl which lived on Ben Macdhui in 1952 and 1953: nearly all snowy owls spend the summer on high-arctic tundras.

Mountain hares are scarce on the highest ground, but a few live even on the summits of the Cairngorms in summer. Like the ptarmigan, they turn white in winter and shelter in holes which they scrape out of the snow. Both pygmy and common shrews occur on the highest plateaux in summer and we have seen shrews running over the snow at 3,500 ft. on mid-winter days. Short-tailed voles and wood mice have been trapped on the highest summits, and sometimes the voles are so abundant on grassland at over 3,000 ft. that most of the grass is eaten by the spring. The highest fox den we have seen is at 2,700 ft., but foxes hunt right up to the highest tops, preying mainly on ptarmigan, hares, voles and insects. Stoats are rare, and red deer occur on the high plateaux only occasionally in summer, though more frequently in the sheltered corries.

Moorland

Moorland covers half of the North-East of Scotland, almost reaching the sea near Aberdeen and elsewhere, and is very extensive in the hills, where it is only partly broken up by arable farming in the lower grassy glens. The economy is based largely on the sporting value of red deer and red grouse, but much of the lower moorland is being planted increasingly with conifers. The dominant plant is heather, which is the main food of grouse and mountain hare. There are no grassy sheep-walks as in western Scotland, but large numbers of blackface sheep and some hill cattle graze the heather on both the grouse moors and the deer forest. Peat banks lie deep on the gentle slopes and flat places, often broken up by deep gullies or to form hags. The frequent roots of pine and other trees embedded in the peat, at heights over 2,000 ft. show that these moors were forests in the past. Pine, birch and juniper are still regenerating on many moors, and undoubtedly the moors below 2,000 ft. are maintained by man's burning, livestock grazing, and the removal of seedling trees.

The deer forests lie on higher ground, or to the southwest where rainfall is heavier and the vegetation is consequently more grassy and mossy, and less heathy than on the grouse moors. Grouse are less common on the higher deer forests than lower down. Keepers burn the heather on both types of ground to destroy old, rank foliage and allow growth of the more nutritious, young shoots which are preferred by sheep and grouse.

Many of these grouse-moors are among the best in Scotland. The heather is usually burned with small fires and grouse reach densities of a pair per five acres in spring. In the neighbouring county of Angus alone, the annual bag varies from 15,000 to 50,000, and in Aberdeenshire it is known to be much greater. Mountain hares, though fairly scarce on the deer forests, are commoner on many of the grouse moors than anywhere else in Scotland, locally reaching densities of one per acre. Unlike continental sportsmen, British shooters do not value them highly, but many thousands are shot annually in each county for export and local consumption.

The density of red deer, at about one per twenty acres, is as high in the North-East deer forests as anywhere in the country. About 10 per cent. of the stock, or roughly 2,000 deer, are shot every year, and in severe winters many hundreds starve. Deer are scarce or absent on the lower eastern moors, but since the war many have colonised the higher grouse moors, where they damage nearby crops and constitute a serious economic problem. Roe deer occur widely on the lower moors and hills, reaching 2,500 ft. in summer and sometimes living far away from trees. Many rabbits and a few brown hares live on the hill farms and lower moors, overlapping with the lowest of the mountain hares; rabbits occur commonly to 1,500 ft. and occasionally to 1,800 ft. The various small mammals of the mountains are common on the moors, especially the short-tailed vole in grassy places. In addition, moles occur in fertile, undisturbed grassland up to 2,100 ft.

Foxes reach a density of at least a pair to five square miles in the deer forests but are scarcer on the grouse moors, where control measures are more intensively applied and more effective. However, the numbers of foxes do not change much despite a local bounty of ten shillings per tail. Though rare up to the last war, wild cats have become numerous and increased their range in all the counties and are now quite common in upper Deeside, Moray and Nairn. Stoats, which turn white in winter, and weasels are widespread on the moors, as well as in the forests and on agricultural land; however, they became much scarcer when myxomatosis decimated the rabbit population after 1955.

About 25 pairs of golden eagles breed in the area, nearly all on the deer forests where they are little disturbed. About ten pairs of peregrine falcons breed on the moorland crags and a few pairs of ravens. The buzzard has bred in the area, but only a few pairs occur in summer; however, many move into the North-Eastern moors in autumn and spend the winter there. Hen harriers are increasing as winter visitors to the grouse moors and a few breed there in spite of much shooting and trapping. Merlins are uncommon but widespread, and the short-eared owl is frequent on moors below 2,000 ft.

Blackgame are locally common on the lower moors and in the open birch and pine forests. The moors are also the summer home of many meadow pipits, cuckoos, curlews and golden plovers, with redshank, snipe, mallard and teal in the bogs, ring ouzels in the rocky and scrubby places, and wheatears among the boulders. Lapwings and skylarks are very common in the grassier areas, and a few pairs of greenshank nest in the boggy glens around the Cairngorms. Many common and black-headed gulls and fewer lesser black-backed gulls nest in colonies on the open moors. Flocks of hundreds of snow buntings from the arctic live on the moors and upland farms in winter.

Adders and viviparous lizards are frequent up to 1,500 ft. Frogs are common in the bogs and both toads and palmate newts are fairly widespread on the lower moors.

Locally, on moors below 1,500 ft., the heather may be badly affected by larvae of the heather beetle. Sheep ticks, living on hares and grouse as well as sheep and cattle, are locally a pest in parts of Moray, Banff and Kincardine. With the large numbers of deer, hares and grouse in the area, various parasitic animals such as intestinal nematodes and warble flies are common and so also are blood-sucking mosquitoes and midges. Blood-sucking black flies are common near the streams, horse flies in the deer forests and house flies abundant everywhere up to 3,000 ft. These flies are all much scarcer on the lowland farming areas. Many characteristic Lepidoptera live on the moorland plants, for example the northern arches feeding on grasses, the northern eggar and the peacock butterfly feeding on heather, and the very local underwing moth *Anarta cordigera*. Some need two years to complete their development in the cold brief summers of these moors.

Forests

The North-East of Scotland contains some of the finest remnants of the old Caledonian forest. Extensive stands of natural pine exist at Glentanar, on the Royal estate at Ballochbuie, and in the glens of Mar, where they occur up to 2,000 ft., and there are many old birch woods on Deeside and Speyside. These forests with their scrubby undergrowth of juniper, heather, blaeberry and other plants and many dead trees, standing and fallen, retain something of the richness of truly natural woodland communities with a very varied fauna and flora. Unfortunately in many of these areas natural regeneration of the trees is being prevented by the high grazing pressure of superabundant red deer and by sheep.

Lying adjacent to deer forests, the old pinewoods offer winter shelter for large numbers of red deer which summer much higher on the treeless hills. They have permanent populations of roe deer, rabbits, mountain hares in the open parts and red squirrel. So far, on the east, the invading grey squirrel has not penetrated north of Angus. Bird life is abundant. The capercaillie, which became extinct around 1760, and was successfully reintroduced from Sweden in 1837, is now common. The Earl of Fife tried unsuccessfully in 1827/29 to re-establish it at Mar Lodge, in upper Deeside. They feed mainly on pine shoots and buds. Blackgame are abundant and even red grouse live in the more open areas. Seed-eating finches include the abundant chaffinch with some siskins and a few bullfinches and the highly specialised crossbill, which feeds entirely on the seeds of pine and the introduced larch, its bill being curiously adapted to deal with the cones. Insectivorous species are also present in great variety. Great spotted woodpeckers which became extinct about 1850 have now recolonised many of the mature woods. Coal tits are abundant with smaller numbers of goldcrests and tree creepers. Speyside has been the main stronghold of the Scottish crested tit, an endemic species whose range had been greatly reduced. Now it has moved out again to colonise Forestry Commission plantations on the shores of the Moray Firth in Nairn, Morayshire and Banffshire. Willow warblers are abundant in summer with small numbers of redstarts, tree pipits, robins, wrens, spotted flycatchers and woodcock, and clearly a great variety of insect life must be available to support them. A few woodpigeons also nest in the old woods, up to 1,700 ft. The birch woods have a similar fauna, except that lesser redpolls are abundant and there are no capercaillie, crested tits, crossbills and red squirrels.

Among predators, shrews and moles are common, and foxes and wild cats occur more sparsely. There are a few recent records of animals that may have been pine martens, a species spreading rapidly in the west and likely to colonise the North-East forests before long. Golden eagles nest in the old pines and long-eared owls, tawny owls and sparrowhawks prey on the ubiquitous bank voles, wood mice and small birds. Crows eat carrion and take many eggs in season. In this part of Scotland the hoodie and carrion crows overlap and hybridise freely.

Adders, viviparous lizards and frogs are common in the old woods, and there are a few slow-worms, toads and palmate newts.

A great variety of insects live on both the native and planted pines and on the birches. Many of the herbivores are defoliators. Generally the larvae feed on the leaves during summer and overwinter in the soil: the adults have a brief life in spring. By far the most important of these are the pine looper moth, the pine beauty, and sawfly larvae of several species. The breeding of the insectivorous birds usually coincides with the periods of larval abundance in the canopy. Several species of geometrid moths occasionally cause locally severe defoliation of the birches. The commonest in this area is *Eraunis aurantiaria*. In the pine the bark beetles *Myelophilus piniperda* and *M. minor* are common and the latter is characteristic of the old forest with Glentanar its best-known stronghold. In Banffshire the sub-species of the wood wasp is *Urocerus gigas taiganus*, a form known to occur also in northern Eurasia. This North-East corner is also one of the known areas for the bee-beetle *Trichius fasciatus*, an inhabitant of old birch forests. A striking feature of pine woods, natural and planted, is the abundance of tall nests of the ants *Formica lugubris* and *aquilonia* and their associates. These ants range widely all over the canopy.

While the old pine and birch forests are of the greatest interest to the naturalist, there are three other kinds of woods in the North-East: the remnant oak forests of Deeside and Moray, the old woods of mixed conifers and hardwoods planted in the eighteenth and nineteenth centuries on private estates, and the recent private and Forestry Commission conifer plantations. These small patches of oaks and estate hardwoods and parkland are the only deciduous woodlands of the area, apart from the birch woods. The oak woods are the northern haunt of the nightjar and the wood warbler. In a fairly treeless area, such as Buchan, the small woods carry an amazing density of birds which feed on the neighbouring agricultural land, typical of the ' edge effect ' in animal communities.

The young conifer plantations provide a good example of ecological succession. As the trees grow, the thick sward of tall grasses which surrounds the young trees and supports a dense population of short-tailed voles and short-eared owls, meadow pipits and skylarks, is gradually choked out as the tree canopy meets overhead and light is excluded. Then mice become scarce, and the owls, pipits and skylarks are replaced by tits, magpies and other woodland birds, with woodpigeons in very large numbers. These plantations of exotic pines, spruces and firs have their own, usually genus-specific, insects.

Agricultural Land

Below about 500 ft. the area is intensively cultivated apart from some small unreclaimed bogs, and mixed farming is practised. In Kincardine, Deeside and Donside, and the sheltered Moray Firth areas, these lowlands are quite well wooded, but the undulating northeast corner of Buchan offers a bleak, treeless appearance. Here even hedgerows are few, thin and straggling in quality, and the uncompromising wire fences with cultivation to within inches of them offer no cover for even the least demanding of animals. The normal agricultural practice involves a regular rotation of cultivation of all fields so that permanent grasslands scarcely exist except in marginal areas on the hill farms. There are, however, numerous old moss-covered stone dykes, often supporting scattered bushes and small trees which harbour a variety of animals.

The most characteristic birds of these farmlands are the rooks, which have a very dense population in this part of Britain: almost one bird to every 3 acres of lowland. Rookeries tend to be large and a dozen or so exceed 2,000 nests. The largest rookery in Britain is at Hatton Castle, near Turriff: here there are about 6,000 nests in old beech trees and coniferous plantations and 10,000 or so young are shot annually by farmers in a vain effort to reduce their numbers. In the last year or two rooks have nested in trees at the busy intersection of two of Aberdeen's main streets (Union Street and Union Terrace): their nests can be observed almost at eye level from the upper deck of Corporation buses. Corn buntings are also common, extending inland to about the 600 ft. contour. They sing from fences, posts and telephone wires, unlike their neighbours, the skylarks and meadow pipits, which sing on the wing. Oystercatchers and curlews breed on the arable land along with lapwings; and starlings, which nest mainly in farm buildings, feed in flocks in the pastures. Hedgerow birds are locally abundant. Flocks of woodpigeons are a conspicuous feature of the farmland, and very large numbers nest in the small spruce plantations and shelter belts: ten nests per acre of wood have been found. Thousands are shot each year, but they remain very common. Stockdoves are locally common in the old planted hardwoods with hollow branches. Throughout the year there is a conspicuous daily movement of herring gulls from their coastal roosts to feed on fields far inland. Many southern species are absent. We have no hawfinches, nuthatches, or marsh tits, and many of the warblers do not come so far north. Jays, goldfinches and willow tits are rare. In autumn large numbers of fieldfares and redwings come from Scandinavia and Iceland, continental starlings join the local residents to form large roosts throughout the area, and mixed flocks of finches and buntings gather in the stackyards and stubble fields. The commonest birds of prey are the tawny owl and the kestrel; sparrowhawks are scarce except in well wooded districts, and buzzards, so common in the west, are seen only locally.

Small mammals, especially bank voles and wood mice, are numerous along the edge of fields in stack yards and waste ground. All three mainland voles occur: the water voles are large and black, the brown southern form being uncommon. All three of the mainland shrews occur, the water shrew showing a great variety of melanistic types. Stoats and weasels are widespread though persecuted by game-keepers, but larger carnivores are surprisingly scarce. Badgers occur sporadically but are nowhere common, and likewise foxes are scarce though recently both these species have increased in numbers and appeared in unusual places.

Shooting is actively practised in the lowlands, but there is little game-keeping and killing of predators except in moorland or well-wooded areas. The absence of fox and badger requires some other explanation. The commonest species shot are partridges and brown hares on open arable ground, pheasants and woodpigeons near patches of woodland, and geese and duck on the marshes, rivers and lochs.

Rabbits were greatly reduced by myxomatosis after 1955, but are again a common pest on agricultural land, particularly on the lighter sandy soils. Brown hares also are abundant on low ground and many thousands are shot and sold to game dealers each year.

Intensive cultivation brings with it problems of control of many insect pests. Many of these are country-wide, but several are unusually significant in the North-East. Of these the turnip mud beetle, whose first record as an economic pest came from Aberdeenshire in 1889, and the turnip root fly are important to farmers. The apple fruit miner, a moth whose larvae commonly feed on the fruit of the rowan, may cause much damage to apples. Although there are some interesting records of thrips, aphids and other groups, there seems to be no outstanding feature in the insect fauna of the North-East lowlands.

Rivers and Lochs

The area is well watered with rivers running east and north. Since distances from source to mouth are quite short and gradients often steep, the rivers are consequently rapid and subject to spates. The biggest rivers are the Dee and Spey with impressive valleys 80 and 100 miles long, and the North Esk, Don, Ythan, Deveron and Findhorn. All carry cold, clear water of fairly high acidity and with little calcium. Temperatures increase slowly, from near freezing in winter to about 42°F. (17°C.) in late July, and the pH is usually close to 7 though a little higher near scattered limestone outcrops. These rivers are well known to anglers for their brown trout and migratory salmon and sea-trout.

There is an abundant insect fauna of mayflies, stoneflies and caddisflies, as well as midge and mosquito larvae. *The* mayfly, *Ephemera danica,* common in the south, occurs only sporadically on the Don in years and in places fairly free from the scouring action of spates. A moderate variety of water snails and fresh-water limpet occur but the pearl-bearing river mussel is found only in the slower unpolluted reaches of the Don. These invertebrates provide food for the fish and some birds, notably the dipper which is common on rivers and streams, walking freely under the water searching for its prey. Apart from the game-fish, eels are abundant and minnows and sticklebacks are sporadically distributed all over the area. Perch and pike are present in many small lochs and the slower reaches of some rivers, and in most cases were introduced there. Gudgeon have been introduced locally, e.g. in the Don.

Water voles are plentiful and otters widespread from sea level to the hills: the former is a harmless herbivore, the latter an effective predator on fish, frogs, birds and small mammals. Mink are occasionally trapped, having escaped and wandered from the mink farms. Mergansers breed on the rivers and goosanders on streams far inland, often nesting in holes in dead pines high in the Caledonian forest. Grey wagtails are widespread but local from sea level to 1,500 ft. Scattered pairs of common terns breed along the rivers far into the hills and black-headed gulls have colonies on some of the reedy lochs. One or two pairs of kingfishers live on the lower Dee, Don and North Esk. Around 1925 ospreys bred on the Deveron and hunted over a Buchan reservoir, but they now occur only on passage.

Lochs are numerous and apart from one or two lying in rich agricultural land, are generally acid and oligotrophic. The highest tarn is Lochan Buidhe at 3,700 ft. on Ben Macdhui, there are several small lochs between 3,000 and 3,200 ft. and the lowest is the Loch of Strathbeg, at sea level between Peterhead and Fraserburgh. In Loch Davan, Aberdeenshire, occurs a northern species of mosquito, *Theobaldia alaskaensis.* Its life-history is apparently quite unknown.

Several of the upland lochs have isolated populations of char, members of the circumpolar arctic fauna. Lochs Muick and Builg, both at 1,500 ft., are examples. Great crested grebes breed at the northern end of their British range at Lochs Spynie and Strathbeg, and the Slavonian grebe at the eastern end of its range at Loch Oire. In October the Loch of Strathbeg is at its best. More than 500 whooper swans use it as a staging post on their way south, and some hundreds of mute swans may be seen. Ducks are there in thousands: mallard, wigeon, pochard, teal, tufted and fewer individuals of other species. Up to 5,000 geese, mostly pink-feet, but with a fair proportion of greylags, graze on the surrounding fields or sit on the loch.

Coast and Sea

The coastline between Montrose and Nairn is on the whole fairly smooth, and although there are no marked indentations and no off-shore islands yet there is a great variety of habitat. Fine sandy beaches occupy most of the east coast and nearly all of the Moray Firth coast west of Buckie. There are some fine cliffs at Fowlsheugh near Stonehaven, Bullers of Buchan between Cruden Bay and Peterhead, and at Troup and Pennan on the Aberdeen-Banff boundary. These cliffs are the homes of vast numbers of sea-birds during summer. Perhaps the most spectacular sea-bird colony on the mainland of Britain is the great conglomerate cliff of Fowlsheugh with many thousands of nesting guillemots, kittiwakes, and herring gulls. In smaller numbers are puffins, razorbills, fulmars, shags, rockdoves, crows and jackdaws, and a pair of peregrine falcons live here among abundant food. The other cliffs support the same species but in rather less spectacular numbers. Although cormorants are numerous along the coast throughout the year, none breeds there, and greater and lesser black-backed gulls nest very sporadically. Many great black-backs live far inland in winter, eating dead spawned salmon, and even searching snow-covered hills up to 3,000 ft. for carrion.

Of special and unusual interest are the small colonies of house martins scattered along these rocky coasts. In this region they are host to two unusual fleas in addition to their usual ones. These are *Frontopsylla laeta* known from coastal nests from Kincardine to Caithness, with an odd record from Berwick, and otherwise only from Switzerland and the Caucasus and *Orneacus waterstoni* with a similar distribution in this country and otherwise found only once in Switzerland.

The extensive areas of sand are relatively barren for birds, though several places have colonies of common and arctic terns and little terns. Among the dunes at the Sands of Forvie at the mouth of the Ythan, a large breeding colony of these species is accompanied by Sandwich terns and black-headed gulls. A few stockdoves breed in old rabbit holes in dunes and ringed plovers occur on the pebbly places. Few animals live on the sandy beaches; in winter there are sanderlings and many gulls of several species and common seals occasionally haul out at low tide. A variety of clams and razor shells may be obtained by digging and in the drift-line of decaying weed large numbers of sandhoppers of several species occur, and many species of Diptera breed. Off these shores, where the salmon netsmen have their stake nets and bag-nets, the grey seal is a common visitor and does much damage to both nets and captured fish.

There are two conspicuous muddy inlets: the Ythan estuary at Newburgh, and the mouth of the Findhorn near Forres, both with a characteristic fauna. Invertebrates occupy the mud in great abundance. Recent studies on the Ythan show densities of 15,000 *Corophium volutator*, a burrowing amphipod, and, in sandier places, 200-300 cockles per square metre. Annelid worms, mainly *Nereis diversicolor* and the lug worms, are also abundant, and the small snail *Hydrobia ulvae* is very common. These invertebrates support large numbers of waders in autumn and winter. While many golden plovers, knots, dunlins, lapwings and oystercatchers stay all winter, species such as ruff, whimbrel, greenshank, spotted redshank, and bar- and black-tailed godwit pass through in the autumn and spring. In spring and summer some 100 pairs of shelducks are dispersed over the Ythan mud and move in to the nearby dunes and heather moor to nest. Red grouse also nest on the heather here at sea level. A feature of the Ythan salt marshes is the thrip *Aptinothrips nitidulus*, which breeds on the grasses *Puccinella maritima* and *Festuca rubra*, and survives regular submergence by the tide. Another thrip, *Chirothrips ruptipennis*, occurring on the dunes of North-East Scotland, is otherwise known only from central Europe.

The Ythan also has extensive mussel beds which provide the main food for a spectacular breeding population of 1,500 pairs of eider ducks, of which 600 or so birds remain in the area all winter.

SCIENTIFIC NAMES OF SPECIES MENTIONED

Worms

Lug worm—*Arenicola marina*

Arachnids

Sheep tick—*Ixodes ricinus*

Insects

Heather beetle—*Lochmaea suturalis*
Turnip mud beetle—*Helophorus porculus*
Peacock butterfly—*Vanessa io*
Northern Eggar — *Lasiocampa quercus callunae*
Black Mountain moth—*Psodos coracina*
Broad-bordered White Underwing—*Anarta melanopa*
Northern Arches moth—*Apamaea exulis*
Mountain Burnet moth—*Zygaena exulans*
Pine Looper—*Bupalus piniarius*
Pine Beauty—*Panolis flammea*
Apple Fruit Miner—*Argyresthia conjugella*

Molluscs

Fresh-water limpet — *Ancylastrum fluviatile*
River mussel—*Anodonta cygnea*
Cockle—*Cardium edule*
Mussel—*Mytilus edulis*

Fish

Salmon—*Salmo salar*
Sea trout—*Salmo trutta*
Brown trout—*Salmo trutta*
Char—*Salvelinus alpinus*
Pike—*Esox lucius*
Perch—*Perca fluviatilis*
Gudgeon—*Gobio gobio*
Minnow—*Phoxinus phoxinus*
Stickleback—*Gasterosteus aculeatus*
Eel—*Anguilla anguilla*

Amphibians

Frog—*Rana temporaria*
Toad—*Bufo bufo*
Palmate newt—*Triturus helveticus*

Reptiles

Lizard—*Lacerta vivipara*
Adder—*Vipera berus*
Slow-worm—*Anguis fragilis*

Birds

Great Crested Grebe—*Podiceps cristatus*
Slavonian Grebe—*Podiceps auritus*
Fulmar Petrel—*Fulmarus glacialis*
Cormorant—*Phalacrocorax carbo*
Shag—*Phalacrocorax aristotelis*
Mallard—*Anas platyrhyncha*
Teal—*Anas crecca*
Wigeon—*Anas penelope*
Tufted Duck—*Aythya fuligula*

Birds (contd.)

Pochard—*Aythya ferina*
Eider—*Somateria mollissima*
Red-breasted Merganser—*Mergus serrator*
Goosander—*Mergus merganser*
Sheld-Duck—*Tadorna tadorna*
Grey-Lag Goose—*Anser anser*
Pink-footed Goose—*Anser brachyrhynchus*
Mute Swan—*Cygnus olor*
Whooper Swan—*Cygnus cygnus*
Golden Eagle—*Aquila chrysaëtus*
Buzzard—*Buteo buteo*
Sparrow-Hawk—*Accipiter nisus*
Hen-Harrier—*Circus cyaneus*
Osprey—*Pandion haliætus*
Peregrine Falcon—*Falco peregrinus*
Merlin—*Falco columbarius*
Kestrel—*Falco tinnunculus*
Red Grouse—*Lagopus lagopus*
Ptarmigan—*Lagopus mutus*
Black Grouse—*Lyrurus tetrix*
Capercaillie—*Tetrao urogallus*
Partridge—*Perdix perdix*
Pheasant—*Phasianus colchicus*
Lapwing—*Vanellus vanellus*
Oyster-catcher—*Hæmatopus ostralegus*
Ringed Plover—*Charadrius hiaticula*
Golden Plover—*Charadrius apricarius*
Dotterel—*Charadrius morinellus*
Snipe—*Capella gallinago*
Woodcock—*Scolopax rusticola*
Curlew—*Numenius arquata*
Whimbrel—*Numenius phæopus*
Black-tailed Godwit—*Limosa limosa*
Bar-tailed Godwit—*Limosa lapponica*
Common Sandpiper—*Tringa hypoleucos*
Spotted Redshank—*Tringa erythropus*
Greenshank—*Tringa nebularia*
Knot—*Calidris canutus*
Dunlin—*Calidris alpina*
Sanderling—*Crocethia alba*
Ruff—*Philomachus pugnax*
Great Black-backed Gull—*Larus marinus*
Lesser Black-backed Gull—*Larus fuscus*
Herring Gull—*Larus argentatus*
Common Gull—*Larus canus*
Black-headed Gull—*Larus ridibundus*
Kittiwake—*Rissa tridactyla*
Common Tern—*Sterna hirundo*
Arctic Tern—*Sterna macrura*
Little Tern—*Sterna albifrons*
Sandwich Tern—*Sterna sandvicensis*
Razorbill—*Alca torda*
Guillemot—*Uria aalge*
Puffin—*Fratercula arctica*
Stock Dove—*Columba ænas*
Rock Dove—*Columba livia*
Wood Pigeon—*Columba palumbus*
Cuckoo—*Cuculus canorus*
Snowy Owl—*Nyctea scandiaca*
Tawny Owl—*Strix aluco*
Long-eared Owl—*Asio otus*

5

Short-eared Owl—*Asio flammeus*
Nightjar—*Caprimulgus europæus*
Kingfisher—*Alcedo atthis*
Great Spotted Woodpecker—*Dendrocopus major*
Skylark—*Alauda arvensis*
Swallow—*Hirundo rustica*
House Martin—*Delichon urbica*
Raven—*Corvus corax*
Hooded Crow—*Corvus cornix*
Carrion Crow—*Corvus corone*
Rook—*Corvus frugilegus*
Jackdaw—*Corvus monedula*
Magpie—*Pica pica*
Jay—*Garrulus glandarius*
Coal Tit—*Parus ater*
Crested Tit—*Parus cristatus*
Marsh Tit—*Parus palustris*
Willow Tit—*Parus atricapillus*
Nuthatch—*Sitta europæa*
Tree Creeper—*Certhia familiaris*
Wren—*Troglodytes troglodytes*
Dipper—*Cinclus cinclus*
Fieldfare—*Turdus pilaris*
Redwing—*Turdus musicus*
Ring-Ouzel—*Turdus torquatus*
Wheatear—*Œnanthe œnanthe*
Redstart—*Phœnicurus phœnicurus*
Robin—*Erithacus rubecula*
Willow Warbler—*Phylloscopus trochilus*
Goldcrest—*Regulus regulus*
Spotted Flycatcher—*Muscicapa striata*
Meadow Pipit—*Anthus pratensis*
Tree Pipit—*Anthus trivialis*
Grey Wagtail—*Motacilla cinerea*
Starling—*Sturnus vulgaris*
Hawfinch—*Coccothraustes coccothraustes*

Goldfinch—*Carduelis carduelis*
Siskin—*Carduelis spinus*
Redpoll—*Carduelis flammea*
Bullfinch—*Pyrrhula pyrrhula*
Crossbill—*Loxia curvirostra*
Chaffinch—*Fringilla cœlebs*
Corn Bunting—*Emberiza calandra*
Snow Bunting—*Plectrophenax nivalis*

Mammals

Hedgehog—*Erinaceus europæus*
Mole—*Talpa europæa*
Pygmy Shrew—*Sorex minutus*
Common Shrew—*Sorex araneus*
Water Shrew—*Neomys fodiens*
Fox—*Vulpes vulpes*
Pine Marten—*Martes martes*
Stoat—*Mustela erminea*
Weasel—*Mustela nivalis*
Badger—*Meles meles*
Otter—*Lutra lutra*
Scottish Wild Cat—*Felis silvestris*
Grey Seal—*Halichœrus grypus*
Common Seal—*Phoca vitulina*
Red Deer—*Cervus elaphus*
Roe Deer—*Capreolus capreolus*
Brown Hare—*Lepus europæus*
Scottish Mountain or Blue Hare—*Lepus timidus*
Rabbit—*Oryctolagus cuniculus*
Red Squirrel—*Sciurus vulgaris*
Grey Squirrel—*Sciurus carolinensis*
Field Mouse—*Apodemus sylvaticus*
Bank Vole—*Clethrionomys glareolus*
Water Vole—*Arvicola terrestris*
Short-tailed Vole—*Microtus agrestis*

THE REGION BEFORE 1700

T H E three northeastern counties of Scotland, Kincardineshire (or the Mearns), Aberdeenshire, and Banffshire, may be described as a clenched fist thrust forward into the North Sea. If Aberdeenshire and Banffshire are taken by themselves they represent an area cut off from the remainder of the country by marked physical features. On the east and north they are ' swilled with the wild and wasteful ocean '; on the west—the wrist of our ' clenched fist '— they abut on the great mountain *massif* of the Cairngorms; while on the south a barrier of much historical importance is imposed by the Mounth, the chain of hills stretching from the Drumochter Pass along the south side of the Dee valley to the coast at Girdleness near Aberdeen. To the north of the Cairngorm mountains a natural boundary of our district is formed by the broad valley of the river Spey.

Kincardineshire, situated on the south of the Mounth, lies somewhat apart from the well-defined area whose limits have been indicated above. Moreover this county itself falls into two well marked divisions. The northern part, beyond the Highland Boundary Fault, belongs to the Highland area, while the southern half forms the northern apex of the Old Red Sandstone basin of Strathmore. Nevertheless, owing doubtless in great part to the dominance, political and commercial, of the Royal Burgh and City of Aberdeen, the Mearns has always been regarded as pertaining rather to the northeastern group of counties than to its neighbour, the ancient province of Angus on the south.

Geology is the womb of history, and no understanding of the human record in our area is possible without some appreciation of its rock structure. Broadly speaking, Aberdeenshire, Banffshire, and Kincardineshire north of the Highland Boundary Fault, may be considered as consisting of a worn-down platform of resistant and very ancient metamorphic rocks belonging mostly to the Dalradian series. These have been invaded on at least two occasions by masses of granite, which form the principal mountain areas of the district. The change to a softer and much more fertile country is markedly apparent south of the fault at Stonehaven. So far as the metamorphic and igneous area is concerned, the country cannot be described as naturally fertile, though it has been made highly productive by the energy and industry of many generations of patient farmers. The kindliest land is found in the lower valleys of the Dee, Don and Deveron, and in the district at the ' back o' Bennachie '. This formed the old lordship of the Garioch, which used to be described as the ' meal girnal of Aberdeenshire '. Throughout its history the Garioch has been associated with the great Earldom of Mar, which comprised, broadly speaking, the Dee and Don valleys and the country between them. The northeastern knuckle of our 'clenched fist' formed the ancient Earldom of Buchan; while another important territorial division in former times was the Lordship of Strathbogie in the northwest of our area. From the fifteenth century onwards Strathbogie acquired great importance as the headquarters of the famous and powerful family of Gordon.

Practically throughout the area the country rocks are blanketed with immense masses of boulder-clay and gravels, representing the rubbish left behind by the general ice sheet and the later valley glaciers at the close of the Pleistocene period. It was probably between ten and twelve thousand years ago that the ice finally withdrew from our area, which thus became fit for human habitation but when the first human beings appeared in this remote northern tract nobody can say. We do, however, know something about what manner of folk they were. We must picture them as small isolated groups of primitive food-gatherers, ignorant alike of husbandry or of the domestic animals. Their camping sites have been found at a number of places, notably in the lower valley of the Dee in the neighbourhood of Banchory. Here have been found their hearths and their characteristic 'pigmy flints'. These are tiny slips or spalls of very delicately worked flint, showing a marked tendency to crescentic or geometrical shapes. It is believed that such tiny tooth-like implements were hafted in wood like the teeth of a saw so as to form a primitive kind of sickle for cutting edible grasses and the like. Upon these, and upon such nuts and berries and small game as they could collect amid the primeval forests, these early men contrived to maintain what must to our minds have been a wretched existence.

Such settlements as those at Banchory take us back to Mesolithic times, though the absolute date when these primitive food gatherers settled in the lower Dee valley is quite unknown.

At various places among the sand dunes fringing the coast, large numbers of worked flints and flint cores are found, together with middens containing oyster shells, fish bones and the like. These point to the settlement along the coast of primitive strand-loopers who quite probably may have been contemporary with the pigmy flint workers on Deeside. Here again, however, no precise chronological data are available; and none of the flints picked up among these seashore deposits appear to belong to distinctive types. Most of them in fact, seem to be the waste products of an early flint-knapping industry, whose date is uncertain.

The source of all this flint, both now and in later times, was in Buchan, along a moorland ridge stretching roughly from Ellon towards Stirling Hill behind Buchan Ness. On this area many flints are found containing, or associated with, Cretaceous fossils. It is evident that there was once a large extent of the Chalk formation here, which probably was removed by erosion before or during the Ice Age. The heavy residue of flints remained to be exploited by prehistoric man.

It is probably true to say that the great majority of the flint tools and implements throughout the prehistoric period, found in our area, were worked from the Buchan flint. Flint factories, if we may call them so, have been found as far west as Strathdon and the Hill of Skares near Insch. It is obvious that for this valuable material the dwellers in the interior must have traded their own produce—skins and furs, perhaps; timber for making dugout canoes; bone and deerhorn for tools. We may therefore infer the beginnings both of industry and commerce in our district as far back as the Stone Age.

The name 'Mesolithic' has been given to the culture of the pigmy flint workers and the strand-loopers, because it is believed that these people were the descendants of the Palaeolithic hunter folk making their way northwards in pursuit of game as the climate of Pleistocene times slowly improved and herds of animals followed the retreating front of the ice sheet. It must of course be understood that all these stages in the evolution of prehistoric man represent sequences, which occurred at widely different periods in different regions of the globe. They are in no sense an absolute chronology.

What is known as the Neolithic period is marked out from preceding stages by the great fact that man has now become an agriculturist. He is a grower of barley and a breeder of cows and sheep. The transition from a hunter's life to that of a farmer and stock breeder represents by far the greatest step forward that humanity has taken during its whole long history on our globe. The hunter is perforce a wanderer who must forever be shifting his ground in pursuit of the herds of game. The farmer, however, is forced to lead a settled life. He is anchored to the spot where he has planted his crops. These he must tend till harvest time; he must protect them from the inroads of wild beasts and hostile neighbours. A settled life inevitably brings organisation; the growth of village communities; the emergence of tribes; and, ultimately, the formation of states and nations.

In addition to the practice of agriculture, Neolithic man had mastered the important art of making pottery. Furthermore, he had learned to make larger and much superior stone tools and weapons. These were no longer now chipped out of intractable flint, but were smoothed and sometimes highly polished out of the large variety of very hard stones which were available in this metamorphic and igneous area. For the first time, therefore, man found himself in possession of a kit of tools which enabled him to make a real impression on the vast primeval forests. Clearance of the ground for agriculture could therefore commence. We may say that in Neolithic times man is at last able to undertake the mastery of his environment.

Of course many useful smaller tools and weapons continued to be made of flint. This is particularly true of the very beautiful arrow heads for which our area is justly famous. There are three kinds of these—the lozenge-shaped type, the barbed type and those that have both barbs and a tang. It must be remembered that such arrow-heads continued to be used long after the introduction of metal. Since neither tin nor copper are found in our area, all the bronze used in the first age of metal had to be imported. It was therefore a valuable commodity that would not be used for making such things as arrow points, which were liable to be lost.

Moreover it seems clear that throughout the Age of Bronze many other weapons and tools continued to be manufactured out of stone of various kinds. Stone axes and hammers cannot therefore be necessarily taken as proof of the presence of Neolithic man. The one certain evidence is furnished by his graves. Neolithic man had arrived at some notion of a future life. He buried his dead—or at least the great ones among his dead—ceremonially in large and carefully constructed cairns. These are usually elongated in shape but sometimes round. Within them is a chamber which served as a family vault—the dead of the kindred who had erected the cairn being buried here for several generations. Usually the bodies were inhumed, though sometimes cremation is found. The evidence seems clear that Neolithic man entered Scotland by the Atlantic seaboard; penetrated to the northeast along the Great Glen; and in this way reached our area from the north.

Unfortunately, very few of his characteristic long cairns have been recorded from our area. There is, however, one overlooking Macduff, one on the western outskirts of Aberdeen, and one at Gourdon. A certain amount of Neolithic pottery has also been recovered sporadically from our district. Skeletons found elsewhere show that Neolithic man was slightly built, that his skull was long from front to back, that his face was oval and his features delicate. Anthropologists sometimes call the race which he represents the Iberian folk; and it is believed that they reached Britain from the Mediterranean area. Their journey, which probably must have taken them some centuries to accomplish, was from Spain to Brittany, from Brittany to Ireland and from Ireland (as indicated above) to the western coast of Scotland. Ultimately they penetrated as far north as the Shetland Islands. In case this prehistoric voyaging may seem incredible, it is worth while pointing out that you can sail from Gibraltar to the Muckle Flugga (the northmost inhabited point of Britain) without ever being out of sight of land.

At what precise point in time the first Neolithic settlers appeared in our area cannot be said with certainty. Evidence, however, is accumulating that the period was not earlier than say 3000 to 2500 B.C. They appear to have been few in number and it is unlikely that they have left much trace of themselves in the present racial make-up of the three counties.

A very different story falls to be told about the next race which occupied our area. About 2000-1800 B.C. a new people began to land in large numbers along the eastern and northern coasts, particularly where there were sandy beaches. This people came overseas from Holland, and have been traced back from the mouth of the Rhine to Central Europe. In marked contrast to their predecessors the chambered cairn folk, they were taller and very powerfully built, with round skulls, square jaws and broad faces. Their burial customs also are wholly distinct from those of their predecessors. Their dead were inhumed singly in a crouched position in short stone cists, usually without any cairn or other visible mark above ground. Alongside the body was placed an urn, which from its peculiar shape is called a beaker. To the new race accordingly, the name of ' beaker folk ' has been given. All over the fertile lands in our area their graves are found in extraordinary numbers. A careful distribution study of such burials shows very clearly that they did not penetrate into it from the south along Strathmore, but that they came ashore in groups at suitable landfalls along the whole coast from Montrose to the inner alcove of the Moray Firth.

The number of their recorded burials is so great that we can fairly describe this as a prehistoric colonisation. In fact it is to the beaker folk that we owe what may be called the first real settlement of our area.

The Department of Anatomy and Anthropology in the University of Aberdeen has long been a reception centre for the contents of these short cist burials. It therefore possesses a unique collection of the skeletons and tomb furniture of this early people. These skeletons have been the subject of intensive anatomical study, which has brought out the interesting fact that the beaker folk have left enduring traces of themselves in the physical make-up of the present inhabitants of the northeast. It is indeed not too much to say that the beaker folk are the original strain in the present Aberdeenshire peasantry.

Although the grave goods found in our short cists are few and unimpressive, the beakers are often elaborately and tastefully ornamented and make a very handsome appearance on our museum shelves. Doubtless much of the equipment of the beaker folk was made of materials such as wood or bone or horn which are apt to perish. Anyone who has seen the Lapland Museum at Oslo will understand how rich such a culture can be, and how few of its materials—of wood, bone, horn, leather and basketwork and different kinds of cloth—could have survived from prehistoric times. We should not therefore picture the beaker folk as a race of skin-clad savages. They certainly must have had craft seaworthy enough to carry them across four hundred miles of open and stormy water from the Rhineland to our Scottish shores.

When they first landed, the beaker folk, in our area at all events, seem to have been ignorant of metal. Very soon, however, the use of bronze was introduced among them. The first metal to be discovered was copper; but, as pure copper is too soft for practical use, it was not until some unknown genius had discovered the art of hardening it by an admixture of tin, that mankind had in bronze a metal hard enough for use as a tool or weapon. As explained above, all the bronze used in prehistoric times in our area had to be imported.

There is evidence that this trade was in the hands of itinerant bronze-smiths. The stone moulds in which they cast their tools and weapons have been frequently found, while the large hoards of bronze implements, many of them broken or damaged by use, which are a feature of the period, were obviously buried by these wandering craftsmen with the hope of being recovered at some future date.

Another change which took place very soon after the introduction of bronze was the incoming of cremation. It looks as if the new mode of burial spread from the south northwards with something of the rapidity of a religious craze—so that in the Northern Islands we find cremation in use in the chambered cairns of the Neolithic folk. In our area the ashes of the Bronze Age dead were usually placed in a hole in the ground underneath what is called a cinerary urn, shaped like a plant pot, and placed upside down over the cremated bones. As in the case of the short cist burials, these cinerary urns—particularly in the earlier period—are often buried without any mark above ground. Since they are not protected by an enclosing cist, they are apt to be knocked to pieces in the process of discovery by the ploughman or the gravel digger. Hence in most of our Museums you will find far more beakers than cinerary urns. For the reasons stated, however, this must not be taken to infer any decline of population during the Bronze Age. On the contrary, there is plenty of evidence that the population expanded rapidly and was making steady progress in clearing the forests and bringing more country under cultivation.

As in the case of the short cists, the cinerary urns are often found associated in groups, forming what are known as urn fields. These imply the existence of village communities. That the practice of cremation was not brought in by a new race is evident from many proofs of continuity. A notable example of this was found at Ardoe, on Lower Deeside, where in the same gravel bank were found short cists, cinerary urns and a small bronze bowl of a type belonging to the Iron Age. It is clear that this site must have been occupied by a prehistoric community dwelling there from the close of Neolithic times until perhaps the early centuries of the Christian era.

In the later Bronze Age cremated burials of important persons were often placed beneath large cairns now always circular in outline. These cairns were usually placed on commanding sites, with the result that even today, after centuries of spoliation, the round cairns of the Bronze Age are a conspicuous feature of the northeastern skyline.

Another type of sepulchral monument belonging to the Bronze Age in our area is the stone circle. The country between the Dee and the Spey is famous among prehistorians because of the presence therein of a special kind of stone circle which is almost peculiar to our area, though a number have been recorded from either flank. This type is known as the recumbent stone circle, from the presence on the southern side (and usually in the southwestern sector) of a large flat stone between two pillar stones generally of superior height. About 70 or 80 of these recumbent stone circles are on record; and of course many others will have been destroyed during centuries of cultivation. What this particular type of monument may represent in ritual and possibly

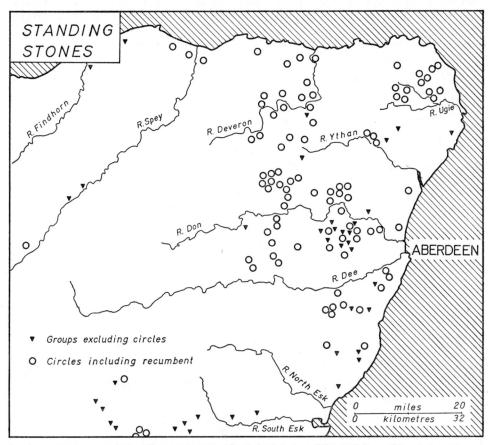

FIG. 8. Standing stones. Based on one-inch Ordnance Survey maps and *P.S.A.S.*

racial practice is quite unknown. A famous example of a recumbent stone circle, which has been thoroughly excavated with all the precision of modern archaeological science, is the one at Loanhead of Daviot in Aberdeenshire, now preserved as a national monument by the Ministry of Works.

It is impossible here to give any adequate account of the variety and beauty of the tools and weapons of the Bronze Age which have been recovered in large numbers all over our area. Mention may, however, be made of the gold torques and *lunulae* or crescent-shaped collars; also of the jet necklaces which reproduce in a different material the pattern of the ornament on the *lunulae*. Jet of course had to be imported, and our northeastern necklaces appear to have been made out of material brought from Whitby in Yorkshire.

Probably about a century or two before the birth of Christ the use of iron was introduced into North-East Scotland. There is evidence that throughout the Bronze Age Scotland as a whole was receiving fresh streams of racial emigration from the south. By the time of the Roman invasion, it is certain

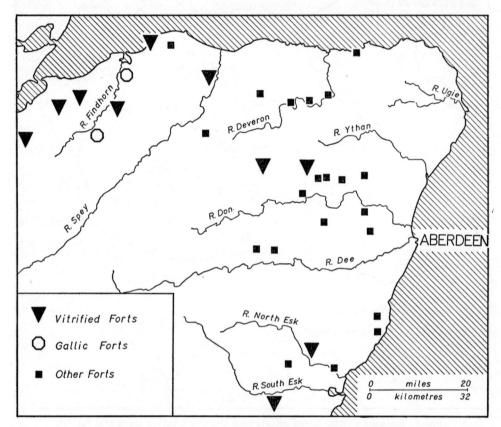

FIG. 9. Forts. Based on one-inch Ordnance Survey maps and *P.S.A.S.*

that the inhabitants enjoyed the full use of iron, and that at all events the upper strata of the population were of Celtic race—though no doubt the rank and file of the people were still the descendants of the old Bronze Age folk.

Tools and weapons assignable to the Iron Age are somewhat scarce in our area—no doubt owing to the perishable nature of the type-material. There is, however, ample evidence of a great increase in the arts and crafts. Mention can here only be made of two classes of objects assignable to this period which seem to be specially characteristic of the North-East of Scotland. The first is the carved stone balls, the use of which is unknown. The second are the massive bronze armlets, decorated with Celtic patterns and often enriched by enamel work, an art in which the ancient Britons are known to have been specially proficient. These armlets have been found on a number of occasions within the ' earth houses '—a type of construction very characteristic of the Iron Age in eastern Scotland, and of which the classic area is Kildrummy on Donside. These *souterrains* were constructed with great skill, and they appear always to have been associated with huts above ground. They were not therefore refuges, since the presence of the hut would betray the existence of the *souterrain*. No doubt they were stores, but also they served as sleeping quarters during the cold weather. Hearths and food refuse are often found in them, and one or two earth houses possessed a regular chimney. Their approximate date is fixed by the relics found in them. In one Aberdeenshire earth house a coin of the Emperor Nerva (96-98 A.D.) was picked up; while another earth house in Midlothian is built partly out of stones taken from some Roman edifice.

Another characteristic monument of the Celtic Iron Age is the crannog or lake dwelling. Our area contains at least two of these, one in Loch Kinnord and the other in the now drained Loch of Leys near Banchory. It should, however, be noted that such buildings were constructed in the Scottish Highlands as late as the sixteenth century.

Perhaps the most notable monuments surviving from the Iron Age in our area are the group of massive hill forts, generally built out of stone, but in one or two cases of earthwork. These military works are of great size and skilful construction. They must have involved immense labour and efficient direction. Clearly they must be the response to some great stress laid upon the Iron Age population of the North-East. While the problem can be solved only by large-scale and careful excavation, there is a good deal of evidence supporting the suggestion that this great group of hill forts in central Aberdeenshire may be the answer of the local inhabitants to the Roman invasions.

One of the best known of these hill forts crowns the Mither Tap of Bennachie. Its main wall, 15 ft. thick, possesses a regular wall-walk and parapet. This seems to be an imitation of Roman military engineering practice. It recalls similar features on certain hill forts in North Wales, which are now believed to have been built by the local folk under Roman supervision.

In at least two cases—Dunnideer and Tap o' Noth—the hill fort is vitrified, i.e. large portions of the dry-built masonry have been wholly or partially fused together by intense heat. It is now known that vitrification is a by-product of the burning of a wall of a type known in Roman days as a *murus Gallicus*—that is to say a wall in which the uncemented stonework is disciplined or tied together by a framework of logs. If such a structure takes fire, either by hostile action or by the accidental kindling of the wattled huts within the rampart, a great heat may be engendered, which under suitable conditions will vitrify the stone. The truth of this has been proved by practical experiment. It is quite possible, therefore, that our vitrified forts in the North-East may have been set on fire by Roman soldiery.

Of the Roman penetration into our remote northeastern area ample proof exists in the great series of marching camps which stretches northwards from Strathmore through the Howe of the Mearns and Aberdeenshire as far as the neighbourhood of Keith in Banffshire. These entrenched bivouacs have been found to belong to two categories. In the larger group each camp encloses an area of between 90 and 100 acres. Camps of this size are computed to be large enough to contain an army of as much as 12,000 men. Thus they indicate that in one at least of their invasions the Romans must have been present here in very large force. The varying sizes of the camps and their position with relation to each other suggest that more than one expedition is involved; but none of the series has yielded coins or other relics from which a definite date might be deduced. It is usual to think either of the invasion of Julius Agricola which culminated in the Roman victory on an unknown site at Mons Graupius in A.D. 84; or else of the punitive expedition of the Emperor Septimius Severus in A.D. 208-211. Severus is said to have penetrated further north than any of his predecessors, and to have reached the northern seaboard. But it is a mistake to think in terms only of the Agricolan and Severan expeditions. We know nothing of the campaigning that must have preceded the building of the Antonine Wall in the year 143. Moreover, recent excavations are showing that the robust and radical reorganisation of Roman Britain carried out about the year 300 under the Emperor Constantius Chlorus involved action against the Picts vigorous enough to include a reoccupation of the naval base at Cramond near Edinburgh. We cannot therefore exclude the possibility that some at least of the northern bivouacs may be as late as this time.

It is in connection with the campaign of Constantius that we first hear of the Picts. After the collapse of the Roman power we find the kingdom of this gifted and powerful people in possession of the whole of Scotland north of the Forth and east of the central mountain backbone. It is among the Picts that Christianity was introduced in the post-Roman period. The circumstances under which the Christian faith reached our area are the subject of much contention; and it is unlikely that owing to the paucity of evidence full agreement will ever be reached among scholars. The Celtic Church was organised upon monastic lines. Its monasteries, often of large size, were beehives of missionary enterprise rather than cloisters of men who had rejected the world around them. Of such missionary monasteries our area contained a number. The most famous was the Abbey of Deer in Buchan. This place owes its celebrity through the survival of the Book of Deer, the most precious relic of the Celtic Church in Scotland. This little volume, now preserved in

Cambridge University Library, contains the complete Gospel of St. John and fragments of the other three Gospels; a short Creed; and an Order of Service for Communicating the Sick—which last is the only surviving remnant of the ritual of the Celtic Church in Scotland.

What makes the book of still greater interest is the fact that the monks of Deer used its fly-leaves and margins to write down jottings of gifts of land and privileges made to their house by early Celtic kings and local magnates. Apart from the light which these *notitiae* cast upon social and economic conditions in Celtic Buchan, their supreme importance lies in the fact that they are in Gaelic. These Gaelic *notitiae* in the Book of Deer are centuries older than any other specimen of Scottish Gaelic known to us.

There were also Celtic monasteries in our area at Mortlach near Dufftown; Turriff; Monymusk; and Clova, in the uplands of Kildrummy. Monymusk is famous through the survival to our own times of what is known as the Monymusk Reliquary, a rich and splendid example of Celtic ecclesiastical art, now one of the treasures of the National Museum of Antiquities in Edinburgh. The Monymusk Reliquary, however, had nothing to do with the Celtic monastery there. Its custody was attached to the lands of Forglen in Banffshire, and with these it came into the possession of the territorial family of de Monymusk.

The most remarkable relics of the Celtic Church in our area are the magnificent series of sculptured stones. Taken together, these form a *corpus* of early Christian art of which any nation might be proud, and afford a vivid glimpse of local culture in what we choose to call the Dark Ages. What gives these stones a special interest is the fact that many of them display those mysterious forms which for want of a better term are usually grouped together under the descriptive heading of ' Pictish symbolism'. In the oldest class of these stones, which are believed to date from before c. A.D. 800, the symbols are incised and are not associated with a cross or any other recognisable Christian symbol. It has therefore been maintained by many that the symbols were in their origin pagan. In the second class (about 800-1000) the symbols are now associated with a Christian cross, while both cross and symbols are carved in relief and enriched with Celtic ornament. The final stage is reached when the symbols pass out of use, and only the great Christian cross graven on a slab remains.

The richness of this art may be understood from the fact that the total of known examples of all three classes between the Dee and the Spey may be reckoned as upwards of one hundred. We have only to remember how many must have been destroyed without trace in the last thousand years to realise how rich is the artistic heritage that still survives to us from the Pictish period in our area. Much of the carving is of the highest merit: in particular its sprightly and joyous animal forms are a delight to behold. To the meaning of the symbolism, despite any amount of speculation, no key has been found. Nothing like it is known anywhere else in the world.

The Celtic period in Scottish history was drawing to an end in the twelfth and thirteenth centuries, when the powerful kings of the House of

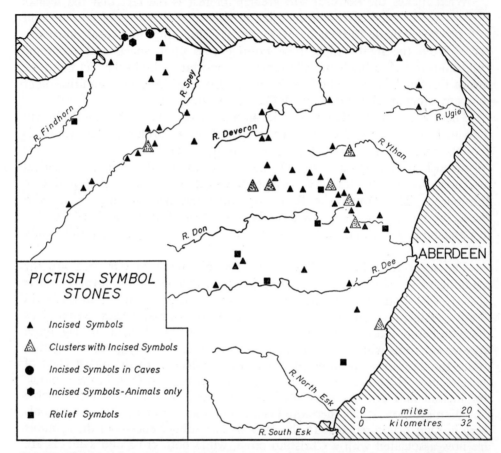

PICTISH SYMBOL
STONES

▲   Incised Symbols

△   Clusters with Incised Symbols

●   Incised Symbols in Caves

⬟   Incised Symbols–Animals only

■   Relief Symbols

Fig. 10. Pictish symbol stones. The Dee marks the southward limit of the main concentrations of these stones. The few stones recorded north of the Ythan may be due to the extensive clearance of stones during the agricultural improvements. Based on C. L. Curle, 'The Chronology of the Early Christian Monuments of Scotland.' *P.S.A.S.*, **75** (1939-40), 60 et seq.; R. B. K. Stevenson, 'Pictish Art' in F. T. Wainwright (Edit.), *The Problem of the Picts*, Edinburgh, 1954 etc.

Canmore sponsored a policy of what may be described as Anglo-Norman infiltration. Under their patronage large tracts of land passed into the hands of Norman immigrants—either through direct gift from the Crown, or because these incomers married Celtic heiresses. This last is what happened in the old Celtic province of Buchan, where in 1210 an Anglo-Norman noble, William

Comyn, married the heiress of the old Celtic mormaers or rulers of the province. In other cases, as in the province of Mar, Celtic mormaers themselves adopted Anglo-Norman ways, and came to be known as feudal earls. By both of these methods the feudal system gradually overlay the old Celtic landholding arrangements. Concurrently with this process, the medieval Church, with its territorial organisation into parishes each served by a priest and grouped into dioceses presided over by a bishop, superseded the old Celtic monastic organisation. The small monastic houses such as Mortlach, Turriff and Clova were converted into parish churches, while larger establishments such as Monymusk were usually transformed, more or less against their will, into houses of Augustinian canons-regular. The Celtic monastery of Deer was thus replaced by a Cistercian Abbey.

In this way throughout Scotland during these two critical centuries a peaceful revolution was accomplished, as a result of which the country, from being a congeries of loosely knit Celtic tribes, emerged finally as a strongly organised feudal monarchy.

The Celtic period in our area was also the time when Scotland as a whole suffered sorely from the Viking raids. So dreaded were these that a new petition was added to the Church's litany: *A furore Normannorum libera nos, Domine.* As is well known, the Norse invasions resulted temporarily in the colonisation of the Northern and Western Isles and their allegiance to the kings of Norway. It appears, however, that the main track of the invaders was down the west coast, where they found the scenery of fjord and mountain that reminded them of their homeland. Although therefore there are records of Viking raids on the North-East, and at least one account of a Norse settler in Buchan, the Vikings do not seem to have had much permanent influence on our area. Expert opinion declares that there is only one place-name of undoubted Norse derivation in Aberdeenshire.* A notable event was the plundering in the year 1151 of Aberdeen (Norse: Apardjon) by Eystein, King of Norway.

The outward and visible signs of the Anglo-Norman penetration were the parish and cathedral churches and the feudal castle. Of the Norman cathedral of Aberdeen only a single stone now survives; but a fine Norman parish church is still in use at Monymusk. In the 13th century the Norman or Romanesque style of architecture gave place to First Pointed Gothic. Good work of this period still remains in the ' town's kirk ' of St. Nicholas in Aberdeen, and in the Cistercian Abbey of Deer—the only place in our area where a complete monastic plan may be studied. Somewhat later is the very interesting church of Kincardine O'Neil, which appears to be an example unparalleled in Scotland of a parochial church having a hospital attached to its eastern end.

* According to W. M. Alexander, *Place Names of Aberdeenshire,* p. xvii, the only undoubted Norse name in the county is St. Olaf's Church, Cruden Bay.

The earliest feudal castles were not structures of stone and lime. They consisted of earthen mounds, crowned by a palisade enclosing a wooden tower. The tower formed the keep and the lord's residence in time of trouble. Usually an entrenched base court was attached containing the subsidiary buildings of his household. Good examples of this early type of castle exist in our area;

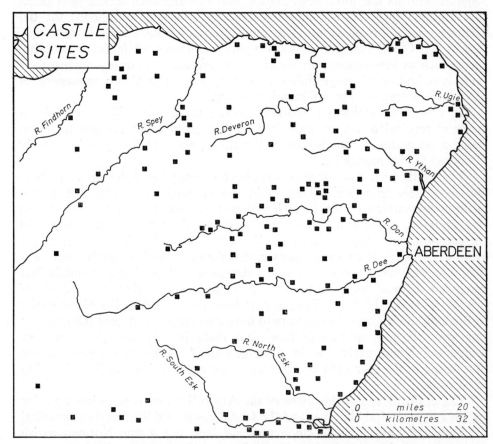

FIG. 11. Castle sites. Based on A. C. O'Dell and K. Walton, *The Highlands and Islands of Scotland*, Edinburgh, 1962, p. 81. By permission of Thomas Nelson & Sons Ltd.

notably the Bass of Inverurie, the Peel of Fichlie, the Peel of Lumphanan and the Doune of Invernochty. The latter ranks with Duffus Castle in Moray and the Mote of Urr in Galloway as one of the three grandest examples of Norman military engineering in Scotland.

A third element in the Anglo-Norman penetration of Scotland was the establishment of burghs—trading settlements inhabited largely by English or Flemish colonists. Royal burghs, whose only superior was the king, were thus planted at Aberdeen, Inverurie, Kintore, Banff and Cullen; while burghs of barony were founded by the enlightened feudal magnates, such as Ellon and Newburgh on the Ythan, creations of the Comyn Earls of Buchan. The Church also had its burghs: it was in this way that Old Aberdeen, which had grown up around the Cathedral and Chanonry, became an ecclesiastical burgh of barony in 1489. A notable event was the settlement in the upper Garioch, during the twelfth century, of a colony of Flemish wool growers, who were allowed to retain their own legal system, 'Fleming law', as late as the fourteenth century. In these and other ways the old Celtic population, in the lowland parts at least, gradually lost its distinctive racial character and its ancient language—though the Gaelic speech survived in Braemar until the beginning of the present century.

The Normanisation of Scotland was not achieved without vigorous protest from certain of the old Celtic provinces. In particular the province of Moray, beyond the Spey, bitterly resisted the centralising and Normanising policy of the House of Canmore. Here the quarrel was sharpened by the fact that the rulers in Moray belonged to the rival house of Macbeth. Hence the struggle between Malcolm Canmore and Macbeth was fought out in our area. It was at Lumphanan that Macbeth was slain on the 15th of August, 1057; and the conflict between the rulers of Scotland and the rulers of Moray was not finally settled until the forceful measures of Alexander II, after the last rising in Moray in 1228, finally incorporated this recalcitrant province in the body-politic of Scotland.

With the conquest of the western islands after the victory at Largs in 1263, Scotland achieved substantial unity and peace within her own borders—though the northern islands continued to form part of the Scandinavian kingdom until the year 1470. The achievement of peace and the introduction of feudal order led to a burst of prosperity, and the latter part of the thirteenth century is looked back upon as a Golden Age in Scottish history. It was in this period that the great cathedrals took on their most splendid form. Aberdeen Cathedral was rebuilt in the fourteenth and fifteenth centuries, but the fragments of First Pointed work that survive show us that the thirteenth century building here was fully abreast of the high standard shown, for example, at the Cathedral of Moray in Elgin. The great stronghold of Kildrummy—'noblest of northern castles'—also belongs to this period.

Unhappily for Scotland, its peaceful penetration from Anglo-Norman England was followed by the attempt to carry out complete political incorporation made at the close of the thirteenth century by Edward I. In the long and desperate struggle for independence that ensued, our area played a notable part. At Stracathro in the Mearns Edward's puppet, John Baliol, in 1296 formally handed back his crown to his English overlord. In the first War of Independence the two most notable events in our area were the heroic defence of Kildrummy Castle in 1306 and Bruce's victory at Inverurie on Christmas

6

Eve 1307. This was the turning point—the Alamein or Stalingrad—of the long struggle. After the death of the liberator king in 1329, Edward III took advantage of the minority of Bruce's son, David II, to renew the Plantagenet effort to subjugate Scotland. Here again the turning point in the second War of Independence took place in Aberdeenshire in the victory of Culblean, gained by the Regent Sir Andrew de Moray over the anglophil Earl of Atholl (St. Andrew's Day, 1335).

Thus the struggle for independence lasted for upwards of forty years, with the most disastrous results on the civilisation of Scotland. In our area, Aberdeen, both the Old and the New Town were given to the flames by Edward III in 1336. St. Machar's Cathedral was so badly damaged that it had to be entirely rebuilt, with the result that there is no work *in situ* older than the fourteenth century. Many of the Anglo-Norman nobles who had estates also in England fled or were exiled thither; those who remained in Scotland were impoverished by the loss of their English property or by the wasting of their Scottish lands. Sweeping changes followed in territorial ownership, since King Robert Bruce had to reward, out of confiscated estates or grants of royal property, those barons who had supported him, or had come over to his side, in the long struggle. In this way new families and new rivalries appear in our area, notably the Forbeses and the Gordons in Aberdeenshire.

The power of the Crown having been disastrously weakened by these great changes, a period of feudal anarchy now set in which was accentuated by the series of minorities that afflicted the unfortunate house of Stewart. This period of anarchy reached its climax in the great battle of Harlaw (24th July, 1411), fought in the Garioch between Donald, Lord of the Isles and the Earl of Mar, acting on behalf of the government of Scotland. The pretext of the quarrel was a purely feudal dispute about the right of succession to the Earldom of Ross; but Donald of the Isles was in secret league with the ever-hostile English government. It was in this way that the ' red ' Harlaw—the most bloody conflict ever fought on the soil of our region—came to be looked upon as a national deliverance. Those who fell in the struggle were exempted from death duties by a special act of the Scottish Parliament. One who died on that crimson field was Robert Davidson, Provost of Aberdeen—so far as is known the only Provost of a Scottish burgh who fell in defence of his city during his term of office. So terrible were the losses on the ' sair field ' of Harlaw that men told, long afterwards, how ' the Coronach was cried from the Tay to the Buck of the Cabrach '.

It is thus obvious that during the fourteenth and fifteenth centuries the burgh of Aberdeen was a dangerous place to live in. On the one side it was liable to be attacked by the English landing from the sea, on the other side by the Celtic Highlanders descending from the mountains. Evidence of such stark conditions is vividly apparent in the nave of St. Machar's Cathedral, rebuilt between 1424 and 1440. The aisles and nave were formerly crested with embattled parapets, while the two western towers have great machicolated war-heads in the manner of a contemporary castle. Thus the Cathedral of Aberdeen is one of the finest examples of a fortified church surviving in western Europe. Incidentally, the fifteenth century work is faced throughout with granite ashlar. This is the first instance of the large-scale use of dressed granite in our area.

Nevertheless, not everything in the North-East was mere strife and anarchy in the fifteenth century. On the contrary, civilisation was making rapid progress in many ways. In particular the church, though suffering from grievous economic and social evils, was full of beneficent vigour. Its success was largely due to the high character of most of the bishops of Aberdeen during the fifteenth and the first half of the sixteenth centuries. Our greatest bishop was undoubtedly William Elphinstone, who in 1495 obtained a Papal Bull founding the University of Aberdeen. Under his vigorous and high-minded direction the church took a prominent part in the intellectual and cultural life of the vast diocese. Round him he gathered a distinguished band of helpers, such as Alexander Galloway, who managed his building and artistic undertakings, and Hector Boece, the first Principal of the University—a distinguished scholar, the friend and correspondent of Erasmus. Elphinstone's zeal for fine building may be seen in King's College Chapel and in the Bridge of Dee —though he did not live to see the building of the latter work, which was carried out by his distinguished successor, Bishop Gavin Dunbar. It was Elphinstone also who introduced the art of printing into Scotland; and one of the first books issued from his press was the famous Aberdeen Breviary compiled by the good Bishop. It contains collects dealing with the life and missionary activities of Scottish saints, and was designed in this way to supersede the English Use of Sarum.

The liturgical and artistic upsurge caused by the powerful inspiration of Bishop Elphinstone and his coadjutors produced a notable result in the series of very beautiful sixteenth century sacrament houses still preserved in a number of our ancient parish churches in the North-East. Fine examples may be seen in Aberdeenshire at Kintore, Kinkell and Auchindoir and in Banffshire at Deskford and Cullen. Right up to the Reformation of 1560 Gothic art continued to flourish in the North-East with unabated vigour, as may be studied in such fine examples as Arbuthnot Church in Kincardineshire or Cullen Church in Banffshire, and in the transepts and western spires of St. Machar's Cathedral.

The general history of our area at this time is conditioned by the unfortunate political void left in the area betwixt Dee and Spey by the collapse of the old Celtic Earldom of Mar, the annexation of this dignity to the Crown, and the consequent fragmentation of its demesne lands. We have in our own times unhappy experience of the disastrous effects which result from the demolition of an existing states-system, whatever its defects, without putting anything in its place. One need only reflect on the Balkanisation of Eastern Europe after the fall of the Austrian empire in 1918, of the struggle for power now going on in the vacuum created by the disappearance of the German *Reich*, and of the present chaos in the Congo. The lessons of history are ever the same, whether its stage be large or small. Exactly the same thing happened, on a much smaller scale, in our area after the disappearance of the old well-organised Earldom of Mar. In the political void thus created the two kindreds of Gordon and Forbes embarked on a ruthless struggle for power. Inevitably with the Reformation both parties took opposite sides. In the main the Forbeses embraced the Protestant cause, while the Gordons for the most part adhered to the ancient faith. Thus religious fanaticism was combined with feudal or clan rivalry. In this way the civil war between the rival factions that followed upon the dethronement of Mary Queen of Scots, took on, in our area, an aspect of peculiar savagery, marked by the battles of Corrichie (1562), the Craibstone, Aberdeen (1571), and Glenlivet (1594)—and above all by the burning in 1571 of Corgarff Castle, in which the lady of the manor and all her children and household perished.

On the other side of the medal the Reformation led to a great quickening in matters intellectual. Of this the most notable result was the founding in 1593 of Marischal College by George Keith, 5th Earl Marischal, one of the most distinguished statesmen, scholars and travellers of a period exceptionally rich in gifted personalities. It is important to note that Marischal College was founded not as a second collegiate establishment within the existing university of Aberdeen—like the various colleges at Oxford or Cambridge—but as a separate University in its own right granting degrees in all the Faculties. In those days the Royal Burgh of New Aberdeen and the Episcopal Burgh of the Aulton were entirely separate corporations and so remained until 1891. But if, as was already the common practice, they are considered together as one—' the two Aberdeens '—then the remarkable fact emerges that from 1593 until the ' Fusion ' of 1860, Aberdeen possessed two universities, as many that is as during the greater part of this period there existed in all England.

One remarkable result of the fragmentation of the Earldom of Mar still forms a conspicuous feature in the Aberdeenshire scene. The rise amid its wreck of a large number of comparatively small estates or baronies resulted in a huge increase in the number of castellated manor-houses. Thus the castles of Aberdeenshire form one of the county's greatest charms; and the same is hardly less true of Banffshire and Kincardineshire on either flank. We have first of all the great castles of the leading barons, such as the Keith stronghold of Dunnottar, near Stonehaven, or Strathbogie at Huntly, the chief residence of the great house of Gordon. As finally reconstructed in the early seventeenth century, Huntly Castle became one of the most magnificent examples of Renaissance architecture in Scotland. Even finer is Fyvie Castle as remodelled by the Lord Chancellor Seton, first Earl of Dunfermline, in the last decade of the sixteenth century. The buildings at the Earl Marischal's Castle of Dunnottar are of less architectural distinction; but dignity is lent them by the unequalled grandeur of the storm-beaten isolated rock on which they are perched.

All our evidence shows that this late efflorescence of castellar construction was the work of local masons. Two families in particular are on record—the Bells and the Leipers. To them are due such splendid examples of ornate semi-fortified castellated buildings as Midmar, Castle Fraser, Craigievar, Fyvie and Tolquhon. In the internal decoration of these fascinating buildings two methods were adopted. The first was the provision of painted ceilings in tempera work. Here again we have the work of local craftsmen. The best examples of such decoration in our area may be seen at the Castles of Crathes and Balbegno, both in the Mearns. The other method was the employment of plaster ceilings, usually with emblematic subjects portrayed in high relief. These were the work of imported English craftsmen. Examples may be seen at Craigievar and Fyvie in Aberdeenshire and at Muchalls and Arbuthnot in the Mearns.

So far from settling the religious question, the Reformation in Scotland committed the unhappy country to another century of bitter strife between the two rival versions of the reformed faith, Episcopacy and Presbyterianism. Here again in our area the old alignment between opposing interests was continued. In the main the Gordons supported King Charles I and his policy of imposing Episcopacy upon his Scottish subjects, while the Forbeses in general espoused the cause of the Covenant. An added bitterness was therefore lent to the great civil war of the seventeenth century. It is worth recalling that this disastrous struggle, involving all three British Kingdoms, began in our area. The first man to fall was David Pratt, slain in the attack on Towie Barclay Castle (10th May, 1638), while the first battle of the war was the skirmish known as the 'Trot of Turriff' (14th May, 1638). In the same way the great civil war may be said to have ended within our area: for the last castle to submit to Cromwell was Dunnottar, which after a heroic defence, hauled down the flag of Charles II on 24th May, 1655. This siege has been rendered epic in Scottish history through the fact that in Dunnottar had been secured the Crown Jewels of Scotland, which by a woman's ingenuity were smuggled out before the surrender. They remained concealed beneath the floor of the neighbouring church of Kinneff until after the Restoration in 1660.

Two of Montrose's famous victories during his marvellous campaign in the Royalist cause were gained within our area—the battle of Aberdeen (13th September, 1644) and the battle of Alford (2nd July, 1645). The story of the part played by the North-East in the long and cruel and desolating conflict is vividly portrayed by our three local historians, John Spalding, James Gordon and Patrick Gordon.

After the Restoration in 1660 the opportunity of carrying out a healing policy in a land weary of ecclesiastical strife was wantonly cast aside by the stupid government of Charles II and James II. In the resulting resistance and cruel treatment of the Covenanters, our area played little part. The people were overwhelmingly in favour of a moderate Episcopacy, and the post-reformation Bishops were men of good character. One tragic episode, however, cannot be omitted even in this brief chronicle—the imprisonment and shocking sufferings of 122 men and 45 women, mostly westland Covenanters, within the 'Whigs' Vault' at Dunnottar Castle in the summer of 1685.

Our district saw much of the marching and counter-marching of Claverhouse and Mackay during the Revolution campaign of 1689. With this event the military and political history of the period covered by this article may be said to close—though it may be said in conclusion that in the eighteenth century the continued sympathy of many folk of the North-East with the Stuart cause and Episcopacy found expression in the large part taken by the three counties in the '15 and the '45.

REGIONAL SETTLEMENT

THERE are many features of the North-East which distinguish it from the other lowlands of Scotland. Not least are the settlement types which have evolved from the primary colonisation to the complex pattern visible today. Although some of the rural settlements common at the beginning of the eighteenth century have been swept away or considerably modified in the last two hundred and fifty years, there are many whose site, plan and name give indications as to their origin and blend past influences into the modern mosaic. Each of the settlement types may be related to a phase in the historical development of the region. It will be shown, for instance, that the crofts, an important feature of the interfluvial and poor soil tracts of the lowlands, are in the main the products of colonisation during the Agricultural Revolution and represent, to a certain extent, the successors to the cottars' dwellings of the farming townships. The villages in the same situations are also a product of colonisation with a mixture of agricultural and industrial influences. These, however, are comparatively recent types which fit into a more ancient pattern of hamlets whose function is indicated by their names— kirktown, milltown, seatown, etc. Sometimes ancient sites have settlement continuity but with different forms, as when individual farmsteads took the place of the nucleated farming townships. The inter-relationship of changes in land-use with settlement modifications is very clear.

At the time this survey begins, the traveller in the North-East saw a vastly different settlement pattern as he crossed from Strathmore to the lowlands on the shores of the Moray Firth, a pattern which is crystallised in the pages of the Aberdeenshire Poll Book of 1696,[1] and represents the layout of the countryside before reclamation and enclosure changed the face of the landscape. Interlocked with the ubiquitous shifting cultivation of the infield/outfield system of land management, the dominant pattern was one of farming townships with occasional small hamlets of ecclesiastical or rural industrial significance. The continuity of settlement names to modern times makes the identification of their location fairly straightforward except in the highland zone where extensive depopulation has taken place with loss to knowledge of settlement names and sites. Here, however, field work reveals traces of former infield as grassy stretches among the encroaching heather and bracken with heaps of building stones to indicate the derelict dwelling places.

Contemporary descriptions of the townships are not very common. Sinclair gives a general description in not very glowing terms: ' The houses were not built according to any regular plan but scattered in every direction.

The roads and alleys were inconceivably bad, especially in wet weather, as few of them were paved, and what added greatly to their miserable state was the abominable practice of placing the dunghill, in which every species of filth was accumulated, before their doors.'[2] This description which could be applied to most of the rural settlements in Scotland in the eighteenth century may be brought into sharper focus by reference to old estate maps and plans. The estate of Monymusk on Donside in the shadow of Bennachie has been closely investigated,[3] which reveals that the heart of the Grant domain was the Kirkton, a small village of about one hundred inhabitants with church and school and a meal mill driven by the Monymusk Burn. About a quarter of a mile away stood the House of Monymusk with, nearby, the Mains or Home Farm worked directly by the proprietor or leased to a substantial tenant. Beyond and scattered over the valley floor and up the slopes of the hills to the west were the 'touns' or townships, each consisting of about eight houses, although occasionally there were many more so that the 'toun' became a small hamlet with its smith, weaver and tailor as well as the truly agricultural population of tenants, subtenants, cottars and grassmen (or women). The general layout of such a township was a central nucleus of irregularly grouped houses with one or two detached cottages standing on the periphery of the township's land. It is possible that the cottars may have lived as a separate community since there are references to 'cottouns' in the Poll Tax Returns and the name has been handed down to a few farms at the present day. 'Cot-town wood' appears on the modern Ordnance map in more than one locality in the North-East. Pratt[4] refers to the 'cottouns' as being generally near the 'Haa'. The cottars were rarely displaced and they and their children formed a colony attached to the township.

The general distribution of the townships on the lowlands reflects the dependence of pre-improvement agriculture on the most fertile and easily worked ground. Accordingly, there is displayed a preference for terraces and lower slopes as in the valleys of the North and South Ugie to the west of Peterhead. These and other townships in similar environmental situations were situated well above the flood plains which had not yet been brought under control but below the stony infertile wastes of the ridgelands which, as in the country between Isla and Deveron in the northwest, were practically devoid of settlement. Wet and mossy land on these higher, gently sloping remnants of old erosion surfaces, bleak in aspect and swept by cold winds, seems to have kept the farmed land and the farming settlements in the valleys and basins. Here, the lowest lying land was frequently wet and so slopes were sought for house sites as, for example, at Nether, Mid and Upper Anguston on the east-facing slopes of the Leuchar Burn and its tributary, the Gormack Burn, which are incised in a black-soiled peaty depression near the junction with the Dee at Peterculter. These three townships with adult populations in 1696 of six, eight and thirteen persons respectively, were paralleled on the opposite side of the basin by a ring of townships, such as that of Ord, which overlooked the old alluvial flat drained by the Leuchar Burn. This preference for well-drained slopes was especially common in the Insch and Garioch lowland developed on the gabbro outcrop between the slates of the Foudland Hills in the north and the granite of Bennachie in the south. Here the farming townships were located on gentle swellings of the boulder clay cover and showed a marked relationship to the deep, freely drained soil pockets found in this area.[5] Small hamlets such as Insch, Old Rayne and Daviot were found to occupy similar small oases of fertility.

In the highland zone the townships spread along the banks of the Dee and Don and their tributaries, and crept into the hills of Banffshire by the Upper Isla and Deveron. In these highland valleys they were frequently sited on the kame terraces above the flood plains of the rivers, yet below the steep rocky slopes of the glaciated valley sides. Although settlement reached as high as 1,500 ft. in some of the glens, the bulk of the townships were to be found below the 1,000 ft. contour, and in the hills surrounding the Alford Basin were often below 600 ft. above sea level. High basins such as the Cabrach were well populated since here gentle slopes and shelter offered possibilities for a little arable grazing for the poor black cattle. It was in such situations, however, that the worst effects of the famine years at the close of the seventeenth century had been felt; disasters which were shared by the poorer lands of Buchan where, for instance, in the parish of Monquhitter many townships were bereft of their population and were converted into a sheep walk. In spite, however, of this and other famines in the first few decades of the eighteenth century there does not seem to have been any substantial modification of the basic agricultural settlements by the time General Roy's surveyors were constructing their map of mainland Scotland from 1747 to 1755 (Fig. 12). The symbol used for the rural settlements, usually three small squares together, indicates that the farming townships lay at the heart of a nucleated settlement pattern.

Thomson's map of 1828 (Fig. 13) shows a vast transformation. Gone are the symbols used by Roy; instead a single dot suffices to indicate the location of an agricultural settlement. Between 1750 and 1830 most of the farming townships had been broken up into single farmsteads dispersed among the new enclosed fields in the long-farmed areas, while the empty spaces of the lowland landscape had been filled in wherever natural conditions allowed by a new settlement type, the croft, which is found in many areas of the North-East at the present day. The deciphering of the settlement pattern is made more difficult by confusion in terminology. The term 'crofter' seems to have been applied indiscriminately to sub-tenants and cottars without adequate definition. By calling sub-tenants 'crofters' it is possible to infer that the small crofts in the primary settled areas of the North-East are long established and also that the break-up of the farming townships occurred at the time of the Seven Ill Years. Anderson, for instance, says that the break-up into small farms happened at that time, but Skene Keith[6] refutes this suggestion and claims that the effect of the great famine was to enlarge the farms since, as tenants or sub-tenants died or were reduced in circumstances by the famine, the lairds persuaded the remaining tenants to take over adjacent farms.

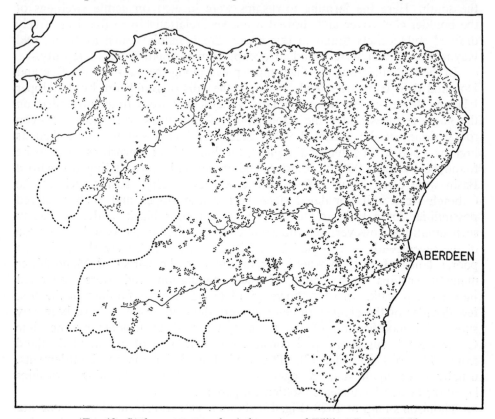

FIG. 12. Settlement pattern from the survey of William Roy, 1747-55.

Certainly the evidence from Roy's map is that the nucleated settlement survived the earlier famines, even though the holdings may have been larger and the number of tenants reduced below the figures given in the Poll Book.

The great changes seem to have begun with the general awakening of interest in agricultural improvements about 1750. As enclosures became necessary for the improved farming and the growth of root crops, the old run-rig system based on the Scottish openfield agriculture underwent drastic changes and individual holdings became common. The size of the farms then established depended on the ideas of the individual landowners. Some let the old townships into large farms, others parcelled out the land into small

farms and crofts, but the effect was the same. The spaces in the old settlement
pattern were filled with a multiplicity of small units, some of which took the
name of the old township and added a prefix to indicate the different site.
Easter or Wester, Nether, Mid or Upper are common all over the region,
although not all of them derive from these changes since some are recorded

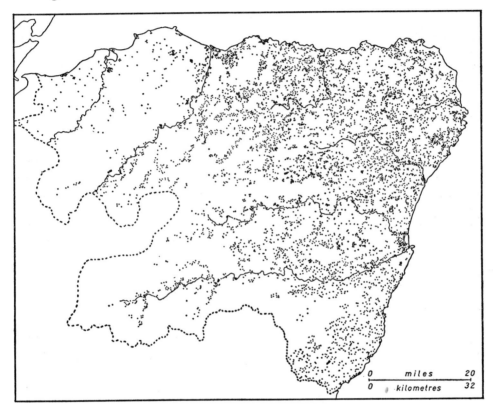

FIG. 13. Settlement pattern from the atlas by James Thomson, 1828.

in the 1696 Poll Book. Although the modern agricultural settlement pattern
was thus created, not all the settlements of this period have survived to the
present day. In the pages of the Old Statistical Account there is much
reference to the enlargement of the farms following the original break-up of
the old townships, which seems to have been most common in the fertile good
soils areas such as the Howe of Cromar, lower Donside and the Insch and
Garioch lowland. It is noteworthy that there is little reference to farm
enlargement in the northeast of Buchan at this time.

The date when the farms began to be enlarged varied in different parts
of the North-East; in some areas it began about 1755; in others it seems to

have occurred after the great famines of 1782-3. In Foveran (south of the Ythan estuary) twenty-four farms were reduced to only seven or eight,[7] while in the parish of Skene a few miles to the west of Aberdeen the fifty-one farms produced by the break-up of the farming townships were much reduced in number. Similar stories are recorded from Strathisla, Strath Deveron and Strath Bogie.

The causes of the enlargement of the farms and the diminution of the number of agricultural settlements were many. The landowners, who had broken up the farming townships into small farms in the hope of furthering the improvements, found that the system was not working to their satisfaction and began to amalgamate the small units by taking them into their own hands or letting them to more substantial farmers, who were better able to improve and enclose the ground. Not only were the improvements the cause of amalgamation. The peat mosses which supplied the country with fuel were beginning to be exhausted in the long-settled areas. In part this was caused by the introduction of carts in the latter part of the eighteenth century which enabled more peat to be taken away in a shorter time than by the old-fashioned creel. Alarm at the exhaustion of the mosses was shown by many of the landowners, who began to prohibit the custom of sub-tenants as on the plateau slope behind Portsoy in Banffshire, where the peat was being exhausted by its use for firing limestone. A restriction in the use of badly-needed lime was imposed to prevent it. The famines of 1782-3 had also played their part since the bad harvests were the ruin of many tenants and small farmers who gave up their holdings and migrated to urban centres or further afield.

In the first decade of the nineteenth century, however, a reversal to the practice of encouraging small farms became evident. Proprietors, seeking labourers for their estates during the Napoleonic Wars, offered land in an attempt to recruit labour to compensate for the serious shortage of workers now that the old system of services had broken down. References to this shortage are universal and the wages demanded were high in proportion.

Meanwhile, the reclamation of the wasteland which was proceeding concurrently with the changes already noted led to the development of new agricultural settlements which, like the crofts and the farms of the good soil districts, were dispersed among the fields. The extent of this internal colonisation was remarkable; well-defined groups of crofts were planted in apparently unfavourable situations such as on the interfluves of Buchan where they were often associated with peat mosses, or on the fluvio-glacial sands of the lowland valleys, or spreading up the higher slopes of the valley sides in the highlands or on to the summit surfaces of the lower plateaux. The attraction of the peat mosses for this colonisation is quite clear as, for instance, on the Kincardineshire Plateau between Aberdeen and Stonehaven. Douglas referred to this district as being ' populous . . . everywhere numbers of poor huts and starved cattle . . . poor people have special inducements to settle in this district . . . They have peat and turf in great abundance, they are on the sea coast and can at most seasons have fish reasonably; they have a superabundance of stone for building their houses, and there are some pine woods in the neighbourhood where they can purchase timber for them.'[8] Later the same district was said to have a ' great abundance of moss for fireing, which last occasions a population pretty thickly scattered over the face of the interior '.[9] Nearby, on the estate of Findon, the same recorder noted that the proprietor let out extensive moors in small parcels to cottagers on long leases. He first of all built for each a substantial cottage of stones procured in the vicinity and then allowed them two or three acres as they found ' courage and ability ' to cultivate from the adjacent stony moor. For this they paid, for the first seven years, twenty shillings a year for the rent of the house alone. In the next seven years they paid annually 5s. an acre and for the last seven years to the end of the lease, 10s. per acre. The site of these cottages is interesting since, while the farm houses were frequently to be seen on top of a hill or sunk in the damp of a bog, ' the cottages (were) generally placed in warm and dry situations in the recess of a glen by the side of a stream, in corners and sides of plantations. Even when on a muir for the sake of the fireing, care (was) taken that they (were) sheltered.'[10]

On the stony, often infertile interfluves, which were practically empty of settlement in the early part of the eighteenth century, there was great activity as lowland landlords sought to improve the less attractive portions of their estates by letting the ground to crofters. There was extensive reclamation in the parish of Monquhitter, once given over to a sheep run and desolate; new crofts sprang up on the ridge between the Ugie and Ythan rivers and on the eastern and western slopes of the quartzite Hill of Mormond. In the Banffshire plateau there was an intensive attack on the Hill of Aultmore, where the valleys which dissect the plateau were cultivated by the crofters and the hill itself ' was studded far and wide with the cottages of the poor '.[11] In the western Uplands the slopes of Bennachie and the Coreen Hills were attacked by the crofter's plough while the Commonty of Bennachie became a favourite site for squatters, who were considerably inferior to the crofters in social and economic status.

These examples show that the colonising crofting settlements filled in some of the gaps in the pattern wherever environmental conditions permitted but even they have not survived intact to the present day. As the acreage of improvable land gradually decreased in both long-settled and colonisation areas many of the small farms were taken over by large farms and a limitation to further crofter enterprise took place. By 1867, at the time of the Scottish Agricultural Commission, there were many references to the decrease in the number of farms especially since 1841 when many leases ran out. The Duke of Richmond and Gordon amalgamated many small crofts and farms in the parish of Cairnie where, for instance, the farm of Newton comprised the land which had previously belonged to seven different farms whose names and sites were extinguished. The crofts of the estate of Greens in Monquhitter almost disappeared, as many as five or six crofts going to make up one farm. In this case the proprietors claimed that they wished to keep down pauperism by the removal of crofters after the passing of the Poor Law Act of 1845. A few new crofts were established but while the earlier crofters had sought the lower lying and more fertile areas, the later crofts were forced on to the bleakest and most exposed parts of the lowland interfluves.

Throughout these settlement changes the highland areas of the North-East lagged behind the lowlands, and many of the old township types erased fifty years earlier on the lowlands, fifty miles away, still survived. In 1837 at Coilacreich between Ballater and Braemar, there were still five tenants in the township who paid rent to the laird and six cottars, each occupying a house and kail-yard, who worked the land on the system of run-rig. In the same district five other townships still survived the changes and the depopulation which was well established in upper Deeside.

The state of occupancy of the County of Aberdeen in 1867 is shown by an analysis of the valuation roll. The total number of holdings of all sizes was 11,422 and of these, no fewer than 8,022 had a rental of less than £50, and of this number 5,525 had rentals of between £4 and £20. The proportion of small farms and crofts was thus very large and statements made to the Scottish Agricultural Commission indicate that conditions were approximately the same for Banffshire. The North-East is still primarily a region of small farms and crofts.

The rural hamlets and villages

The original nucleated settlement pattern has survived in the hamlets and villages which stud the North-East landscape but even here profound changes have occurred since the beginning of the eighteenth century. Foremost among the changes indicated by a comparison of the maps of Roy and Thomson are the planned villages erected in the northeast of the Buchan lowland, especially in the Ugie Basin. The influence of these new settlements was profound and they deserve more attention than the static kirktowns and other rural nucleated settlements. Many of the small hamlets listed in the 1696 Poll Tax Returns have not changed appreciably in size or form to the present day. In the long settled Insch and Garioch lowland, for instance, the small hamlets of Insch, Clatt and Daviot with weekly and yearly markets scarcely changed until the twentieth century and none of the eighteenth century descriptions of these settlements compares in detail or pride with the reports of the new villages.

The lack of market villages, as in other parts of Scotland before this time, was the result of the exclusive marketing monopolies of the Royal Burghs such as Inverurie, Kintore, and Aberdeen, and the baronial markets established on estates in the sixteenth century and later were of little value in raising the size and status of the hamlets. After the '45, however, the new

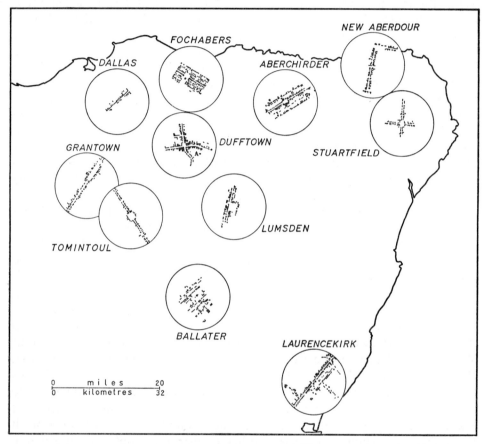

FIG. 14. Selected planned settlements of the North-East. The diameter of the circles represents half a mile. Laurencekirk, Tomintoul and Grantown-on-Spey are over half a mile in length. Based on six-inch O.S. First edition.

planned villages were erected; some were needed to stimulate rural industry where an unfavourable environment necessitated employment to supplement poor agricultural resources; it became necessary to erect villages to absorb the surplus rural population displaced by the revolutionary changes in agricultural management; others were built to beautify the estates. Altogether the North-East produced a remarkable number of these new settlements not only in the landward areas but along the coasts as well.

The basic design of these new settlements consisted of two rows of houses facing each other across a street, although some developed on the grid iron pattern and others incorporated a central square or green (Fig. 14). Sinclair in his analysis of the Old Statistical Account set out a list of desiderata for the new villages but most had been in existence long before 1831. New Keith, for instance, was commenced in 1750 near Old Keith, which ' is a very ancient place '.[12] It was said the ' late Lord Findlater divided a barren moor and feued it out in small plots, according to a regular plan still adhered to, on which there now stands a large, regular and tolerably thriving village called New Keith, containing 1075 inhabitants. The village is the residence of all manufacturers of note in the parish; according to the success of their business therefore it must either prosper or decline.'[13] Soon after the commencement of the village of New Keith, more land was feued out at the New Town of New Mill. Here resided a few weavers but the bulk of the population was ' very poor people who have fixed their abode there for convenience of land and moss '.[13] In 1817 a new village was erected to complete the Keith group on the north side of the Isla. This village in the commercial sense was a complete failure for, except for a few merchants' shops and some three or four tradesmen, the population depended almost entirely on their crofts which were attached to the village houses.

The village of Cuminestown, in the north of the former Monquhitter famine area, extends along the north side of the Waggle Hill for nearly a mile and is built of the Old Red Sandstone which outcrops in a narrow belt running south from Troup Head. Settlers flocked to this new settlement created by one of the great North-Eastern improvers, Cumine of Auchry. He established linen manufactures in the village which brought weavers and spinners and created home rural industries which were later to disappear. Many other villages on the Buchan lowland had the same original function. New Byth, built on the ridge of a hill, was founded in 1764 with small plots of land for the inhabitants. In the same year Lord Strichen founded the village which bears his name for the purpose of ' promoting the Arts and Manufactures of this country and for the accommodation of tradesmen of all Denominations, Manufacturers and other industrious people to settle within the same.'[14] His son sought to develop the linen industry by laying out the village of New Leeds a few miles to the southeast. In 1787 on a derelict moss on the east slope of Turlundie Hill was established New Pitsligo, which it was hoped would rival in a few years the other flourishing villages of Buchan. New Deer was established about 1805 and remodelled from an older settlement, Auchreddy, with a regular feuing and building plan. This was in marked contrast to its namesake, Old Deer, which like most old hamlets, was of organic growth and consisted of one street separating into two branches at the Kirkstile, most of the houses being built with the gable-ends to the road.

Apart from these industrial villages, some such as Fochabers were built to improve the appearance of the estates but there were two other main types as well, the spas and the fishing villages. At the time of the *New Statistical Account,* Ballater, though of recent origin, was said to be frequented by summer visitors from a distance attracted by the scenery and the medicinal well of Pannanich. It was, of course, to develop still more with the movement initiated by Queen Victoria—'Balmoralism'. The grid iron pattern of this settlement on the lowest terrace on the north side of the Dee is comparable with that of Huntly where the old settlement was extended at the north end of Strathbogie.

The fishing villages were mainly erected by the individual landowners. At Cullen, for instance, a new settlement was added in the shape of a crofter community displaced from the land. The older 'seatoun' with an untidy plan on the low raised beach shows only one regular feature, the gable-ends aligned in the direction of the winds from the sea. The new town of Cullen on the cliff top is built on a regular plan. Other villages were extended and the name changed. At Cruden Bay, for instance, a river was diverted to form a small inlet where fishing craft could obtain shelter and a harbour was constructed later in 1875-1880. At the same time the name was changed from Ward of Cruden to Port Errol. Gardenstown on the north coast of Aberdeenshire was built in 1720 on a very restricted raised beach site at the foot of high cliffs of Old Red Sandstone by Garden of Troup.

Each of these new villages brought new population to, and assisted in the internal colonisation of, areas which had previously been very sparsely populated. Most of the villages of Buchan have an interfluvial situation and the development in them of rural industries, which later declined and disappeared, became an important cause of the population increase of northeast Buchan between 1750 and 1850. Other villages were, however, established later than these planned villages; many were the products of improved communications or were built to house quarry workers engaged in the extraction of granite.

The development of the new turnpike roads at the beginning of the nineteenth century produced many settlement changes since the older hamlets, situated on earlier lines of communication, were frequently ignored. There are several examples of these older hamlets in the vicinity of the Loch of Skene about a dozen miles to the west of Aberdeen. The Kirktown of Skene, for instance, situated north of the present main road from Aberdeen to the Tillyfourie gap, was placed at the junction of routes where the old east-west road along the interfluve between Dee and Don was crossed by a branch of the important north to south route from the Cryne Corse Mounth. At Cairnton Cottages another north-south road crossed the east to west route, while at the Lyne of Skene the majority of the cottages flank the old road. With the arrival of the turnpikes later settlement tended to string out along

7

the new roads. The industrial suburbs of Aberdeen on lower Donside developed along the Aberdeen-Inverurie turnpike which was opened in 1800, although at the end of the nineteenth century there were still a few houses marking the line of the older road, of which many sections had been ploughed up.

If the turnpikes stimulated new settlement along the lines they followed so did the railways, while the terminus of Aberdeenshire canal was marked at Inverurie by the creation of Port Elphinstone. On Deeside the line of the Great North of Scotland Railway took a loop to the north thus by-passing Kincardine O'Neil, which declined until the renewed increase of road traffic in the twentieth century, whereas Torphins on the railway grew in importance. The present village of Lumphanan is a creation of the Deeside Railway since the ancient kirktown was left stranded. This hamlet which had been an important post on the ancient road from the Cairn o' Mounth to the north was superseded by a group of houses near the railway station.

Meanwhile the rural towns have had a somewhat chequered career. Eighteenth century travellers were almost universally scathing on the condition and prosperity of some of these centres. Pococke, for instance, passed through ' Inverury and saw to the east (south) Kintore, both Royal boroughs, tho' poor villages '.[15] It was not until the construction of a bridge across the Don at Inverurie and the opening of the Aberdeenshire canal at the beginning of the nineteenth century that Inverurie began to develop, a process which was accelerated at the turn of the century by the establishment of the Great North of Scotland railway works displaced from Kittybrewster in Aberdeen. Huntly, ' the Paisley of the North ' in the late eighteenth century, so-called because of its ascendancy in the linen industry, has a regular lay-out of streets on a grid iron pattern, compared with the old medieval style of Inverurie with the broadening of the main street to form a market place (as also in Old Aberdeen).

These examples will suffice to show the complex evolution of the modern distribution of rural town, hamlets and farms in the countryside of the North-East. The nucleated farming settlements, so common at the beginning of the eighteenth century, have disappeared and in their place a dispersed settlement pattern created. In some ways, however, the wheel may be coming full circle since it is more convenient to supply services to nucleated rural settlements while the advantages of community life in the remoter districts also tend to group new rural housing.

SELECTED REFERENCES

1. *List of Pollable Persons within the shire of Aberdeen 1696.* 2 vols. (Aberdeen, 1844).
2. SINCLAIR, SIR J., *Analysis of the Statistical Account of Scotland* (Edinburgh, 1831), p. 74.
3. HAMILTON, H. (Ed.), *Life and Labour on an Aberdeenshire Estate, 1735-1750* (Third Spalding Club, Aberdeen, 1946).
4. PRATT, J. B., *Buchan* (1901).
5. GLENTWORTH, R., *The soils of the country round Banff, Huntly and Turriff* (H.M.S.O., Edinburgh, 1954).
   WALTON, K., 'The distribution of population in Aberdeenshire, 1696.' *S.G.M.*, **66** (1950), pp. 17-26.
6. SKENE KEITH, G., *The Agriculture of Aberdeenshire* (Aberdeen, 1811).
7. *O.S.A.* Foveran Parish, **6**, No. 8, p. 66.
8. DOUGLAS, F., *A general description of the East Coast of Scotland* (Edinburgh, 1782), p. 68.
9. ROBERTSON, G., *A general view of the agriculture of Kincardineshire* (London, 1807), p. 6.
10. Ibid. p. 85.
11. *O.S.A.* Grange Parish, **9**, No. 39, p. 216.
12. *N.S.A. Keith* **13**, pp. 390-1.
13. *O.S.A. Keith* **5**, p. 421.
14. 'History of Strichen.' *Transactions of the Buchan Field Club*, **2** (1891-2), p. 68.
15. POCOCKE, T., *Tours in Scotland* (Scottish History Society, Edinburgh, 1877), Vol. 1, p. 200.

FISHING VILLAGES, 1750-1880

In the eighteenth century fishing and farming were the two main supports of the economy of the North-East. Physically, the people of the two occupations lived in intermixed groups, with the fishing villages strung along the edge of the agricultural plain and separated from each other by farms and open land. Yet, in fact, at the deeper social levels of marriage and occupational recruitment, they held severely apart; fishermen married only their own kind; every boy born to a family of fishers would in his turn become one, generally to live in the same village and to marry a woman of the same small group; and nobody would be received into the trade—and, what is the same thing, the community—who was not by birth and family brought up to it.

The economic processes could scarcely be so self-contained: fish had to be sold, capital raised, men might travel to other parts to fish or to trade. Yet the technique and economic purpose of the time allowed the isolated group to carry on most of its tasks with its own people and its own resources; the village, the characteristic unit of settlement, could pursue a much more self-sufficient way than was to be possible in the technologies and marketing systems of the nineteenth and twentieth centuries. There were many such villages by the later eighteenth century—more, probably, than before 1750 and as many as there were to be at any time in the nineteenth century—but they were individually small, between one and three hundred people being the characteristic size. Materially, too, they had only the barest equipment—without harbours (except for the few groups who happened to live in the fishing quarters of the larger towns such as Peterhead, Fraserburgh, Aberdeen, Montrose), and compelled to operate with the small craft that could be pulled up the open beaches, beyond the reach of the tide. The siting of the villages, then, depended on the detailed natural configurations of a coast that normally offers only bare wide sweeps to a restless and treacherous sea. On some stretches, indeed, soft sand with a wide level stretch between low and high tide-marks offered little foothold. But elsewhere, whether on the foreshore of low tumbled rock or in the clefts of the cliffs where the swell of the land hung above the sea, the villages clustered close; most closely of all, perhaps, on the Banffshire coast, thinning to the eastern side of the country, gathering again in the cluster of the northeast corner, then giving way to a sandy and empty coast, broken by the Peterhead cluster, as far south as Aberdeen and finally stretching in a regularly spaced chain south to Montrose. All told there were said to be 70 villages along this 150 mile stretch, with 300 boats, say 9,000 people—possibly the greatest aggregation in Scotland, at least in such a coastal space, of people devoted entirely to fishing.

For the fisherman was that and nothing else; he had no land, he followed the one occupation through the year and through his life. He had to answer the frailty of his equipment by bold and skilful operation. So indeed, he did, making out of this harsh environment, with little material protection, a livelihood that was generally estimated to be above that of the general run of labourers or even of small farmers. His main purpose was the catching of the ' great ' fish—cod, ling, skate or halibut, but most of all cod—on the known prolific banks. To these, when the weather eased in the spring and when the fish were in prime condition, with his fellows in the crew of six or seven, he might drive his 25 ft. boat up to 60 miles distance from his home shore, remaining continuously at sea for four or five days. The means of capture was the long-line, a continuous stretch of line to which hooks were attached at regular intervals, the whole being paid out to lie on the sea-bed for a short period; the equipment of a boat would run to two miles of line and 2,000 hooks. Thus, from his precarious platform the open-boat fisherman of the North-East was able to operate an apparatus just as lethal as that of the line fishermen from the English ports, men equipped with powerful, cutter-rigged, decked vessels. The offshore cod fishing alternated with a fishing in nearer waters, mainly for haddock, the second important commercial fish. The principle of capture was the same, but a different apparatus, with smaller hooks and a line of lesser gauge. The fish when landed were mainly cured, although a small proportion might be sold fresh according to local circumstances of market: Aberdeen, for example, took a large proportion of the fish of its surrounding villages. Cod were cured by light salting, splitting and drying in the sun, the haddock by smoking with simple domestic appliances. In either case, since supplies were steady and labour could be drawn out over a period and since little fixed equipment and few stores were required, the whole process from beginning to end could be performed by the fisherman and his family. Moreover, with his boat as means of transport, he could carry his season's catch to the busier commercial centres of the south, there to sell at the price of the day in open and competitive markets.

Such a technical and commercial scheme was consistent both with a good deal of individual independence and with a simple social structure. In fact, the fisherman did receive from landowners aid in the purchase of boats, but on rigid, conventional terms which allowed him to pursue his business independently, selling nearly all the catch as his own and only making a small annual fixed payment to his landlord-creditor. Indeed, this outside provision of capital helped to maintain within the village the conditions of equality between families, in substantial business independence. The regulator of income and status was the possession of a share in a boat and this was an operational not a property concept, not something which could be accumulated or subdivided; as long as the ownership of the boats lay outside the village incomes remained fairly equal, and what wealth could be accumulated had little accessory social power (for it did not bring control of the main form of capital); there was no slightest tendency for the small community to break into groupings of employers and employed. Furthermore the path to independent status was easy; a boy went to sea at fourteen and by his early twenties—because little capital was required and because the landlords were ready to provide it—he was free to marry and take a share in a boat, the step which gave him the full equality of status and the rough equality of income with nearly every other family man in the community. It was, of course, a community of one occupation. Even an increasing population then —and the population of the villages was increasing through the second half of the eighteenth century—did not throw up a class of ' boatless men ' or of families in exceptional poverty. Everybody in these communities went through the same annual routine, moved in the same rhythm over the fluctuations, enjoyed much the same income, held exactly the same status. Without anxiety for his social position, the fisherman pursued a trade always physically perilous; operations were bold, skilful, arduous and dangerous—and also rewarding. Catches were reasonably high and fairly steady, capital costs were low, almost the whole catch was shared among the fishers themselves, the prices were those of an open and competitive market. In addition the fisherman received free land for building (or as part of the agreement which gave him a share in the boat), together with perhaps a small garden patch on which he might grow potatoes or vegetables. His house he would build himself—quite well to judge by the accounts of observers.

By the last decade of the eighteenth century a shiver of change could be felt passing through the North-East villages. The excitement came from a distance—from the Caithness coast where herring were coming to be taken and sold in quantities over a short summer season. It was the beginning of great things: an emergence it seemed from that stinging second-rate status that the Scots had so long held in an industry which they had the best situation in Europe to pursue. The herring was to become the predominant interest of the whole of the numerically increasing body of full-time fishermen on the east coast, and also to give wages to the hands temporarily hired for the summer season. From its beginnings in Caithness—which remained the predominant centre until about 1860—the rising surge was to sweep along the coast into all the old centres of the white fishing: along the southern shore of the Moray Firth, to East Aberdeenshire, Kincardineshire, Angus, Fife, East Lothian and Berwickshire. But the orchestration of the different regional elements was to be a varying one, sometimes concerted, but sometimes thinning to a contribution by one or other section. For a time, apart from the predominance of Caithness, landings were fairly evenly divided between Banffshire, East Aberdeenshire, Fife and Berwickshire; but Banffshire and the southern sections were to fade, Kincardineshire to rise somewhat, and finally the leadership was to pass to East Aberdeenshire. Rise and fall on the different sections of coast did not carry the fortunes of the resident fishermen on a similar curve. For they had learnt to move, seasonally, to the successful area of the moment and the numbers, success, wealth and incomes moved on a curve, mainly of growth, independently of local chances. Particularly the fishermen of the North-East villages were firmly set on this path; men from the southern side of the Moray Firth had played an important part as innovators in Caithness and they retained a leadership over the men of this area in which at first activity mainly concentrated; and when Banffshire landings declined, the men of that coast continued to rank among the best equipped and the most successful herring fishers in the whole of Scotland. In fact, the men of the North-East villages, white fishers by tradition, turned concertedly to the new prospect of profit in the herring fishing; and through the nineteenth century this never ceased to be for all of them the predominant source of income.

But participation in the new industry challenged effort as well as offering easy profit; and it opened new economic connections, set in motion tendencies of accumulation, created demands for new types of labour, rested upon expensive forms of capital. It was bound, then, to strain the old scheme of social relationships and customs. Above all, this was a time of rapidly increasing numbers. Around the northeast, however, no new villages were settled; rather the old villages increased in size. Increases were uneven, but between the 1790s and 1861 population in most villages at least doubled, commonly trebled, and in some cases multiplied five-fold. Such increases indicate migration at least between villages, and, on the whole, would suggest that the barrier of isolation was at least temporarily breached. The increase of population in the country as a whole over much the same period was of 90 per cent.; unless the natural increase within the villages was unduly large, their rate of increase could only be explained by some in-migration of the country population. Yet if there was a breach, it was speedily stopped. By the time of the 1851 census there is little sign of people living in the villages who had been born outside the fishing community. Most men had been born in the village where they now dwelt; a perceptible number of wives came from outside, sometimes from considerable distance (from, say, Fife to Banffshire), but always from other fishing villages or towns. So it continued till at least 1891, a now steady rate of increase, in line with that of the country as a whole, maintained by natural increase.

The first stages of growth were accomplished in temporarily favourable natural conditions, where a small capital addition allowed the fisherman the freedom of a fishing which offered the chance of a profit in a six-weeks' season as great as had been his gains from the yearly round of the cod-fishing; and this income was additional to the continuing return from the white fishing. A small haddock boat, equipped with no more than four nets and manned by four men, might expect to take in the short season between 50 and 100 crans,

for which the fisherman would get about 10/- per cran. A train of nets—
even a train as small as this—was more expensive than a set of long-lines,
and it was, of course, specific to the one short fishing; but the cost was well
within the compass of a man enjoying the new profit opportunities. But, once
started, there was continuous pressure to further accumulation. Increase in
the number of boats, coupled with the custom of hiring outside labour for the
season, allowed the full-time fisherman to man a much larger catching
equipment and to draw a larger proportionate share within each operative
boat; the number of boats in the villages grew, and grew more than the
number of indwelling population. The catching capacity of each boat could be
raised too, by carrying more nets; but nets were bulky, especially before the
invention of the cotton net in the forties, and the greater train required a
matching increase in the capacity of the boat. Such expensive improvements
were being enforced by shifts in the location and yield of the fishing grounds.
Through the nineteenth century the return from a given set of equipment—
a train of nets and a boat of fixed area and capacity—moved steadily downwards; or, to put it in another way, catches, per boat, were scarcely improved
by the great increase in the size of boats and the equipment of nets that
was taking place through the century. It became necessary, too, to move
further offshore—an added reason for increasing the size of the boat. For many
decades the east coast fisherman stuck strongly to his belief in the open boat;
but by the seventies even he was going over to the safety and comfort, but
also the greatly added expense, of the decked vessel. Thus, by the forties the
standard herring fishing boat would cost £50 or £60 and the train of nets
about the same; by 1880 the cost of building and equipping a boat was £300
to £400. And these increases scarcely increased the yield of the boat fishing
through the summer season. This remarkable feat of capital accumulation—
an increase in the value of the fisherman's equipment of at least tenfold in 80
years—was the cost of survival as a herring fisherman.

Inevitably it created strains within a society where every man had been an
independent agent. Under the older system fishermen had enjoyed rights
of virtually independent operation, even though landlords had provided some
of the necessary capital. The new capitalists and likely lenders were merchants,
but, interested as they were in controlling the supply of fish, their help was
more likely to lead to subservience and substantial restrictions on the freedom
of operation and marketing by the fishermen. In fact, new compromises were
worked out which allowed the fisherman the continuing substance of his
freedom of operation. Every year he made a bargain with a merchant to whom
he would turn over all his catch; but he was not tied to one merchant from
one year to the next, at least so long as he kept out of debt. The substantial
point of his status, then, lay in his ownership of boats and equipment. This
ownership he was able to maintain, but only at the cost of prodigious efforts
of personal saving. Merchants would make advances for the purchase of boats,

and, while the debt was unpaid, would control the debtor-fishermen; but the evidence, at least for the Moray Firth and Aberdeenshire villages, is that fishermen quickly struggled free of debt. In doing so, they maintained intact the structure of their village society. Property, it is true, now meant more, and was probably less equally distributed. But all families would have some share in a boat or the nets that went with it; none would fall to dependent status—or at least to wage-earning dependence on the people with whom they lived in the village. It remained so till the eighties, and possibly even until the steam drifter increased indebtedness of even the owning fishermen and turned most of them into pure wage-earners.

The needs of the rising trade also brought the villages into more intricate contact with the diverse and open society of the mercantile centres. Partly this arose from the way in which the new trade operated. Herring were landed daily and had to be processed quickly (by gutting, salting and packing); this demanded a specialised labour force, an accumulation of stores of barrels and salt, and conditions of swift handling of boats. Thus, landing and curing came to be centralised more in centres fewer than the scattered villages where the fishermen continued to live. The main centres, like Buckie, Banff, Fraserburgh and Peterhead, took most of this activity but for several decades secondary centres, such as Rosehearty and Pennan, might do a small amount of curing. The enlargement and deepening of the main harbours to give safe entry at all states of tide and ease of unloading at the quayside made itself felt even before the increase in the size of boats in the seventies sealed the fate of the lesser centres. Physical centralisation covered a developing financial relationship. The accumulation of stores and the hiring of labour were beyond the financial scope of the fisherman; further the barrelled herring had to be sold quickly in markets where sensitively fluctuating prices demanded constant and skilled attention; thus inevitably the processing and the selling fell into the hands of the middlemen—the curers. These were men, sometimes, of wealth and substance in long established businesses; sometimes they were wage-earners, craftsmen, or petty traders who would put their savings into a small curing venture, it might be for no more than a year at a time. They lived where their businesses were—in the larger towns; they were seldom recruited from the ranks of the fishermen themselves, and their rise did not disturb the inner balance of the villages.

Thus, neither the growingly intricate daily contracts of fishermen and people of other trades and classes, nor the increasing capital requirements, broke into the isolation of the fishing community. Fishermen continued to live apart, either in villages which were still dwelling places and communities even if they were not operational centres of fishing, or in the fishing quarters of the towns, where the fishers were segregated not only physically but also socially and biologically, in terms of their choice of occupation, their habits of marrying and the internal structure of their society. Few males moved into the fishing communities from outside; wives were still being chosen solely from the like communities of fishers; sons of fishermen were universally brought up to follow their fathers' trade. With all the mixing and migration that went on people neither moved into or out of the fishing community. Nor was the social equality of the different fishing families disturbed. The fisherman was more and more a small man of property; he owned his boat and his equipment; he engaged in a trade of strangely unequal fortunes, and also one where skill brought in a regular addition to incomes. Yet the successful men did not coalesce as a superior or employing class. There were no wage-earners in the villages, and every head of family had some property in boats or equipment. Finally his community was not infiltrated by men of other occupations. The closing decades of the century, then, found the fishermen, much more numerous than they had been in 1800, living still in many smallish villages along the coast, their mode of operation, their level of property, the daily routine of their work much changed; but their way of life was still distinctive and isolated.

AGRICULTURE

FARMING and related industry and trade together make up a large part of the economic life of the north of Scotland. Of the gainfully employed recorded in the 1951 census, including those (38 per cent.) in Aberdeen city, 18 per cent. were occupied in agriculture and horticulture, or work directly ancillary thereto such as in contracting firms and rural estates. Further substantial proportions were engaged in the processing and distribution of machinery, feedingstuffs, fertilisers, seeds, and other farm requisites, in the marketing, processing and distribution of farm produce, and in banking, legal, educational, research and other services to farmers.

Yields

The average yields of the crops grown compare well, in the lowland areas at least, with those of the same types of crop grown elsewhere in the United Kingdom (Table 1).

Table 1

Crop Yields and Density of Stocking

(North of Scotland in relation to United Kingdom as a whole)

	England & Wales	Northern Ireland	Scotland	Inverness-shire	Aberdeen-shire
	Cwts. per acre				
Yields (1948-57 average)					
Wheat	23·2	21·6	24·8	25·4	21·7
Barley	21·5	22·8	24·0	16·7	23·2
Oats	19·4	18·6	18·0	12·7	18·7
Potatoes	7·7	7·4	7·6	6·5	7·1
Turnips and swedes	14·8	16·1	17·6	13·2	16·8
Rotational hay	29·5	30·7	31·8	22·1	29·6
Other hay	21·1	34·4	29·0	16·0	23·7
	Animal units grazed in summer				
Grazing livestock (1958)					
— per 100 acres permanent pasture equivalent[a]	62·4	48·6	58·1	48·4	50·3
— per 100 acres grass[b]	67·4	53·0	66·2	50·4	67·2

[a] 10 acres rough grazing taken as equal to 1 acre permanent pasture.
0·4 acres rotational grass, mown, taken as equal to 1 acre permanent pasture.
0·3 acres other grass, mown, taken as equal to 1 acre permanent pasture.
0·7 acres rotational grass, not mown, taken as equal to 1 acre permanent pasture.
[b] Equivalents in footnote a taken as 10, 0·3, 0·3 and 1·0 respectively.

The number of ruminant stock carried per 100 acres of grassland in summer is also comparatively high despite a climate not especially favourable to grass. This is largely because most of the grass in these lowland areas is young rotational grass and clover ' leys '. In the Highland counties the very extensive rough grazings are not equal in stock carrying capacity to one-tenth their area of grassland—as assumed, for comparative purposes, in calculating the total areas for grazing in all parts of the United Kingdom; the density of stocking is, therefore, shown to be relatively low in the Highland counties. The fertility of sheep is also low there, and mortalities high, so that the lambs average in June only some 58 per 100 ewes in Inverness-shire as against 112 per 100 ewes in Aberdeenshire. The productivity of cattle in the Highlands is similarly much restricted by climatic conditions and infertile soils, as well as by poor management of grazings following the Highland ' clearings '. But other parts of the North of Scotland are famous for their early maturing beef cattle. Milk yields in the main dairying area—that near Aberdeen city—average some 800 gallons per cow, as against an average of some 780 gallons per cow in the milk selling herds of England and Wales, and 768 gallons per cow in the main Scottish Milk Marketing Board's area. The outputs per head of the pig and poultry populations are also comparatively high.

Determinants of farming systems

The high rainfalls, short growing seasons, poorly drained, acid peat covers, and shallow mineral soils of the Highland areas have severely restricted their use. Over much of Zetland, and westwards of a line that roughly follows that of the 1,000 ft. contour and the 35 ins. (889 mm.) rainfall isohyet from Caithness irregularly to west of Inverness and southeast to near Fettercairn, hill sheep farming now predominates. On the lower land in the far west, and particularly in parts of the Outer and Inner Hebrides and south Zetland, more cattle are reared. On the whole, their nutrition, like that of the sheep, is poor and fertility low. Also the marketing charges on their output are heavy. Progress is, however, now being made in these western parts in improving substantial areas of grassland by cheap liming with local materials, including shell sand, and surface seeding. Without such improvements, and they are not everywhere feasible, the livestock cannot be adequately fed and modern standards of production achieved.

East of the extensive hill farming area, in the counties of Caithness, Ross, Inverness, Nairn, Moray, Banff and Aberdeen, there is an irregular, narrow strip of upland country about 500 ft. to 1,000 ft. in elevation where also cattle rearing, along with sheep of the Blackface and North-country Cheviot breeds, is the predominant farming enterprise. The climate and soils here are not suited to cash crop production nor to dairying, and marketing costs on bulky or highly perishable products would anyway be high. This irregular strip includes the uplands of Nairnshire, Moray and Banffshire, with Strath Spey famous for the Ballindalloch and other pedigree herds of Aberdeen-Angus cattle. The single suckled calves produced in ordinary commercial herds in this area are also of exceptional quality.

Below the upland rearing area in Aberdeen and Banff is a broad extent of country, stretching from Aboyne to Fraserburgh, and from near Stonehaven to Buckie, where cattle rearing and fattening and sheep production are the main enterprises. The balance between them now probably varies more from farm to farm than between localities because, with the improvements to soil fertility resulting from generations of 'good farming', even the higher farms can produce feedingstuffs of fattening quality. The Buchan Division of Aberdeenshire—the 'cold shoulder' of the North-East—is included in this area and is famous for agricultural improvements brought about during the nineteenth century. These required great investments of labour for the clearing of rocks and building of field boundaries, for drainage, liming and manuring (including the use of phosphates) and for the following of rotations based on oats, turnips, oats, followed by three years of 'ley'. Such 'leys' were common here long before they were widely promoted in Wales and England. During the late 1870s the first reliable statistics available indicated that, for the whole of Aberdeenshire, the area of permanent grass was only 6 per cent. of the total area of crops and grass, excluding rough grazings, while leys had been sown on so much as 41 per cent.

Apart from the difficulties of soil improvement this area of cattle and sheep rearing and fattening faces continuing restrictions on choice of farming systems. Soil temperatures are late in rising in spring, not reaching, at Craibstone, near Aberdeen, 48°F. (8·8°C.) at 4 inches deep until about 6th May. This is about one week later than at Boghall in Midlothian, and three weeks later than in Rothamsted, Hertfordshire. Nor do summer temperatures rise as high as further south. Near the coast, 'haars' are common in early summer and humidities can also be comparatively high later, so that weather for hay-making and the cereal harvest is somewhat 'chancy' and potato blight can be serious. Moreover, ways have not yet been generally found of maintaining, at a level judged sufficiently high, the productivity of the land without the use of crop rotations that include cereals and entail the sowing each year of not much less than 25 to 30 per cent. of the total area of leys. Oats have been for decades the main cash crop but potatoes, especially 'seed' potatoes, comparatively free of virus diseases and true to variety, have become important since the late 1920s. Barley is now being more extensively grown because its requirements are better understood and higher yielding, stiffer-strawed varieties are available. Other cash crops are difficult to foster: sugar beet requires a longer growing season and warmer soils, and bulky perishable crops in excess of the needs of Aberdeen and the smaller towns would have to pay high transport costs. Some production of peas for canning has been introduced near Peterhead.

The restrictions on dairying in this area are similar although pricing arrangements and continually improving techniques have helped to raise production in the small dairying area near Aberdeen far above local demands for milk for local consumption.

From Stonehaven southwestwards into the Howe of the Mearns and Strathmore, and along the coast, and again in the Laigh of Moray and lower Nairnshire, Inverness-shire and Easter Ross, soils are warmer and more fertile (see page 43) and comparatively more land is used for grain and roots and less for grass. But even in these areas cattle and sheep are more important end products than are crops sold for cash.

The Orkney islands, like Aberdeenshire, are famous for their agricultural improvements and the main products there are similar to those of Aberdeenshire, although cattle are not finished to the same extent.

Pig and poultry production can be carried on with less regard to the restrictions on other farm enterprises imposed by climates, soils and

Table 2

Stocking of Full-time Farms

(Five type-of-farming groups, North of Scotland, 1947)

Region, and types-of-farming[a]	Distribution of:		Dairy cattle	Beef cattle	Sheep	Pigs, horses	Poultry
	Farms	Animal units[b]					
	Per cent of regional totals		*Per cent of total animal units in each type-of-farming*				
North-East counties							
Hill sheep rearing	1	2	1	9	88	1	1
Stock rearing	28	21	13	47	18	7	15
Stock rearing and feeding	42	50	7	65	11	4	13
Cropping, with livestock	21	16	7	61	23	2	7
Dairying	8	11	75	8	5	4	8
Total—per cent	100	100	16	53	15	4	12
—thousands	11·1	399	…	…	…	…	…
Highland counties							
Hill sheep rearing	22	45	5	12	81	1	1
Stock rearing	46	28	16	38	38	5	3
Stock rearing and feeding	7	9	7	57	30	4	2
Cropping, with livestock	7	4	13	47	29	8	3
Dairying	18	14	73	4	14	4	5
Total—per cent	100	100	18	24	53	3	2
—thousands	3·6	213	…	…	…	…	…

[a] For definitions see: *Types of farming in Scotland*, Department of Agriculture for Scotland, H.M.S.O., Edinburgh, 1952, pages 99-101.
[b] One animal unit is the equivalent of 1 beef cow or 9 ewes or 70 poultry (all ages).

marketing costs. Egg and poultry meat production are especially heavy in Aberdeenshire, the number of poultry per 100 acres of crops and grass there being 413 in June, 1961, as against comparable figures of 495 in Orkney, 214 in Scotland as a whole, 389 in England and Wales, but 528 in Northern Ireland.

The Department of Agriculture for Scotland has carried out a classification of farms based on information collected in 1947 and this permits some statistical description of stocking and cropping in the counties of the North-East and the Highlands (Tables 2 and 3). In the North-East, 28 per cent. of the full-time farms were classified as 'stock-rearing'. 'Stock-rearing and feeding' farms were 42 per cent. of the full-time farms, and had 50 per cent. of the livestock and 47 per cent. of the acreage of crops and grass. Another class, 'cropping, with livestock', also undertook a substantial amount of fattening and included 21 per cent. of the full-time farms, 16 per cent. of the livestock

Table 3

Land Use on Full-time Farms

(*Five type-of-farming groups, North of Scotland, 1947*)

Region, and types-of-farming[a]	Distribution of:		Cereals	Pota-toes	Tur-nips, Swedes	Total tillage	Leys	Per-manent grass	Rough graz-ings
	Farms	Area of crops and grass							
	Per cent of regional totals		Per cent of total area of crops and grass in each type-of-farming						
North-East counties									
Hill sheep rearing	1	1	6	...	5	13	21	66	5422
Stock rearing	28	16	33	3	9	45	43	12	140
Stock rearing and feeding	42	47	35	3	11	50	44	6	40
Cropping, with livestock	21	25	42	6	11	59	39	2	12
Dairying	8	11	33	4	11	49	45	6	17
Total—per cent	100	100	36	4	11	51	42	7	100
—thousands	11·1	1104 acres	...	...	...	...	...	...	...
Highland counties									
Hill sheep rearing	22	13	10	2	2	19	21	60	8166
Stock rearing	46	31	22	4	6	35	31	34	914
Stock rearing and feeding	7	18	28	6	10	44	40	16	138
Cropping, with livestock	7	13	39	8	11	59	37	4	18
Dairying	18	25	22	4	8	34	38	28	410
Total—per cent	100	100	24	5	7	37	34	29	1475
—thousands	3·6	282 acres	...	...	...	...	...	...	...

[a] See footnote, Table 2.

(animal units) and 25 per cent. of the acreage of crops and grass. Only 8 per cent. of the full-time farms were 'dairy farms' and these had 11 per cent. of the livestock and of the area of crops and grass. Of the total livestock, 53 per cent. were beef cattle and 15 per cent. sheep. Dairy cattle and poultry made up 16 per cent. and 12 per cent. respectively.

In the Highland counties, 45 per cent. of the livestock were on 'hill sheep' farms although these had only 13 per cent. of the total area of crops and grass. The importance of rough grazings on these farms, about 82 times the crop and grass area, is thus evident as also is their relative poverty. They raise many problems in grazing management and improvement and problems in sheep and cattle nutrition which have been studied mainly by the Rowett Research Institute, the North of Scotland College of Agriculture and the Hill Farm Research Organisation. Almost half (46 per cent.) of the full-time farms were 'stock-rearing' and these had a further 28 per cent. of the livestock and 31 per cent. of the crop and grass area. Sheep were as important as beef cattle to these farms and fully twice as important as dairy cattle.

Even in the Highland counties the tillage area and about an equal area of leys covered fully 70 per cent. of the total area of crops and grass: only 29 per cent. was under permanent grass. The 'hill sheep' farms had the highest proportion of permanent grass. Much of this is poor stuff.

Sizes of farms

Between 1801 and 1871 the total human population of the North-East counties, excluding that in Aberdeen city, increased from 241 thousand by 53 per cent. to 378 thousand. The increases were greatest in Aberdeenshire (66 per cent.), Banffshire (67 per cent.), Moray (58 per cent.), and Caithness (77 per cent.).

Such rises in population pressure raised rents of farm land and influenced decisions on farm sizes. The high rents enable large investments to be made in substantial buildings suited to the current circumstances of these farm sizes. By 1931, the total population pressure was not much less: in rural Aberdeenshire, it was down only 6 per cent. The most recent figures from the 1961 census show, however, a fall in the total for the North-East counties as a whole (excluding Aberdeen city) of 43 thousand (11 per cent.) since 1871, and the farming population has fallen more than this. Indeed the latest figures indicate that rural areas (i.e. the 'Landward' areas of counties excluding the small burghs) lost significant portions of their populations between 1951 and 1961—Aberdeenshire 7 per cent.—but the more outlying areas about twice that—Kincardineshire, Banffshire, Nairnshire and Caithness 11 to 13 per cent. and Orkney 16 per cent. Moray lost 6 per cent. But these and earlier losses were farm workers and their families much more than farmers and crofters and their families. The number of farms has not been

Table 4

Measures of Size of Farm Business

(Full-time farms,[a] seven type-of-farming groups, North of Scotland, 1947)

Region	Hill sheep rearing	Stock rearing	Stock rearing and feeding	Cropping, with: Live-stock	Cropping, with: Live-stock feeding	Dairy	Dairy and hill sheep
North-East counties							
Number of farms	77	3090	4687	1451	817	914	*
Total acres a farm of:							
Crops, grass	85	58	110	108	149	136	*
Rough grazings	4611	81	44	15	12	23	*
Animal units/farm	91	27	43	26	28	49	*
Man equivalents/farm[b]	2·4	2·1	3·1	3·2	4·0	5·0	*
Rent/farm:	*Number of farms*						
£0- 50	21	2439	1808	465	80	157	*
50-100	29	444	1626	524	260	263	*
100-150	14	101	570	214	179	169	*
150-200	6	46	324	112	121	121	*
200-250	3	} 39	} 243	57	64	87	*
250-300	—			32	45	44	*
300+	4	21	116	47	68	73	*
Highland counties							
Number of farms	796	1639	262	224	26	552	101
Total acres a farm of:							
Crops, grass	48	54	193	137	202	106	104
Rough grazings	3926	494	261	25	53	199	1693
Animal units/farm	120	37	71	32	36	36	102
Man equivalents/farm[b]	3·0	2·4	5·5	3·4	5·7	4·3	4·4
Rent/farm:	*Number of farms*						
£0- 50	317	1189	53	75	2	162	18
50-100	243	304	57	63	4	175	42
100-150	112	89	45	26	3	94	14
150-200	53	28	21	13	4	54	14
200-250	29	} 19	} 41	10	2	32	5
250-300	17			7	5	18	5
300+	25	10	45	30	6	17	3

* Less than 10 farms.

a In the Highland counties there were 8,320 'part-time farms' and 6,904 'spare-time farms' with the following averages per farm:—

	Part-time	Spare-time
Acres of:—		
Crops, grass	10	5
Rough grazings	111	58
Animal units	9	3
Man equivalents, excluding the occupier's labour ...	0·4	0·1
Rent	£6	£4

b Including the occupier and his wife as 1·0 man equivalents.

8

much reduced since the latter part of last century, except in the most remote and infertile localities. Thus at the 1951 census, 12,044 farmers and farm managers and 1,111 crofters were recorded, and in the Department of Agriculture analysis of 1947 data there were 11,413 full-time farms, 3,551 part-time farms and 1,842 spare-time farms. Of the full-time farms, only 953 were in multiple-unit businesses, which numbered 403 and consisted mainly of two-farm businesses managed by one man or company. The full-time farms covered 91 per cent. of the total area of crops, grass and rough grazings, so that per business the average area was only 187 acres of which half were rough grazings. The part- and spare-time farms averaged only 25 acres, including rough grazings.

Other measures of the size of full-time farm businesses are set out by type-of-farming in Table 4.

In the Highland counties, the population increase from 1801 to 1871 was 18 per cent. The decrease from 1871 to 1961 was 23 per cent. and began earlier than in the North-East counties. Even so the pressure of population on land is obviously still relatively high in the Highland counties. In 1947, only 17 per cent. of the farms were classified as 'full-time' as against 39 per cent. as 'part-time' and 32 per cent. as 'spare-time'. These latter two categories covered 23 per cent. of the total area of crops, grass and rough grazings. Per person recorded as 'farmer', 'farm manager' or 'crofter' in the 1951 census the area of crops and grass was only 49 acres; the rough grazings were 694 acres. The full analysis of 1947 data showed the following averages for:

	Part-time farms	Spare-time farms
Acres a farm of:		
Crops, grass	10	5
Rough grazings	111	58
Animal units a farm	9	3
Man equivalents a farm	0·4*	0·1*
Rent a farm	£6	£4
Number of farms	8,320	6,904

* Excluding labour of occupier himself.

For full-time farms in the Highland counties, averages are set out in Table 4.

The distribution of farms according to various measures of size (see Table 4 for that according to rents paid or rental values) displays the usual skewness —far more farms being 'small' than 'medium-sized' and few being large. The obstacles to amalgamation of small farms are still great, and they include the distribution of capital, and of managerial skills and energies, as well as the persistent strong demand from many farm folk for the non-monetary benefits of life on small farms. Thus attempts to measure costs and net returns for farms of different area show that the main differences in cost structure lie in the large amounts of family labour used on the smaller farms (see, for example, Table 5). If this labour were charged at the usual rates for hired labour profits on the smaller farms would be decidedly negative!

Table 5

Relation of Inputs and Net Returns per Unit of Output to Area of Farm

(119 cattle feeding farms in the North of Scotland, 1959-60)

Area of farm	Number of farms	Land	Rent and rates	Other measured expenses	Tenants' capital at 10%	Remainder	
						Unpaid manual labour (estimate)	'Profit'
		Acres		£ per £1,000 gross output			
Less than 75	31	25	41	706	135	293	−186
75-150	46	28	50	740	135	143	− 72
150-300	26	31	44	721	136	73	+ 25
Over 300	16	41	57	745	138	47	+ 13
Average	119	29	48	729	136	165	− 78

Source: Based on data in Dunn, J. M.: *Cattle Feeding Farms, 1959-60.* Financial Report, No. 49, North of Scotland College of Agriculture, Agricultural Economics Department, May, 1961.

Trends and research

The comparatively small changes in the average size of farms since the 1860s have to some extent restricted the scope for improvements in labour efficiency, but, as already noted, a substantial reduction in the farm labour force has been brought about. Also, hours of work have been greatly reduced. As elsewhere in Britain the displacement of horses by tractors and improvements in farm machinery have made these changes possible, but it should be noted that they have also been facilitated by farming less intensively, or planting to trees, the less fertile areas.

Improvements in labour productivity have also been achieved through the many changes in crop and animal husbandry that have raised yields per acre and per head of stock. In Aberdeenshire over the 21 years from about 1931-32 to 1952-53 barley yields were raised by 38 per cent., oat yields by 21 per cent., and swede yields by 22 per cent. (Table 6). Potato and hay yields, and crop yields in Inverness-shire were not raised so much, but yet substantially, and the density of summer stocking was raised 22 per cent. in both Aberdeenshire and Inverness-shire in the 22 years from 1936 to 1958—almost as much as in England and Wales and more than in Scotland as a whole (Table 7). Farm improvement schemes and marginal production grants have provided substantial assistance.

Table 6

Trends in Yields an Acre

	Barley	*Oats*	*Potatoes*	*Turnips, Swedes*	*Rotational hay*	*Other hay*
	cwts.	*cwts.*	*tons*	*tons*	*cwts.*	*cwts.*
Average, 1927-36						
United Kingdom	16·5	16·1	6·6	13·3	28·3	20·8
Scotland	18·4	15·8	6·9	15·9	32·6	30·8
Aberdeenshire	16·8	15·3	6·4	13·8	25·8	21·0
Inverness-shire	13·0	11·0	5·2	12·4	21·6	17·0
Index numbers: 1927-36 for each area=100						
United Kingdom:						
1939-48	107	104	106	109	100	100
1948-57	132	117	116	122	105	105
Scotland:						
1939-48	107	103	104	108	96	94
1948-57	131	114	110	111	98	94
Aberdeenshire:						
1939-48	112	111	108	117	106	107
1948-57	138	121	111	122	115	113
Inverness-shire:						
1939-48	115	106	108	98	98	91
1948-57	129	115	125	107	102	94

Table 7

Trends in Density of Summer Stocking

	Animal units per acre of permanent pasture equivalent		
	1936	*1958*	*Per cent. increase*
England and Wales	50·4	62·4	24
Scotland	49·0	58·1	19
Aberdeenshire	41·3	50·3	22
Inverness-shire	39·7	48·4	22

Basic to such changes are the sturdy enterprise of the farming population, and the flow of new scientific knowledge of agriculture. Much of this stems from research and engineering developments carried out elsewhere, but the North of Scotland has itself made substantial contributions both to the international store of knowledge and to the local store required for local conditions. The University was for long interested in agricultural improvements and established a Lectureship in agricultural science by 1840 and a Chair in Agriculture by 1911. The College of Agriculture was founded in 1904, the Rowett Research Institute in 1914 and the Macaulay Institute in 1930 (see below under ' Research Institutes ').

FORESTRY

Introduction

THE area covered by this note includes the counties of Aberdeenshire, Kincardineshire, Banffshire, Moray and Nairnshire and it is no exaggeration to say that this portion of the North-East of Scotland is, for various reasons, one of the most important and most interesting regions for the forester in the whole of the British Isles. This is an area where trees and woods have played a large part in the social history and where the art and profession of forestry is well understood. The valleys of the Dee, the Don, the Spey, the Findhorn and the Nairn have long been famous for their forests as well as the foothills of the Cairngorms which form the western background of the area. Today these five counties are among the most heavily afforested in Scotland, while Moray has the highest and Nairnshire the second highest percentage of woodland of any county in the British Isles.

Historical

In prehistoric times this part of Scotland was not so heavily forested as the more fertile regions of the south but, for various reasons, the original forest remained longer uncleared and there still exist some extremely interesting remnants of the original native pinewoods and birchwoods. The former have been the subject of special study by Professor Steven and Dr. Carlisle of the Forestry Department of Aberdeen University. While most of the remaining examples of the original native pinewoods are found beyond our region to the west and north, there are noteworthy remnants at Glentanar, Ballochbuie and Mar in Deeside and a small one at Glen Avon in Speyside (Fig. 15).

Although so little remains of the original native pinewoods, fortunately several of the great tree planting families of the North-East collected their pine seed from these native stands, notably the originators of the extensive plantations on the Seafield estates in the Spey valley and the Earls of Moray at Darnaway.

The story of the clearance and destruction of the original forest is the same for this region as for the rest of the country, namely the exploitation of the timber and the opening up of the land in the interests of grazing and cultivation. By the beginning of the nineteenth century there was probably less land in the region growing trees than there is today. Sheep farming was never so intensive in the North-East of Scotland as in the hill country of the Borders and Wales and the cleared land became covered with a heathland vegetation.

Scotland in the seventeenth century was a poor country and there is little evidence of any serious tree planting during that period, although some of the Cawdor woods were probably planted at the end of this century.

The eighteenth century was a tempestuous one, but after the forfeitures following 1715 and 1745 the Commissioners of the forfeited estates included afforestation in a serious but not very successful attempt to improve the confiscated properties. Yet it was the latter part of the eighteenth century which became the Golden Age of tree planting in Scotland. Many of the Scottish lairds who had taken refuge on the Continent returned to their native land, many with ideas of planting and afforestation. So, by the end of the century we find some of the more influential landowners vying with one another in the creation of plantations. It is from this period that several of the most famous of the private forests of the North-East originate. It is noteworthy that while the indigenous Scots pine was the principal conifer used, oak was the most desired species. Some of these oak woods still remain, notably at Darnaway and Cawdor. It was also during the latter part of this century that the European larch was introduced and became a commonly planted tree.

The nineteenth century, with the coming of the Industrial Revolution, emphasised the great shortage of homegrown timber and many of the landowners of the North-East embarked on extensive tree planting as a commercial undertaking. Other important events of this period were the founding of the Highland and Agricultural Society and the Scottish Arboricultural Society, the latter the first of its kind in the British Isles. These societies and the increasing literature on forestry gave a great impetus to afforestation which was particularly marked in the estates of Deeside and Speyside. Also at this time, great interest was being shown in the introduction of the North American conifers, notably the Douglas fir and the Sitka spruce, but many of the Aberdeenshire lairds experimented in their policy woods not only with these species but with a great variety of exotics. This zeal and pioneering formed the basis of much which has been done subsequently and has bequeathed to the North-East a great wealth of specimen trees of a wide range of species.

The twentieth century has provided us in this part of Scotland with the most violent events in the forest history of the region. The 1914-1918 war necessitated the felling of many of the woodlands which were so characteristic a feature of the district. These extensive war fellings here and elsewhere were largely responsible for the creation of the Forestry Commission in 1919, and from then onwards State forestry begins to play an ever-increasing part in the story. Unfortunately, the woods established by the Commission were still too young to be exploited when the second and still more demanding war of 1939-1945 broke out so that once again the private woodlands of the region were drawn upon and almost completely denuded of merchantable timber. As might be expected, this well-wooded part of Scotland formed the principal source of these emergency fellings. One further disaster befell the woodlands

of the five counties in the form of the worst storm in living memory. This
devastating storm struck the North-East of Scotland from the Moray Firth
on 31st January, 1953, proceeding southwards, and, in a few hours had blown
down much of the larger and older forest remaining after the war fellings. In
the five counties concerned the damage was especially severe and is estimated
at $39\frac{1}{2}$ million cubic feet. Again, the bulk of the damage, $36\frac{1}{2}$ million cubic
feet, occurred on privately owned forests. To offset this record of exploitation
and devastation, a very large programme of replanting has been undertaken
by both State and private forestry, an account of which, particularly since
1934 when the British Association last held their meetings in Aberdeen, is
given in the following sections.

State forests

Aberdeen is the headquarters for the East Scotland Conservancy of the
Forestry Commission. The area administered by this conservancy includes
the area covered by this note except for the county of Nairn and part of
Moray which are within the North Conservancy. In addition, it includes the
counties of Angus, Kinross, Fife and part of Perthshire which are not dealt
with in this Survey.

The Forestry Commission staff employed in that part of the conservancy
covered by this note are 1 conservator, 4 divisional officers, 7 district officers,
2 engineers, 49 foresters and assistant foresters and 462 forestry workers.

The State Forests administered by the Forestry Commission within the
five counties under review are shown in Figure 15. This shows the location
and extent of the State Forests in 1934 and at present.

*State Forests in the Counties of Aberdeen, Kincardine, Banff, Moray
and Nairn in 1934 and 1962*

Year	No. of units	Total area Acres	Under plantations Acres	To be planted Acres	Agricultural and other land Acres
1934	18	55,521	22,788	25,186	7,547
1962	33	164,765	110,903	22,492	31,370
Difference in 18 years	+15	+109,244	+88,115	−2,694	+23,823

From this it will be seen that the area covered by the State forests has
increased almost three times since the previous visit of the British Association,
while the area under plantations is approximately five times what it was in
1934. These 88,115 acres of new plantations created during the last twenty-
eight years represent an approximate total of 150 million trees planted. The

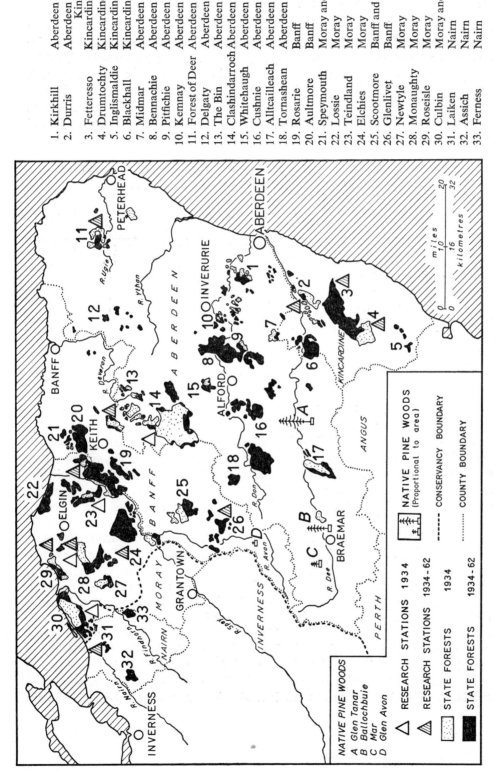

1. Kirkhill	Aberdeen
2. Durris	Aberdeen and Kincardine
3. Fetteresso	Kincardine
4. Drumtochty	Kincardine
5. Inglismaldie	Kincardine
6. Blackhall	Kincardine
7. Midmar	Aberdeen
8. Bennachie	Aberdeen
9. Pitfichie	Aberdeen
10. Kemnay	Aberdeen
11. Forest of Deer	Aberdeen
12. Delgaty	Aberdeen and Banff
13. The Bin	Aberdeen and Banff
14. Clashindarroch	Aberdeen
15. Whitehaugh	Aberdeen
16. Cushnie	Aberdeen
17. Alltcailleach	Aberdeen
18. Tornashean	Aberdeen
19. Rosarie	Banff
20. Aultmore	Banff
21. Speymouth	Moray and Banff
22. Lossie	Moray
23. Teindland	Moray
24. Elchies	Moray
25. Scootmore	Banff and Moray
26. Glenlivet	Banff
27. Newtyle	Moray
28. Monaughty	Moray
29. Roseisle	Moray
30. Culbin	Moray and Nairn
31. Laiken	Nairn
32. Assich	Nairn
33. Ferness	Nairn

Fig. 15. State forests. Counties of Aberdeen, Kincardine, Banff, Moray and Nairn.

greatest activity in afforestation has been in the State forests and it is no exaggeration to say that these new plantations have changed the entire landscape. Much of the planting has been done on bare heather-clad hillsides and probably the greatest advances in techniques have been connected with the afforestation of this kind of land. Deep ploughing with heavy equipment on compacted podsolised soils, together with the use of chemical fertilisers, have made possible the successful afforestation of sites previously considered unplantable.

Species planted (percentages) in State Forests in the Counties of Aberdeen, Kincardine, Banff, Moray and Nairn between 1934 and 1961

Species planted	Aberdeen %	Banff %	Kincardine %	Moray %	Nairn %	Total %
Scots Pine	28·9	37·3	27·0	50·8	57·0	35·4
Corsican Pine	0·5	0·6	0·2	12·5	37·9	3·7
Lodgepole Pine	11·5	18·7	10·0	11·1	2·2	12·9
European Larch	5·1	4·2	2·8	2·4	0·3	3·9
Japanese Larch	12·0	6·9	13·0	7·3	0·7	9·6
Hybrid Larch	2·0	2·2	1·9	1·4	0·04	1·9
Douglas Fir	1·7	1·4	3·1	1·6	0·1	1·6
Norway Spruce	14·5	11·0	10·6	3·2	0·2	10·8
Sitka Spruce	21·7	15·4	27·7	8·2	0·9	18·0
Other Conifers	0·9	0·8	1·4	0·7	0·2	1·0
Oak	0·2	0·2	0·6	0·1	0·07	0·2
Beech	0·6	0·5	1·2	0·3	0·4	0·5
Other Hardwoods	0·4	0·8	0·5	0·5	0·1	0·5

From these figures it will be seen that coniferous species have been almost exclusively planted, and of these the largest percentage is represented by the pines. This is to be expected in this part of Scotland which has a comparatively low rainfall in contrast to the wetter areas of the west where the spruces have been more used. Within recent years there has been a marked increase in the amount of lodgepole pine planted. This species has proved very adaptable on high, exposed heathlands which form a large share of the Forestry Commission acquisitions.

Although the final objective of the State forests is to produce saw logs at the age of about 70 years many of these forests have reached the age when they are yielding a considerable output in the form of thinnings. The present yield of this material from the forests within the area under review is approximately 1,302,000 cubic feet per year and this figure is expected to increase rapidly to about 2,361,000 cubic feet per year in the next ten years. Indeed, the utilisation of this very considerable quantity of coniferous thinnings is one of the major problems of marketing and disposal. While the coal mines absorbed most of this material hitherto, this is now a diminishing market and at the same time increasing supplies of thinnings of pit wood size are becoming available. This has led to current investigations regarding the establishment of one or more pulp mills in this part of Scotland as well as other possible uses for this material which are more fully dealt with in a later section.

Another major development during the last decade in the management of the State forests has been the construction of extraction roads suitable for mechanical transport. At present there are approximately 442 miles of forest roads in the State forests of the five counties.

No note on the State forests of the region would be complete without special reference to the spectacular success of the afforestation of coastal shifting sand dunes at Culbin Forest on the shores of the Moray Firth. The story of the envelopment of the Barony of Culbin in the seventeenth century by windblown sand is well known and has been well described in the Forestry Commission booklet on the forest. The afforestation of the Culbin sands presented very special problems which have been most successfully overcome so that today out of a total of 7,738 acres, 7,254 have been planted, mostly with Corsican pine. This area was acquired by stages by the Forestry Commission between 1921 and 1951, and already very considerable yields of thinnings are coming from this previously completely desolate sandy waste. In 1962 the yield was 65,000 cubic feet, and the estimated yield in 1970 is 151,000 cubic feet.

Mention has been made of the considerable acquisitions of land for forestry by the State since the last visit of the British Association. The question of the best use of land in the interest of the nation is a complicated one, in particular the choice between agriculture and forestry is often difficult and controversial. One of the most marked achievements within recent years has been the evolution of a much more co-operative and amicable relationship between these two competing interests which has already resulted in examples of voluntary and harmonious solutions of these difficulties.

Private forests

The most recent census figures for private woodlands of five acres and over are given in the Table.

Private Forests in the Counties of Aberdeen,
Kincardine, Banff, Moray and Nairn

County	Number of stands	Total area (acres)	Percentage of area of county
Aberdeenshire	7,646	119,702	9·5
Kincardineshire	1,809	24,050	9·9
Banffshire	2,217	36,860	9·1
Moray	2,818	47,585	15·6
Nairnshire	987	18,473	17·7
Total	15,477	246,670	10·6

The total area in the five counties is about one and a half times that of the State forests but it is made up of a large number of properties of very varying size.

For economic reasons, owners found it difficult to reafforest the areas felled during the wars but since the introduction of the Dedication Scheme in 1947, under which in return for certain undertakings by the owners the State offers financial assistance, very considerable areas have been replanted by the owners. There are now 111 estates in the area representing 81,943 acres participating in the Dedication and other grant aided schemes. As recently as 1959 the Scottish Woodland Owners Association was formed. This organisation promotes the interests of private forestry and constitutes a link between the owners and the Government. It employs its own qualified forestry officers and assists members with the marketing of their forest produce, and gives advice on forest management. A large number of the local woodland owners are members of this association.

Many of the larger estates within the region are composed of agricultural land and woodland and a skilful and successful integration of these two interests is practised.

The forestry undertaken by the private estates applies chiefly to the better sites and to the reafforestation of previous woodland in contrast to most of the State forestry which is concerned principally with the afforestation of bare and often very difficult sites. The afforestation accomplished by estate owners has been most praiseworthy and, in many cases, both enterprise and initiative have been shown in tackling difficult areas and using new methods. More and more attention is being given to the choice of species and to the use of selected planting stock. Conifers represent the large majority of the species planted, with Scots pine the commonest, but there is always an important amenity element in private forestry and both broadleaved trees and the rarer exotic species are not overlooked.

Reference has already been made to the very important part which the woodland owners of the North-East of Scotland have played in the local forestry history. Among the foresters and head foresters in charge of these private woodlands there have been some very able and outstanding men. Great woodland estates like Glentanar, Dunecht, Balmoral, Candacraig, Monymusk and Ballogie in Aberdeenshire, Glen Dye and Fasque in Kincardineshire, Seafield in Banffshire, Darnaway, Altyre and Strathspey in Moray and Cawdor and Lethen in Nairnshire, to mention only a few, are continuing to play a very active part in the forestry of the region.

Reference should also be made to the very fine collections of specimen trees which fortunately still exist as reminders of the past interest in arboriculture by previous owners. This is especially true of the arboreta and policy woods in Glentanar, Durris, Paradise Wood at Monymusk, Coull, Cullen, Ballindalloch and Relugas estates. On these and other estates are to be found some of the finest specimens of the exotic conifers in the United Kingdom. In the Table a list is given of some of the outstanding specimens with the most recent measurements.

Specimen trees of special interest in the Counties of Aberdeen, Kincardine, Banff, Moray and Nairn

Species	Estate or Forest	Height (ft.)	Girth at b.h. (ft. & ins.)	Date of measurement
Abies lowiana	Durris, Kincardineshire	145	14′ 7″	1955
Abies nordmaniana	„ „	114	12′ 0″	1955
Abies procera	Inchmarlo, „	124	14′ 2″	1957
	Durris, „	132	14′ 2″	1955
Araucaria araucaria	Kilravock, Nairnshire	49	7′ 6″	1956
Larix decidua	Alltcailleach, Aberdeenshire	102	7′ 9″	1955
„	„ „	116	6′ 3″	1955
„	Ballindalloch, Banffshire	120	7′ 9″	1960
„	„ „	117	9′ 0″	1960
„	Darnaway, Moray	132	10′ 11″	1955
„	Cawdor, Nairnshire	121	7′ 0″	1958
„	„ „	110	9′ 7″	1958
„	„ „	121	8′ 6″	1958
„	Dunphail, Moray	106	10′ 11″	1954
„	Woodend, Kincardineshire	114	7′ 3″	1960
Picea sitchensis	Kilravock, Nairnshire	135	21′ 11″	1956
„	„ „	145	16′ 2″	1956
Picea smithiana	Gordon Castle, Moray	88	11′ 6″	1955
Pinus jeffreyi	„ „	90	7′ 8″	1957
Pseudotsuga taxifolia	Ballindalloch, Banffshire	137	8′ 9″	1960
„	Durris, Kincardineshire	147	16′ 2″	1955
„	Glendye, Kincardineshire	129	9′ 1″	1956
„	Darnaway, Moray	133	10′ 2″	1955
„	Relugas, Moray	143	12′ 3″	1954

Education and research

Aberdeen is one of the four British universities which grants degrees in forestry. The course for the ordinary degree of Bachelor of Science in Forestry extends over three academic years. Candidates who are recommended by the examiners for this degree may proceed to a fourth year of study leading to the honours degree. In addition, the higher degrees of M.Sc. and Ph.D. can be obtained in forestry subjects.

Aberdeen is fortunate in having the Macaulay Institute for Soil Research situated at Craigiebuckler on the outskirts of the city. This famous research station was founded in 1930 to promote land husbandry and is concerned with both agriculture and forestry, especially in connection with the study of peat and heathlands. A close association has been established between the Institute, the Forestry Department of the University and the Forestry Commission, and valuable assistance has been given, especially in connection with tree nutrition and forest nursery soils.

The Research Branch of the Forestry Commission is responsible for carrying out experiments and investigations regarding silviculture, management, pathology, entomology and genetics throughout the country. Many of these are long term projects and a considerable number of these are being carried out in the area under review. Very great strides have been made by this branch of the Forestry Commission since the last visit of the British Association of Aberdeen. Figure 15 shows the forests where silvicultural research was being carried out in 1934 and where long term experiments are now in progress. The Table gives the principal current silvicultural research

Major Silvicultural Experiments under investigation by the Research Branch of the Forestry Commission in the Counties of Aberdeen, Kincardine, Banff, Moray and Nairn

---

ABERDEENSHIRE

Clashindarroch — Provenance experiments with European and Japanese larch and lodgepole pine. Upland heath afforestation, species and cultivation trials. Thinning and mixture experiments.

Forest of Deer — Experiments with spruce species. Provenance experiments with lodgepole pine.

Teindland — Upland heath afforestation experiments.

KINCARDINESHIRE

Drumtochty — High elevation pilot plots. Larch provenance trials. Nursery experiments. Seed orchard for Scots pine, Douglas fir, European larch and *Picea omorika*.

Fetteresso — High elevation pilot plots. Japanese larch provenance trials. Long term experiments to compare mixtures of *Pinus contorta* and Japanese larch with pure crops.

Durris — Provenance trials with European larch. Fertiliser experiments with Norway spruce. Spacing and pruning experiments.

BANFFSHIRE

Glen Livet — Cultivation and spacing experiments with Norway spruce. Provenance and progeny trials with Scots pine.

The Bin — Provenance trials with Norway spruce.

MORAY

Elchies — Provenance trials with lodgepole pine.

Speymouth — Ploughing and planting position experiments. Long term experiments to compare mixtures of Scots pine and *Tsuga* with pure crops.

Monaughty — Pruning experiments with Douglas fir.

Roseisle — Provenance trials with Scots pine. Spacing experiments with Scots pine.

Culbin — Species trials. Provenance trials with Scots pine and lodgepole pine. Nutrition experiments.

Newton — Nursery experiments. Seed orchard and tree bank.

NAIRNSHIRE

Laiken — Provenance trials with Scots pine and Douglas fir.

In addition, extensive entomological investigations are being carried out at Drumtochty on control measures against the larch sawflies and at Culbin and other pine forests against the pine looper moth (*Bupalus piniarius*).

---

experiments. In addition, many permanent sample plots have been established for yield determination investigations.

The timber trade and wood utilisation

The port of Aberdeen has for a long time been one of the principal trading ports with the Baltic and the Scandinavian countries. Since the seventeenth century there has been an important import trade in timber from these countries, and at present they represent the source of most of the timber and wood pulp entering the port of Aberdeen. The current annual imports are approximately 75,000 cu. ft. of round timber, 1,600,000 cu. ft. of hewn or sawn wood, and 487,000 cu. ft. of box shooks. Most of the round timber comes from Finland, the sawn wood from Sweden, Finland, Russia and Poland, and the box shooks from Portugal. The importance of Aberdeen as a centre of the fishing industry and its strategic position as the market for an extensive distribution trade have favoured the timber trade. Several old established firms of timber merchants exist and there are many sawmills. In addition to the general trade of importing, sawing and distribution, chiefly of softwood from Scandinavia, a number of more specialised wood-using industries have been developed. In particular, Aberdeen is a very important centre for the box and crate making trade and also has factories making barrels and bobbins. High grade paper making has for long been a distinctive feature of the region, and while this previously depended principally on fibres other than wood, in recent years more and more wood pulp is imported annually. The present annual imports are approximately 58,000 tons of chemical and 19,000 tons of mechanical pulp and the countries of origin are Sweden, Norway, Finland, Russia, France, Portugal and North America. Shipbuilding requires a wide range of timbers and the construction of wooden fishing craft along the North-East coast demands high quality larch timber. While most of the timber handled by the timber merchants is still imported, there is an ever-increasing use being made of home grown timber. There are in the district a number of efficient and enterprising timber merchants with modern felling and extraction equipment and up-to-date sawmills who are well organised to deal with the larger and better quality home grown material. Several of these merchants have recently developed specialised departments which undertake planting work on contract with private woodland owners.

Mention has already been made of the very considerable quantity of coniferous thinnings which are already coming from the local plantations and this will increase rapidly in the future. Much attention has been given in recent years to the marketing, disposal and use of this source of material. Although no decisions have yet been made for the construction of factories within the region requiring a large sustained supply of raw material, the yields coming from the local forests are suitable for the manufacture of wood pulp, fibreboard and particle board, and already plans are well advanced for the establishment of a pulp and paper mill at Fort William which may draw a part of its requirements from the forests of Moray and Nairnshire.

In addition to the timber trade and other wood-using industries, Aberdeen and the area included in this survey has a nation-wide reputation for its forest tree nursery trade. Several well known firms are engaged on a large scale in the raising of trees for planting and very large quantities of high grade planting stock is distributed annually all over the British Isles.

SELECTED REFERENCES

'Experiments in the afforestation of upland heaths.' *Forestry Commission Bull.*, No. 32, H.M.S.O., 1960.

STEVEN, H. M. and CARLISLE, A., *The Native Pinewoods of Scotland*, Edinburgh, 1959.

MURRAY, J. M., 'An Outline of the History of Forestry in Scotland up to the end of the Nineteenth Century.' *Scottish Forestry Journal*, **49**, Pt. 1, 1935.

STEVEN, H. M., 'The Forests and Forestry of Scotland.' *S.G.M.*, **67**, No. 2, 1951.

GUILLEBAUD, W. H., 'Scots Pine in Morayshire and Strathspey.' *Forestry*, **7**, No. 2, 1933.

'Forestry in Scotland' (Mimeographed notes for British Council Course), Aberdeen, 1950.

International Union of Forest Research Organisations (Mimeographed notes of Tour No. 1, Northern Scotland), 12th Congress, 1956.

CHITTENDEN, F. J. (Ed.), 'Conifers in Cultivation.' Report of the Conifer Conference, 1931. *Royal Horticultural Society*, London, 1932.

MACDONALD J., WOOD, R. F., EDWARDS, M. V. and ALDHOUS, J. R. (Ed. by), 'Exotic Forest Trees in Great Britain.' *For. Comm. Bull.*, No. 30, H.M.S.O., 1957.

Culbin, For. Comm., H.M.S.O., 1949.

Drumtochty, For. Comm., H.M.S.O., 1953.

FISHERIES

IN considering the fisheries of North-East Scotland it is convenient for a number of reasons to regard the area, on the coast, as stretching from Arbroath to Lossiemouth. In addition to these ports it includes Buckie, Whitehills, Macduff, Fraserburgh, Peterhead, Aberdeen and Montrose, as well as other smaller towns and villages, all of which are dependent to some extent on fishing. Current Scottish fishery statistics show that 60 per cent. of the total Scottish catch by weight is landed in this region but this does not represent the full measure of the northeastern fishing industry. For example, many vessels from North-East ports seasonally are based elsewhere in Scotland or in England so that their landings at certain times are credited to other regions. Although it is difficult, in view of the varying sizes and engine powers of fishing vessels, to apportion fishing power to the different parts of the country, it is estimated that from 80 to 90 per cent. of Scottish catching power is permanently based in the region. Furthermore, the North-East collectively is the chief centre in Scotland for the processing of fish by smoking, filleting and freezing, and for ancillary industries such as shipbuilding, the manufacture of nets and of fish-meal, ice factories, ship repairs and supplies of all kinds.

Historical development

In the course of the last century and a half the fisheries of North-East Scotland have undergone many changes and in order to appreciate the situation at the present time it is worthwhile considering their development historically. The traditional fishery of North-East Scotland is the drift-net fishery for herring. This fishery on local grounds developed throughout the nineteenth century mainly as a result of a trade in salt herring with German and Russian ports on the Baltic and North Sea. During most of the nineteenth century the fishery was prosecuted from open boats propelled by oars and by sails. These were replaced by larger decked vessels driven by sails and later by motor power. In turn, the latter were outnumbered by steam drifters, many of them built of steel. This fishery reached its peak in the years immediately preceding the First Great War.

At the end of the war attempts to revive the trade in cured herring with the Baltic ports were unsuccessful with the result that demand for herring diminished and the fishery started to decline. This was hastened by a fall in the home consumption of herring and by the relatively high running-costs of the steam drifter. Consequently, herring fishermen in growing numbers turned to the catching of white-fish and the steam drifter began to disappear from the fleets and to be replaced by smaller, more economical, dual-purpose vessels, powered by diesel motors. Such vessels were adaptable for both drift-netting or seining as circumstances demanded.

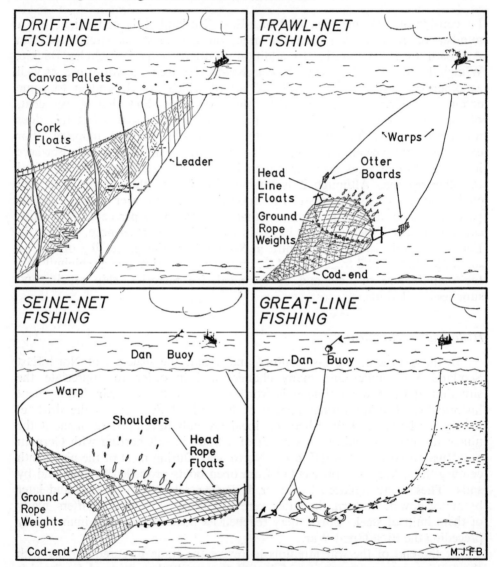

FIG. 16. Methods of fishing used in the North-East.

Throughout the greater part of the nineteenth century white-fish were caught chiefly by baited hook and line. This was the position in North-East

Scotland when trawling was introduced to the area in 1882. This new method of fishing was immediately successful and a rapid expansion followed. For example, white-fish landings at Aberdeen in 1888 totalled 133,000 cwt. while in 1914 they amounted to $2\frac{1}{4}$ million cwt. Not surprisingly this increase in the quantity of fish caught was also accompanied by a comparable development of other branches of the industry and this development was aided by the good rail connections with markets in the south.

Just as the use of the larger steam drifter in the herring fishery had resulted in the concentration of the fleets in the larger harbours of the area, such as Buckie, Fraserburgh and Peterhead, so the employment of even larger vessels in trawling was followed by a concentration of the latter in the port of Aberdeen.

During the First Great War, fishing in the North Sea and its adjacent waters was greatly reduced with the result that stocks of fish were allowed to accumulate. At the end of hostilities trawlers reaped a rich reward for a few years. In a remarkably short time, however, largely owing to improvements in the otter trawl, fish stocks were depleted and throughout the 1930s Scottish fishermen for the first time experienced the effects of overfishing. Aberdeen trawl fishermen shared in this experience and from the boom years of the first decade the industry gradually entered a period of depression in the 1930s.

Reference has already been made to the decline in the herring fishery after the First Great War and to the change-over of fishermen to white-fish. This was largely facilitated by the introduction of a new method of fishing— Danish seining. Adopted first by Moray Firth men its success was ensured to some extent by the existing regulation prohibiting trawling by British vessels in that area. From the Moray Firth ports seining gradually extended to all Scottish fishing ports so that concurrently with the decline in the herring drift-net and white-fish trawl fisheries in North-East Scotland there developed the successful seine-net fishery.

The fisheries after the Second Great War

The effect of the curtailment of fishing in the North Sea during the Second Great War was another accumulation of fish which again resulted in remarkable fishing for a number of years at the end of hostilities. In spite of the mesh and minimum landing size regulations introduced by some nations between the two wars, and of the efforts made by the Permanent Commission set up under the International Fisheries Convention (1946) to avoid another depletion of stocks such as occurred after the First Great War, stocks were quickly reduced so that fishermen soon had to fish harder or to go further afield in order to obtain profitable catches. Fishermen in the North-East of Scotland shared both in the good fishing and in the subsequent scarcity. The resultant trend within each of the three main fisheries however was very different.

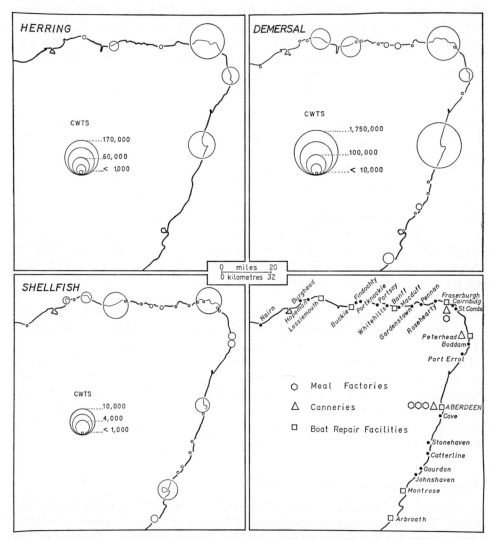

FIG. 17. The fishing industry. Based on *Scottish Sea Fisheries Statistical Tables* for 1961. It must be noted that catches in any one year may depart considerably from an average view and that 'creeks' with a considerable number of boats may land little or no fish since the boats may not fish from that creek.

Herring drift-net fishery

Although the stocks of herring in the North Sea after the second war were shown to be high by the quantities landed in the Continent, Scottish fishermen were obviously unwilling to participate in a fishery which had proved disastrous in the period between the wars. Despite some good fishing in the late 1940s and 1950s, the number of boats taking part in the drift-net fishery for herring off North-East Scotland continued to decline; in 1961 the ports of Fraserburgh and Peterhead, which ever since the days of the steam drifter have been the main centres for this fishery, experienced one of their poorest herring seasons. The extent of the decline of this fishery may be gauged from the following yearly catches of herring from all Scottish grounds:

1913   4·5 million cwt.
1938   2·8   ,,   ,,
1960   1·7   ,,   ,,

and these figures may be regarded as roughly representative of the local fishery off North-East Scotland. Although herring are no longer as plentiful on some North-East Scottish grounds as they were in the early days of this fishery, the decrease in the landings is, of course, primarily due to the diminishing number of drifters participating each year.

In recent years the hopes of herring fishermen have received a further setback by the continued failure of the East Anglian fishery, in which at one time hundreds of drifters from North-East Scotland took part every year; indeed the full effect of this failure has only been offset by some North-East drifters turning to the winter herring fishery in the Minch.

Fishery scientists and fishermen alike have been concerned with the decline of these once important fisheries. Various explanations have been suggested, including overfishing of the adult or of the immature stocks and environmental changes, but whatever part these (or some combination of them) may have played in the striking decline of the southern North Sea fish stocks, scientific evidence suggests that in the northern North Sea as a whole there has been no such diminution, although there have been other changes. In particular, older fish are much less abundant than they used to be on the grounds off North-East Scotland and this has affected the quality and, therefore, the utility of the catch. In regard to quantity, however, as Scottish catches have diminished in the North Sea, so continental catches have increased. Whilst this is partly due to the diminishing Scottish fishery it must also be associated with the remarkable change-over on the Continent from drift-netting to trawling as a means of catching herring.

Although Aberdeen fishermen pioneered the catching of herring by trawl on the Fladen and other grounds, this method has now been neglected in the United Kingdom where the traditional drift-net continues to be the principal method used. On the Continent, however, trawling for herring has grown to be the most important method for catching this fish. Some Scottish fishermen maintain that this active method of fishing for herring tends to break up the shoals compared with the passive drift-net method, and indeed this relatively new disturbance, on such a big scale, of the fish stocks may well be affecting their behaviour, distribution and abundance. On the other hand, scientists have observed a biological change in certain groups of herring, indicating a somewhat faster growth and earlier ripening of the reproductive organs, which would appear to be due to environmental influences and with this change there seems to be associated the decline in the proportions of older fish.

Concurrently with the decline in the herring fishery, a very marked change has been evident in the utilisation of the herring catch. Before the First Great War the bulk of the fish was cured in salt while appreciable quantities were consumed fresh or kippered. Failure to revive the export trade in cured herring ended the main demand for this fish and for a time during the 1920s large quantities of good quality fish had to be dumped at sea for lack of a market. The Herring Industry Board, set up in 1935 to investigate new outlets for herring, turned its attention, among other things, to the problem of unwanted surpluses and after the Second World War erected reduction plants at a number of ports. The capital costs involved and the losses incurred in operating the meal and oil schemes were met by a grant from the Exchequer. However, because of the decline in the herring landings these plants have been working well below capacity. This and the flooding of the European market with large quantities of Peruvian meal at low prices has resulted in the Board experiencing heavy losses on its meal and oil operations, so that the government has had to underwrite these losses since January 1960 in order to maintain the level of prices to the fishermen. In any event British fishermen have neither been encouraged nor have shown any desire to follow the continental practice of fishing solely for herring for reduction to meal and oil, i.e. the so-called industrial fishing. More recently the expansion of deep-freezing facilities at fishing ports has enabled a greater use to be made of herring both in the fresh state and as kippers etc. The post-war years have also seen the development of a sizeable market for herring as pet food, an outlet which ensures a better price than would be obtained for surplus herring to be manufactured into fish-meal.

White-fish trawl fishery

As already indicated the trawl fishery at Aberdeen enjoyed profitable fishing of the accumulated stocks of fish in the North Sea at the end of the second war. Thereafter, however, owing to a combination of factors, including the growing scarcity of fish, the mounting running-costs and the increasing price of new vessels, the industry experienced a period of depression. A committee under the chairmanship of Sir B. H. Neven-Spence had been set up during the war to investigate the state of the white-fish and shell-fish industries in Scotland and in 1951 the Scottish Council (Development and Industry) set up a second committee to investigate the difficulties of the

Aberdeen fishing industry. The reports by these committees made a number of recommendations with a view to improving conditions in the industry and in 1951 the White Fish Authority was set up for the purpose of 'reorganising, developing and regulating the white-fish industry' in the United Kingdom. In particular the Authority was given powers to make grants and loans towards the cost of replacing obsolete vessels. From this point the old coal-burning trawlers, which formed the bulk of the Aberdeen fleet, began to be replaced by modern diesel-powered vessels with a number of oil-fuelled steamers. By the end of 1961 the modernisation of the fleet had virtually been completed with the replacement of the 300 or more steam trawlers by 150 motor or oil-fuelled vessels. The disparity in the number of trawlers in the old and new fleets may be attributed to the increased power and efficiency of the new vessels compared with the old, and to the fact that a big proportion of Scottish white-fish (45 per cent. in 1961) is now provided by the relatively new seine-net fleet.

Most of the Aberdeen trawlers fish the North Sea or other home waters, some making short trips of two to three days to local grounds and landing twice weekly, others voyaging to the Shetlands or to the northwest coast and landing once per seven to ten days. For many years an appreciable fleet, variable in size according to the season, has successfully fished at the Faeroes, making trips of twelve to fourteen days. In the past few years, however, this section of the fleet has been affected by the decision of the Faeroese to extend their fishery limits from three to twelve miles and although British trawlers are temporarily permitted to fish to within six miles of the coast, this concession may soon be again under review. Although a small number of Aberdeen trawlers fish at Iceland in the late spring and early summer, owners have shown little interest in the far distant grounds from which the bulk of the English catch is derived. It is possible, however, that any final decision by the Faeroese to fix their fishery limits at twelve miles may force more trawlers from Aberdeen to operate in the Iceland area.

Seine-net fishery

The end of the second war was followed by a rapid expansion of the seine-net fleet. This was aided by a number of factors including the lower initial cost of the seine-net vessel compared with the trawler, the relatively low running-costs at a time when prices for fuel etc. were rising, the general suitability of seiners for the smaller harbours and by the grant and loan scheme of the W.F.A. Development of the fleet was characterised not only by an increase in the numbers of these vessels but also by an increase in the average size and engine power of the individual units. These changes in turn enabled an extension of the area of operation of seine-net vessels. From being almost entirely inshore fishermen seine-netters have gradually extended their activities into deeper and more distant waters with the result that seining is now carried on in most parts of the North Sea and west of Scotland. The progressiveness of Scottish seine-net fishermen, and this applies particularly to men from North-East Scotland, is revealed by the readiness with which they have adopted modern electronic, navigational and fishing aids. Furthermore, the evolution of the present fishing gear from the original Danish seine introduced in 1921, together with the changes in operational techniques, bears witness to the skill and ability of Scottish seine-net fishermen.

As may be expected the increase in the numbers of seiners of all sizes naturally put a very heavy strain on local fish stocks. Consequently, following the practice of the herring fishermen in fishing seasonally in other areas, many seine-netters from North-East Scotland, at certain times of the year, fish from ports in other parts of the United Kingdom. Vessels from the Moray Firth for example are based temporarily at west of Scotland ports, fishing the North Minch, North Rona and the Butt of Lewis grounds from the small ports of Wester Ross and Sutherland, the Tiree, Skerryvore and St. Kilda grounds from Oban, and the Firth of Clyde from Ayr and Campbeltown. Similarly vessels from Fraserburgh and Peterhead operate on the northeast coast of England at certain times of the year.

Of the thirty or thereabouts species of food fishes landed by Scottish trawlers and seine-netters the haddock is the most important both as regards quantity and revenue. In the last five years from $1\frac{1}{4}$ to $1\frac{3}{4}$ million cwt. of this fish have been landed yearly at Scottish ports, most of it in North-East Scotland. This represents nearly twice the catch of the next most abundant species, the cod and the whiting. These three species together provide more than 80 per cent. of the Scottish white-fish catch and thus form the main objective of Scottish white-fish fishermen. Certain less abundant species such as plaice, lemon sole, turbot and hake, which are also caught by North-East fishermen, are important because of the high prices which they fetch as quality fish on the market.

As every fisherman knows, stocks of fish vary from place to place and from time to time. This may be due to seasonal variations in the habits of the fish or to the effect of fishing intensity. Research has also shown that stocks of fish vary as a result of natural fluctuations in the number of each species 'born' annually. It has also been shown that these fluctuations between 'good' and 'poor' years are sometimes considerable. In the haddock, for example, the variation in annual brood strength over the last forty years has been calculated to be as high as the ratio 60 : 1. Obviously, therefore, the stocks of a species such as the haddock on which Scottish trawl and seine-net fishermen are so predominantly dependent may, at times, be profoundly affected by such fluctuations. In general, good, moderate or poor broods appear at intervals and in proportions to ensure a fairly uniform annual commercial catch. Occasionally a succession of good broods, as occurred every year from 1951 to 1955, gives rise, after a suitable interval to allow the fish to reach a marketable size, to a period in which stocks are high and fishing profitable. On the other hand, a succession of poor or average broods can depress stocks and give rise to unprofitable fishing, as indeed happened from 1956 to 1960 and resulted in the relative scarcity of haddock which has persisted from the end of 1957 to the present time.

Line fishing

Although the proportion of fish caught by line in Scotland (9 per cent.) is now much smaller than it used to be, all three branches of this selective and desirable method of fishing continue to flourish in North-East Scotland. Hand-lining, in the form of ripper fishing for cod and fly fishing for mackerel, is pursued seasonally from small boats on a considerable scale at Fraserburgh and Peterhead. Small-lining in which the baiting of the hooks is done ashore, sometimes by women, continues to prosper on a small scale on the Angus and Kincardineshire coasts and at Fraserburgh and Peterhead.

Great-lining, involving the use of stronger lines and hooks and different methods of operation than in small-lining, is mainly carried on from Aberdeen, although some of the vessels taking part come from the ports of Fife and from Peterhead and Fraserburgh as well as from Aberdeen itself. This fishery, which is mainly carried on in deep water, concentrates chiefly on big fish such as cod, ling, tusk, skate and of course halibut, the most important species of all, since it fetches the highest price for any white-fish on the Scottish market. Some great-line fishing is carried on in the North Sea and off the west of Scotland but on the whole this is a middle- or distant-water fishery with the vessels, now entirely motor-powered, concentrating on the oceanic banks such as Rockall, Faeroe, Lousy, etc., with a few specialising in longer voyages, of three to four weeks, to Iceland and, in season, when ice and weather conditions permit, to east Greenland.

Shellfish

Crabs and lobsters are caught on sections of the northeast coast although not in the quantities in which they are fished in some other parts of Scotland. During the present scarcity of white-fish, however, more fishermen have turned to creel fishing with the result that landings of shell-fish have been increasing at ports such as Fraserburgh, Peterhead and Gourdon.

Reference must also be made to the development of the new fishery, by seine and small trawl, for Norway lobsters. These shell-fish, known to science as *Nephrops norvegicus* and to the trade as prawns and sold in fashionable restaurants as scampi, not so long ago were discarded by fishermen as having no market value. From a modest landing of 3,000 cwt. in 1950 the Scottish catch rose to over 42,000 cwt. in 1959 when it earned more than £270,000 for the fishermen. Stocks of Norway lobsters in the Moray Firth and on the Fladen ground are fished by vessels from Lossiemouth, Buckie and Fraser-burgh, but fishermen from the northeast ports also exploit the more extensive west-coast grounds for this crustacean.

Squid

Another marine invertebrate for which demand has grown in recent years is the squid. Formerly used only as bait there is now a profitable market for this animal on the Continent—the result of the enterprise of Aberdeen fish merchants. Scottish landings of squid in 1960 exceeded 21,000 cwt. for which the fishermen, most of them from the North-East, received over £60,000.

Salmon fisheries

The annual Scottish catch of salmon and sea trout by angling and by commercial methods amounts to between 1,500 and 2,000 tons. Compared with some species of marine fish this is a small total but in value it represents an income to fishermen of between $1\frac{1}{4}$ and $1\frac{1}{2}$ million pounds sterling. (Unlike marine fishermen, salmon fishermen have to pay for the right to fish for salmon whether on the sea coast or in the rivers.) Of the total catch about 80 per cent. is taken on the Scottish east coast and in its rivers and of this rather more than one-third comes from North-East Scotland. All three methods of catching salmon and sea trout are employed in the area—rod and line in the rivers, net and coble in the mouths of the rivers and fixed nets (bag-nets and stake nets) on the coast. Salmon, including grilse, forms the bulk of the catch with the fishery districts of Dee, Spey and the North Esk outstanding. In certain rivers such as the South Esk and the Ugie the proportion of sea trout is higher than elsewhere.

Finally, any account of the fisheries of the area must include a reference to the valuable sporting interests in its rivers, burns and freshwater lochs. Salmon and sea trout have already been mentioned, but of even greater interest to the ordinary angler is the brown trout, which occurs widely throughout the North-East and, as elsewhere in Scotland, provides sport and relaxation for an ever-increasing number of people.

Conclusions

This short review of the fisheries in North-East Scotland has indicated the major changes which have taken place over the past hundred years. Some of these changes have been forced on the fishermen by events, national and international, outwith their control; others have followed the application of technical advances in the evolution of fishing gear and other kinds of marine equipment. The review also reveals the ability of Scottish fishermen to meet the challenge of events and to adapt themselves to changing circumstances. That this challenge is continuing is evident from the problems facing Scottish and English fishermen today. Foremost amongst these is the decision by some nations to extend their fishery limits and thus exclude foreign fishermen from grounds which many of them, including the British, pioneered, and have fished for nearly a hundred years. In consequence British fishermen are having to look for other grounds or to consider the exploitation of other species of fish for which at present there is no great demand. Another problem to be faced at the present time is the remarkable expansion of the fishing fleets of certain countries, which, hitherto, have not been regarded as fishing nations. This expansion adds to the growing fishing power throughout the world and thus increases the ever-present danger of overfishing. It is to be hoped, therefore, that the countries with an interest in fisheries will in time reach agreement on the regulations which are essential to ensure the effective conservation of fish stocks.

INDUSTRIES AND COMMERCE

THE North-East of Scotland, though predominantly an agricultural area, has also a variety of industries. None, of course, are heavy industries, for the area does not possess the natural resources associated with the location of such industries. These industries are of vital importance to the economic life of the people of the region and also to the country as a whole.

The principal industries are fishing, distilling, granite, textiles, shipbuilding, engineering, food preservation and paper manufacture, all of which have long associations with the area, and, indeed, one might almost say are traditional. Many started as family concerns, becoming in course of time quite large companies and, in some cases, amalgamating with larger national interests.

A characteristic is the high degree of specialism that exists both in the processes of manufacture and in the finished products. The woollen mills, for example, produce high quality luxury cloth, involving specialised skill on the part of the workpeople. The engineering firms concentrate on the manufacture of equipment, which can be found in most countries abroad, and hold a distinguished record for the excellence and individuality of their products. Local labour is held in high esteem, not only because of its quality and character, but because of the ease with which it can adapt itself to novel and complicated processes.

The extent to which the many industries of the North-East engage in foreign trade is another notable feature of the enterprise of the area. In this respect, one of the most important is the distilling industry, which has become a great dollar earner. Whisky is one of Scotland's greatest exports and has achieved this position through the skill and enterprise of its distillers. The textile mills also have a large export trade in high quality goods. The paper industry is no exception, a great variety of high quality papers produced at the mills around Aberdeen being consigned to many overseas markets.

Almost all the industries have a long history, although beyond Aberdeen new enterprises have been started up by American companies. These firms were attracted to this area by the availability of labour, and according to their own testimony, the results have justified their choice of site. This would suggest that, despite distance from markets and sources of raw material, business can take root and succeed provided enterprise and a good type of labour are available. But the Americans are not alone in appreciating this. Enterprise in the North-East among the natives themselves is still a living force. The modernisation of the granite industry and the transformation of the fishing industry in the last seven years or so from a decaying to a progressive industry bears witness to this fact. Those who sometimes bemoan the absence of new industries might well reflect on the achievements of many of the existing firms and in the success of local people in establishing new businesses. Yet, it is remarkable that no new industries have been founded in the present generation within the city itself. This is a great defect in its economy and, unless remedied, the drift to the south of skilled men will continue. There is therefore an urgent need for new industries which will offer to young people interesting employment and provide fresh outlets for labour, as mechanisation proceeds in the older established industries.

Fishing

This industry occupies a major place in the economic activities of the city and the whole of the North-East and at June 1960 gave employment to a total of 6,467. Aberdeen itself is the largest fishing port in Scotland and the third largest in the United Kingdom. Other ports in the county, such as Peterhead and Fraserburgh, and those on the Moray Firth, Buckie, Macduff and Lossiemouth, also play a large part in the industry.

The modern history of the industry dates from the end of last century when steam power was introduced. This effected a revolution in both white and herring fishing, which hitherto had been carried on by sail boats. Specialisation and concentration were the first and most significant consequences. White fishing became highly organised and carried on by steam trawlers and liners, while steam drifters engaged in herring fishing. Steam power thus divided the industry into two parts, each with its own methods, its own type of vessel, its own capital organisation and its own system of remuneration.

White fishing concentrated in Aberdeen. Steam trawlers were larger than the old sail boats, so that many of the small creeks around the coast were unable to provide suitable harbour accommodation. Moreover, Aberdeen had the advantage of having good railway facilities, an important consideration for the expanding fresh fish trade.

The port's first steam trawler—a second-hand wooden paddle boat of 28 tons and 50 h.p.—commenced fishing in Aberdeen Bay in March 1882. At first little headway was made in steam trawling, because of the inadequacy of the boats and the lack of fishermen skilled in the new method and with a knowledge of the best fishing grounds. In a few years, however, these difficulties were largely overcome and progress became rapid and sustained. By 1892 there were 38 trawlers fishing from the port, rising to 156 in 1902, to 217 in 1912 and to 249 in 1914.

The change-over from sail to steam power led to concentration of capital. Hitherto boats and gear generally belonged to the fishermen themselves, although sometimes landowners assisted in the provision of capital. But the financing of steam vessels was quite beyond the capacity of the ordinary fisherman and the tendency for land capitalists to invest in ships was accelerated. Capital was readily forthcoming, for the new industry offered handsome profits. In some cases companies were formed, while in others vessels were owned by individuals or by small partnerships. Many who invested in trawlers were also interested in the supply of coal, ice or stores and so the interlocking of directorates, between companies engaged in trawling and in the subsidiary industries, became a marked feature of the industry's organisation. The marketing of fish, however, remained the function of the merchants and between them and the trawl owners there was little community of interest.

Aberdeen city authorities were quick to appreciate the potentialities of the town as a fishing port and from time to time carried out extensive improvements. The new fish market was opened in 1889 and harbour accommodation was extended to cope with the increasing number of trawlers frequenting the port, for not only did it become the headquarters of most Scottish and a large number of English trawlers, but also of Danish and German vessels. Buyers and fish-salesmen also made Aberdeen their headquarters, while various subsidiary industries, like fish curing, ice manufacture, box-making, net manufacture, ship repairing and engineering, were established. Coaling facilities were also provided and shipbuilders concentrated on the special problems of trawler construction.

*Number of Arrivals of White Fishing Vessels and
Quantity of Fish landed in Alternate Years from
1st October 1887 to 1914*

Year ending 30th September	Trawl fishing vessels	Steam and motor line vessels	Sail and motor yawls	Fish landed (cwts.)
1888	2,763	296	7,751	133,180
1890	3,389	958	9,793	230,320
1892	3,764	1,537	11,705	332,240
1894	4,049	1,783	10,522	403,240
1896	4,873	2,215	11,832	532,200
1898	6,473	2,424	9,868	712,660
1900	7,575	1,941	8,357	911,260
1902	9,197	1,843	6,062	1,217,680
1904	9,125	1,825	5,675	1,463,640
1906	9,136	1,708	6,554	1,485,700
1908	10,712	2,170	3,863	1,994,020
1910	11,596	1,555	2,729	2,000,000
1912	11,275	1,668	1,952	2,256,960
1914	12,082	1,436	1,111	2,268,860

Source: Aberdeen Harbour Accounts.

With the larger home fleet and the facilities offered to trawlers from other ports and countries fishing into Aberdeen, landings of white fish showed a marked increase.

The steam drifter brought a period of abnormal prosperity to the herring fishing communities of the North-East. The first drifter sailed from Wick in 1898, but it was at Buckie in Banffshire that the use of this new type of fishing vessel was most quickly developed. Fishermen there were not slow to see the advantages of the steam drifter. Buckie's first, commissioned in 1900, was quickly followed by others, resulting in a revolution, probably the most rapid ever witnessed in the history of fishing of any nation. With amazing speed fishermen turned to steam, the year 1907 being a record when no fewer than 234 drifters were added to the Scottish fleet. In 1914, Buckie district alone had 298 steam drifters and liners on its register, the largest number in any district of Scotland, Peterhead with 186 coming second. Aberdeen district had 113, Fraserburgh district 119, Banff district 100 and Findhorn (Lossiemouth) district (which includes ports in Moray and Nairnshire and also in part of Inverness-shire) 132.

Steam vessels accounted for 74 per cent. of the total catch of herrings in Scotland, motor vessels 7, and sail boats 19. Many small creeks like Crovie, Gardenstown, St. Combs, Inverallochy and Rosehearty, could face the challenge of the drifter only by adopting the motor boat and concentrating on white fishing.

The character of herring fishing was changed by the adoption of the drifter. It became a full-time job and white fishing was largely abandoned by the drifter ports. The drifter, with its greater mobility, greater range and increased capacity, could follow the various fishings from one part of the coast to another and its home port thus became merely a base where it was overhauled and serviced between seasons. There were three great herring seasons, providing a continuous fishing for nine months of the year—first, the winter fishing during the first three months, mainly in the Firth of Forth, Wick and Stornoway; second, the summer fishing from the end of May to September, commencing in the Hebrides, then Shetland, followed by Orkney and the east coast; and third, the autumn or Anglian fishing from September to November.

Within each of these areas landing and curing came to be concentrated at one or two ports. The growing complexity of the industry resulting from the greater range of the fleet and the change in the system of marketing brought into existence a new class of fish-salesman, who employed agents to meet the boats at different ports and dispose of their fish. These salesmen, who were often agents for coal and other supplies, furnished part of the capital required by fishermen to buy their drifters. The banks and landowners also came to their assistance and in some cases engineers and boatbuilders were content to leave balances on the purchase price of the boats. The earnings of the boats were very great and the profits handsome. Fishermen were indeed unlucky if, in a few years, they were unable to clear their boats of all encumbrances.

The fishing industry was completely disorganised by the First World War. Many drifters were requisitioned by the Admiralty while mine-fields and general hostilities limited the extent of fishing operations. Thus at the end of the war a rich harvest from the rested fishing grounds awaited exploitation. But the German and Russian markets, once so important to the herring industry, were closed, a serious matter for the herring fishermen.

In 1919 and 1920 the Government, alive to the precarious state of the industry, guaranteed to take over any unsold portion of the season's cure. But in 1921 this guarantee was withdrawn and the industry, thrown back on its own slender resources, entered a period of acute depression. Two years later, however, the Government placed £150,000 at the disposal of the Fishery Board for the purpose of making loans to fishermen for the replacement of nets and gear, but this period of hope was cut short by the strike of 1926. British coal was rationed on the basis of 25 per cent. of normal consumption, little short of calamitous to steam fishing vessels—still the backbone of the industry. Foreign coal, when obtainable, rose to 90s. a ton.

The white fishing industry also suffered during these years, although at the conclusion of hostilities prospects had seemed bright. The war had given a much needed rest to the fishing grounds, already showing signs of depletion in 1914, owing to over-fishing. By 1920, however, it became clear that a difficult period of readjustment lay ahead. There were signs that the industry was over-capitalised, while the amount of fish landed was almost the same as in 1914, although costs were much higher. In 1921, when the price of fish had fallen to almost pre-war level, only one-third of Aberdeen's trawlers covered expenses. Yet during that year no fewer than 418 vessels were engaged in white fishing in Scotland—an increase of 33 over the previous year. In common with the herring industry, white fishing also suffered severely during the protracted coal dispute. In 1926 long voyages became impracticable and some 90 of the largest trawlers were laid up.

Towards the end of the twenties prospects brightened and it seemed as if the whole industry was at last reaching a position of stability. White fishing, in particular, enjoyed a measure of success in 1928 and 1929, the number of trawlers fishing from Aberdeen rising to 238 as compared with 223 in 1926. From the port's yards 17 new trawlers were launched, 11 for local owners although only 6 were to be attached to the port. The price of fish was rising and there was a remarkable increase in its consumption, resulting from the development of motor transport and the increasing number of fried-fish shops. Motor transport was especially important to Aberdeen, for no less than 75 per cent. of the port's catch was sold fresh in the United Kingdom.

Improvement in herring fishing was not so marked. Each year saw more drifters go to the breakers' yards, although the number of motor boats steadily increased. But the employment of the seine-net was giving new life to some communities, especially along the Moray Firth. Lossiemouth in particular showed enterprise in adopting dual-purpose boats, which could concentrate on white fishing by seine-net in near waters and, at the appropriate season, engage in herring fishing.

The whole industry, however, soon became engulfed in the great depression of the early thirties. White fishing, which depended on the home market, was severely hit by the fall in prices and the herring fishing suffered greatly from restrictions imposed by foreign governments on imports to their countries. So serious was the plight of the industry that in 1933 the Government appointed a Sea Fish Commission to investigate and report on all sections of the industry. Its first report dealt with herring and on the basis of its recommendations the Herring Industry Board was set up in 1935, with power to reorganise this section in accordance with the changed circumstances of the times. One of the Board's first actions was to reduce both the herring fleet and its personnel, but despite the reduction it remained evident that the drifter was no longer an economic proposition. In 1937, for example, the average earnings of a drifter at the two principal herring fishings amounted to £1,588, while at least £2,200 were required to meet wages, running expenses and maintenance costs. Opinion, therefore, tended steadily towards the motor boat, suitable for both white and herring fishing, and in an endeavour to encourage their construction the Government, under the Herring Industry Act of 1938, provided for the expenditure of £250,000 within a period of five years.

The second report of the Sea Fish Commission dealt with white fishing. It drew a striking contrast between Hull, with its modern fleet and organisation, and Aberdeen, with its ageing fleet and its complex and inefficient shore organisation. Admittedly Aberdeen suffered from two disadvantages, the cost of coal to trawlers and the distance from the principal markets, but the most serious feature was the obsolescence of her fleet. In 1934, of a total of 285 steam trawlers, 171 or 60 per cent. were over 20 years old. Attention was also drawn to the very small ownership units, no less than 41 per cent. of the vessels being owned by concerns with fewer than 5 ships each. As a result of the investigations, an act was passed in 1938 setting up a White Fish Commission with supervisory powers over the white fishing industry of the United Kingdom as a whole, but before it got into stride, war broke out and it ceased to function.

The economic position of the industry was profoundly affected by the Second World War. In a sense it enjoyed an artificial prosperity, because of the reduction in the fishing fleet, while the North-East, especially Aberdeen, benefited by the virtual elimination of the intense competition of Grimsby

10

and Hull. Fish was not rationed because of the difficulty of maintaining regular supplies. Although a general control of prices was introduced in June 1941, the level remained higher than before the war. Moreover, the Ministry of Food paid all carriage on fish despatched inland from the main ports, thus securing a wider distribution of supplies, while to reduce charges and save transport, Great Britain was divided into five zones in October 1942 for the distribution of white fish. This scheme continued in operation until March 1946.

Between 1944 and the end of 1946 the de-requisitioning of fishing vessels took place. At the end of 1948 there were 237 trawlers engaged in fishing in Scotland, of which 171 (including 4 new vessels) fished from Aberdeen. Steam drifters or liners had been considerably reduced, 250 as against 442 in 1938, but the number of motor boats had increased, 3,622 as compared with 2,471 in 1938. Aberdeen had 22 steam liners and 119 motor vessels; Peterhead 88 drifters or liners and 119 motor vessels; and Fraserburgh 35 drifters or liners and 170 motor vessels. The Moray Firth districts of Banff, Buckie and Findhorn had a total of 70 drifters or liners and 383 motor vessels.

During the war years the problems of the fishing industry had been closely examined. The herring industry had been the subject of an exhaustive enquiry, resulting in the powers of the Herring Industry Board being greatly extended under an act of 1944. This act provided for grants aggregating £820,000 to assist herring fishermen to acquire boats and equipment and for a further £250,000 and advances not exceeding £1,700,000 towards expenses incurred by the Board, including loans to fishermen. In May 1946 the Board again assumed responsibility for production and export but the Ministry of Food retained control over the home market. While in the thirties the industry had suffered from over-supply and unsatisfactory prices, now there was a general shortage and high prices. Home consumption of fresh herring and kippers had been stimulated during the war and export markets were now open to feed the starving European countries ravaged by war.

In the case of white fishing, attention was drawn in 1943 to the relative decline of Scottish landings in pre-war years, as compared with those of England and Wales, and at the request of the Government the Scottish Council on Industry appointed a committee to consider the problems of both the white and shell fish branches of the industry. This committee submitted two reports (in February and June 1945) making numerous recommendations for consideration by the industry and also for departmental attention. The Government immediately took action and under the Inshore Act of 1945 grants totalling £500,000 were made available to inshore fishermen in Great Britain and loans up to a total of £800,000 for the acquisition, improvement and reconditioning of boats and purchase of gear. This was later increased in 1948 to £1 million by way of grant and £1,800,000 for loans.

In 1945, notwithstanding a much reduced fleet, the total catch of white fish in Scotland equalled 84 per cent. of 1938 and by 1946 it was above the 1938 figure. Between 1938 and 1947 landings by seine-net increased fourfold, the fishing being carried out mainly by motor boats. The import duty of 10 per cent., removed during the war owing to the scarcity of food, was reimposed on imported fish. In 1948 the Ministry of Food granted a subsidy of 10d. a stone on fish caught by British vessels in near and middle waters to offset higher costs. But despite the extensive assistance given by the Government, there was a general decline in white fish landings. To make matters worse the flat-rate transport scheme, operated by the Ministry as an integral part of price control, was withdrawn in April 1950 and the subsidy paid in respect of fish caught in near and middle waters was also terminated. The immediate effect of decontrol was a substantial rise in white fish prices, but they soon fell again below the general level under control, resulting in a number of trawlers and other vessels being laid up. Over-fishing, another difficulty facing the industry, was particularly serious in the case of inshore fisheries, for unlike the near and middle waters, success of these depended to a large extent on the landing of good quality fish which were in short supply. There were also delays in obtaining supplies of essential equipment and a shortage of women labour for gutting and curing.

In 1951, under the Sea Fish Industry Act, the Government established the White Fish Authority to reorganise, develop and regulate the white fish branch of the industry. Steps were also taken to reintroduce, on a temporary basis and in a different form, the subsidy on white fish caught in near and middle waters, and to initiate discussions in the Organisation for European Economic Co-operation on the question of over-fishing, a matter which from time to time had caused much concern.

Broadly speaking, the two sections of the industry were faced with the same problems—modernisation of the fleet, improved organisation of curing and marketing, and over-fishing. In the case of herring, although some progress had been made by the Herring Industry Board, there was a continuing fall in demand and by 1950 landings in Scotland by British vessels were the lowest for half a century apart from the war years. Over 50 drifters were laid up, so that most of the herring was landed by motor vessels. In 1950 the Government took immediate action on proposals submitted by the Board, including the buying and scrapping of all steam drifters and the promotion of a sales campaign at home and abroad. All this gave new confidence to the industry. The drifter fleet was progressively reduced, until in 1957 the only remaining boat was scrapped. But both the white and herring fishing received a setback in January 1953 when an unusual storm severely damaged harbours, gear and vessels.

To encourage modernisation of the near and middle waters fleet, the White Fish Authority was authorised to make loans up to 60 per cent. of the cost of new vessels of not more than 140 feet in length. This, however, did not prove sufficiently attractive to encourage the building of new trawlers and two years later, under the White Fish and Herring Industries Act of 1953, both the Herring Board and the White Fish Authority were given power to supplement loans by grants of 25 per cent. towards the cost of new ships, thus leaving owners to raise only 15 per cent. The fishing industry in all its branches also received further assistance in the form of subsidies. For example, the act of 1953 made provision for the payment of the subsidy on fish caught in near and middle waters, first introduced in July 1950 as a temporary measure. On vessels over 70 ft. but under 140 ft. a subsidy was paid on scales, varying according to gross and average daily earnings of a voyage, the grounds fished and the type of vessel employed. This subsidy was later extended beyond 1958 and under an act of 1961 made available to the distant water section of the industry.

For some years the white fish industry of Aberdeen had been a source of serious concern, not only to many citizens who viewed its decline with alarm, but also to the Government. At the request of the Secretary of State a committee was appointed under the chairmanship of Sir Alexander McColl to examine the local situation. In December 1950, this committee issued a report, recommending a re-organisation of the industry and the framing and adoption of a plan to secure greater efficiency, which included a reduction in the number of firms engaged, especially producers. Subject to the industry's acceptance of these proposals the committee also recommended loans and a 25 per cent. grant towards rebuilding the trawler fleet. Loans of up to 60 per cent. and grants of 25 per cent. were in fact made available to the whole white fish industry under the acts of 1951 and 1953.

The White Fish Authority devoted its main attention in Scotland to Aberdeen. The serious state of the industry, revealed by the McColl Committee, prompted it to open negotiations in 1951-2 with the trawl owners with a view to implementing the committee's proposals for the rationalisation of the fleet. Its approach, however, met with little support and it was made clear that no voluntary reorganisation would take place. Efforts were also made to initiate schemes to improve the marketing organisation, but here too it was apparent there would be no voluntary adoption of the McColl recommendations. The difficulty was the large number of relatively small units of ownership. For example, out of 88 trawl owners, 70 controlled only 87 ships between them, while on the processing side there were several hundred firms, most quite small. In the summer of 1953 the Authority continued negotiations at Aberdeen, but the Owners' Association again declared its unwillingness to pursue amalgamation. In this year the Authority had been authorised to make grants as well as loans, and, it was hoped, this more generous provision would encourage trawl owners to build. But they were slow to move. A group of merchants, however, alarmed at the decline of the fleet, proposed a ' Fleet

Replacement Scheme ', under which 40 or 50 diesel trawlers would be built over a period of ten years, but only one-sixth of the merchants were prepared to subscribe and this naturally limited the scope of the enterprise. Down to March 1955 only four applications for assistance had been received, although subsequently a group of companies, including Aberdeen Motor Trawlers Ltd., sponsored by a number of merchants, applied for grants and loans for nine trawlers to be built over a number of years. But this was only nibbling at the problem of modernisation. Of the 186 Aberdeen trawlers fishing the near and middle waters, seven-eighths were 30 years old and nearly half over 40. The situation was indeed critical and brooked of no delay.

It was not until 1956 that the modernisation of the Aberdeen trawler fleet really got under way. At first local owners had been largely content to purchase vessels from southern ports. Thus between 1945 and 1955 only four new vessels had been added to the fleet. But in 1957, there were 13; in 1958, 16; in 1959, 22; and in 1960, 34. At 30th November, 1960, the trawler fleet of the port comprised 40 steam and 85 motor vessels. The White Fish Authority was naturally gratified at this result. It also welcomed the growing tendency towards larger owning units, although it was felt much more concentration was desirable.

Ownership of Aberdeen Trawlers and Liners in 1950 and 1959

	1950		1959	
	Number of concerns	*Number of vessels*	*Number of concerns*	*Number of vessels*
Concerns owning:				
10 vessels or more	2	27	—	—
5 - 9 vessels	4	25	9	59
4 vessels	4	16	3	12
3 vessels	7	21	4	12
2 vessels	21	42	13	26
1 vessel	67	67	30	30
Total	105	198	59	139

Source: *White Fish Authority Annual Report and Accounts for the year ended 31st March 1960*, p. 23.

Liners and seine-net vessels are also employed in the white fishing industry. Aberdeen again is the main port for this method of fishing, although Peterhead, Fraserburgh, Macduff, Buckie and Lossiemouth are also important. Lossiemouth had led the way in the use of the Danish seine-net and by 1928 was the main centre in Scotland. During the war seine-netting was greatly stimulated and on the conclusion of hostilities expanded greatly. The financial assistance given by the White Fish Authority for the building of vessels of not more than 140 ft. covered the inshore as well as the near and middle waters fisheries. The maximum rates for inshore fishermen were in fact more favourable, as on a new vessel, costing not more than £20,000, a ' working owner ' could obtain a grant of 30 per cent. (joint owners up to 25 per cent.) of the expenditure up to a maximum of £5,000. In addition he could obtain a loan up to 55 per cent., thus leaving only 15 per cent. to be met from his own resources. Inshore fishermen were not slow to avail themselves of this assistance and applications poured into the Authority.

White fishing by seine-net has become the principal fishing of the Moray Firth. The seine-net boat, though smaller than the deep-sea trawler, is larger and has a greater range than the inshore boat and engages in off-shore fishing. These vessels must fish outside the three mile limit, however, but in the Moray Firth are protected from the competition of trawlers which have not been permitted to fish there since 1909. Seine-net fishing is engaged in all the year round and herring fishermen turn to this method with their dual-purpose boats during the off-season for herring. It is a daily fishing, the boats leaving in the morning and returning before night, and is prosecuted all along the north-east coastline. Some boats go as far as the west coast, landing their catches at Kinlochbervie, Ullapool and Oban, whence they are consigned by road to Aberdeen, Newhaven and Glasgow.

By 1960 the seine-net fleet accounted for a larger proportion (47·7 per cent.) than trawlers (43·7 per cent.) of the total landings of white fish in Scotland, and for the first time supplanted the trawler as the chief supplier of fish to the market. The bulk of the catch was landed on the east coast, the principal districts being Aberdeen, Fraserburgh, Peterhead, Buckie and Lossiemouth in that order. Many Moray boats landed their catches at Fraserburgh, Peterhead and Aberdeen. Considerable quantities of white fish were also consigned to the Aberdeen market from other ports, mainly on the east coast.

Distribution of Landings by British Vessels

	1938		1959		1960	
	Weight cwt.	Value £	Weight cwt.	Value £	Weight cwt.	Value £
Aberdeen	1,607,393	1,763,883	1,860,308	6,099,884	1,652,642	5,941,250
Peterhead	7,152	9,595	100,564	288,401	132,679	380,516
Fraserburgh	25,414	30,398	176,356	571,363	218,535	665,575
Macduff	39,530	56,342	83,910	346,394	75,530	344,815
Buckie	9,443	14,064	113,033	418,159	123,241	461,502
Lossiemouth	103,396	129,288	111,647	415,586	104,328	394,862

Source: Fisheries of Scotland Report for 1960, p. 41.

Of the total quantity of demersal fish landed by British vessels at Scottish ports in 1960 (3,367,157 cwt. valued at £11,839,608), 83 per cent. was consumed in Scotland or sent fresh to England and of the remainder 16 per cent. was processed and the balance reduced to fish meal. Aberdeen produced the bulk of the processed fish. The pattern of the disposal of herring was substantially different. In 1960, of the total landings by British vessels in Scotland (1,762,058 cwt. valued at £1,881,496), home consumption absorbed 42 per cent., exports 26 per cent., pet food 18 per cent. and 14 per cent. was processed into meal and oil. Landings in Scotland represented 81 per cent. of the total United Kingdom catch.

Fish, when landed, is laid out on the market floor and the merchant or his manager walks around, notebook in hand, assessing the state of supplies. Prior to this, he has obtained some estimate of landings at other ports and also made contact by telephone or telegraph with dealers throughout the country regarding their requirements. Auction sales commence at 8 a.m. each morning, when the merchant buys his fish from salesmen, generally acting as agents for the boat owners. In 1960 there were some 240 firms of merchants in Aberdeen. The fish is boxed and taken by motor lorry to the merchant's fish house where it is processed and despatched by road or rail to large wholesale markets or direct to fishmongers' shops or fish friers in many parts of the country. Fish is also sent abroad to almost every country in the world.

Fish landed at Aberdeen is processed in a variety of ways. After washing, the fish may be skinned and filleted and cured by smoking to produce finnan haddocks, golden cutlets, smoked fillets or other specialities for which the city is famous. During recent years, much progress has been made in quick freezing and pre-packaging, a development greatly stimulated by the expansion of the export trade and by the installation of 'deep freezes' in shops. This new departure has led to the adoption of mechanisation for skinning, filleting, freezing and packaging. There are two cold storage firms but large firms have also cold storage facilities often in excess of their requirements and are thus able to offer storage to others not so well equipped. Three firms, the most important being Mutual Fish Products Co. owned by the merchants themselves, convert fish offal, and on occasion surplus fish, into fish meal for use as animal food. The distribution of white fish is in the hands of different firms from those on the producing side. This may result from the divergent interests within the industry placing trawl owners and distributors in different camps or from the economic impossibility of combining in one unit two operations demanding different abilities and experience. In recent years, however, there have been a few cases of integration. In 1955, for instance, Aberdeen Motor Trawlers Ltd. was floated by several leading merchants taking the initiative in modernising the Aberdeen fleet. But, although the interests of the two major sides of the industry may appear to be divergent at times, both trawl owners and merchants are primarily concerned in the production of good quality fish. It is true, however, that whereas trawl owners are not enthusiastic about landings of distant water fish, merchants welcome them for, though coarser in quality, they are very saleable when cured or frozen. Since Aberdeen trawlers are engaged almost entirely in near and middle waters fishing, the recent restrictions on trawling in Icelandic waters is of little moment to local owners. But the restrictions imposed by the Danish Government on fishing in the neighbourhood of the Faeroes, restrictions likely to be extended to a 12-mile limit in the future, are more serious and likely to have adverse affects on the port's fishing industry.

Fishing Vessels in each District 1960

District	Total	Vessels 40 ft. and over			Vessels under 40 ft.	
		Trawl		Other methods	Motor	Sail
		Steam	Motor	Motor		
Aberdeen	187	40	85	26	36	—
Peterhead	158	—	—	65	91	2
Fraserburgh	171	—	—	92	79	—
Macduff	174	—	—	101	73	—
Buckie	137	—	6	104	27	—
Lossiemouth*	125	—	—	108	17	—

*Ports in Moray and Nairnshire only.

Source: *Scottish Sea Fisheries Statistical Tables 1960. Table 24, p. 40.*

Since 1960 modernisation has continued. For instance, Aberdeen's trawling fleet now consists of 121 diesel trawlers, 14 oil burning steam trawlers and 1 coal burning trawler.

Distilling

In the popular mind the production of whisky is associated with Scotland and the term 'Scotch' is renowned the world over. This industry has had a long and eventful history in this country and today is an important constituent in her economy. Most malt distilleries are found north of the Tay and within this area the counties of Banff and Moray are by far the most important. Indeed each has more malt distilleries than any other county in Scotland. South of the Highland line there are many other distilleries, but most of these produce a grain whisky. Measured by employment figures the distilling industry is relatively small, but in terms of value of output and value of exports it ranks very high. In the post-war years it has been a famous dollar-earner.

How early and by whom whisky was first produced in Scotland cannot be determined, but it is known that from a very early date there were scores of small stills operating in the Highlands. The chief ingredients for the manufacture of the product, barley, peat and water, were available in most places. The whisky produced was largely for domestic use, although the more enterprising farmers and crofters appreciated the saleability of the spirit, and, indeed, in some cases regarded the revenue from stills as necessary to their means of livelihood. To market the commodity, they made hazardous journeys south, with their ponies loaded with whisky kegs, over the hills and

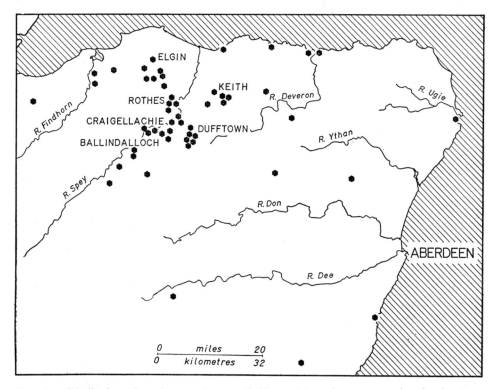

FIG. 18. Distilleries. One dot equals one distillery. Note the concentration in the Spey valley region.

glens by the old drove roads, or conveyed it to the nearest port or creek, from whence it was shipped south or to the Continent. Thus through the efforts of these intrepid pioneers, whisky became known outside the confines of Scotland and it might be said they were the first to plant the seeds of its fame. Even as early as the beginning of the seventeenth century Scotch whisky had gained a great reputation in England.

From time to time the Government attempted to control production of spirits by imposing taxes on malt and by passing legislation designed to restrict the number of stills. This naturally incensed the Highlander, who regarded it as a gross interference with his traditional way of life and bred in him a cold determination to defy the law in an effort to preserve what he considered as his birthright. Thus in the course of the eighteenth century an extensive smuggling trade developed. Glenlivet in Banffshire became one of the great centres of illicit distilling, from whence a lucrative trade was carried on with customers in the south despite all the efforts of authority, while from Moray, where there were also scores of illicit stills, whisky was shipped to England and the Continent from the many creeks along the Moray Firth. By the early years of the nineteenth century practically all the trade of the Highlands was in the hands of smugglers. Indeed, the amount of illicit whisky produced ruled the market price.

In 1820 the Duke of Gordon, who at that time was laird of Glenlivet and the largest landowner in the Central Highlands, raised in the House of Lords the question of the widespread traffic in illicit whisky. He promised to induce other landowners to co-operate with him in an endeavour to suppress smuggling, if the Government would sanction the legal distillation of whisky, of a strength equal to that produced by the illegal distillers, on payment of a reasonable duty. This proposal was approved and under an act of 1823 new rates were introduced, whereby 2s. 3d. was made payable on a gallon of proof spirit and licences of £10 were fixed on all stills of 40 gallons capacity and over. This act not only ensured the production of good whisky but did much to oust the coarse varieties flooding the market at that time. Illicit distilling, however, persisted for a long time after and it was not until near the end of the nineteenth century that it was brought under control by the vigilance of excise officers.

The first distillery in Banffshire to be licensed under the act was in Glenlivet. The pioneer was George Smith, a prosperous farmer who had also carried on a lucrative trade from his illicit still. Realising that the days of such distillation were numbered he applied for a licence to protect and consolidate his hitherto illicit business. His action was not welcomed by many of his neighbours, for it brought the revenue authorities into the Glen and for several years he had to have a military guard to protect his distillery. About this time four other distilleries, which are still in operation today, were licensed in Banffshire, while in the neighbouring county of Moray, Miltonduff in the parish of Elgin was the first to be granted a licence. Before the end of the century numerous other distilleries had been established.

Prior to the 1830s all Scotch whisky was distilled in the traditional pot still, but the invention of the patent or continuous still brought into the market a grain spirit which, although largely tasteless, was very cheap to produce. In the pot still the spirit is always made from barley malt, whereas in the patent still maize and other grains mixed with a little malted barley are used. Thus the patent still brought about a revolutionary change in the industry and laid the foundation of the blending trade. All over the country patent stills sprang up and although many, finding them unprofitable, gave up immediately, this method of producing whisky gained a strong hold in the Lowlands. By the 1850s, when production in this area had increased considerably, trade agreements were entered into by the patent distillers about the division of the market, but these never proved wholly satisfactory. Finally, in 1877, the Distillers Co. Ltd. (known as D.C.L.) was floated with a capital of £2 million, the shares being taken up by six of the largest patent distillers. Before the introduction of the patent still each distillery marketed its own product as an individual brand of whisky of the distillery concerned. With the production of the tasteless spirit from the patent still, however, the first blending of spirits took place, as before it could be sold Highland malt had to be added to give it quality and flavour. Subsequently, the blending of different brands of whisky was developed to a fine art until gradually the blending trade became a major part of the industry. The pioneers in Scotland were Andrew Usher & Company, Edinburgh, agents since 1840 for the produce of the Glenlivet Distillery in Banffshire, but they were soon followed by others in Glasgow, Leith, Dundee and Aberdeen. Today D.C.L. has virtual control of the blending trade or, as it is called, the Scotch Whisky Trade.

By zeal in advertising, both at home and abroad, D.C.L. greatly extended the market for whisky and in the nineties the industry enjoyed boom conditions. New distilleries sprang up, a total of 11 being established in Banffshire and eight in Moray, while existing distilleries doubled or trebled their output, with the result production soon exceeded demand. Then came an inevitable slump from which the industry was to take more than ten years to recover. During this period D.C.L. bought up many distilleries and endeavoured to put the industry once more on a sound footing by introducing a policy of restrictive production.

In 1905 a famous court case, known as ' What is Whisky Case ', reflected the bitter conflict between malt and grain distillers. The former maintained that they alone produced real whisky, while the latter contended that their product was a scientific mixture of grain and malt whiskies and therefore also entitled to be called ' whisky '. The powerful D.C.L. took a lively interest in the case and eventually, urged by the grain distillers and the blending trade, approached the President of the Board of Trade to have the whole matter settled. The Government was forced to appoint a Royal Commission to enquire into the subject and its report, issued in July 1909, pronounced a victory for D.C.L. This decision gave great encouragement to the blending trade and stimulated the art of blending. Today practically all Scotch whisky is a blend, many different whiskies being used to produce one specialised brand.

The need to conserve grain supplies for food during the First World War struck a heavy blow at the industry. Some distilleries had to close down while others were required by the Government to concentrate on the production of industrial alcohol and acetone. During these war years D.C.L. strengthened its hold on the industry by forming subsidiary companies for the production of by-products of alcohol. Thus when peace came it was in a strong position to commence an intensive programme of distillation to meet the large demands for whisky. But many of the independent distillers were not so fortunate. They were ill-equipped to enter the market and in the difficult years that followed the collapse of prices in 1921, coinciding as it did with the enforcement of total prohibition in the U.S.A., they readily accepted terms of purchase offered by Scottish Malt Distillers, a subsidiary of D.C.L. Year by year more and more distilleries were taken over by the combine, so that by 1960 it possessed 13 out of 25 distilleries in Banffshire and 11 out of 22 in Moray.

The great depression of the early thirties had a serious effect on the industry but prospects brightened with the ending of American prohibition in 1933. Three years later approximately 100 of the distilleries which had been closed throughout Scotland were once more in full operation and down to 1939 the industry experienced boom conditions. The outbreak of the Second World War, however, ushered in a period of uncertainty and ultimately stagnation. At first during the ' cash and carry period ' the industry was encouraged to expand exports to the U.S.A., but with the entry of America into the war and the dire necessity to conserve food supplies it was forced to curtail operations. Distillation at the patent or grain distilleries ceased after 1940 while in 1943, when food stocks were at a dangerously low level, barley supplies to distillers were cut entirely. Towards the end of 1944, production at both malt and grain distilleries was resumed, when an allocation of cereals amounting to approximately one-third of pre-war quantities was granted, but it was not until 1948-9 that production reverted to normal. The running down of stocks was particularly serious for the industry, for the maturing time-lag forces both distillers and blenders to think ahead in terms of up to ten years at least, before the product is available for sale.

Immediately after the war the Government instituted a national export drive. There was an insatiable world demand for Scotch whisky. The United States was by far the largest market, and whisky became a great dollar-earner, but large shipments were also made to Canada, South Africa, Australia, New Zealand and Venezuela. The total exports of Scotch whisky to overseas markets rose from 4·7 million proof gallons in 1945 to 9·7 in 1950 and to 19·3 in 1958. In the last-named year almost 11 million gallons went to the U.S.A., a greater quantity than was sold in the home market, which was severely handicapped by the steep rise in excise duty from 8s. 6d. per bottle before the war to £1 4s. 7d. in 1951.

Of the 94 malt or pot-still distilleries in the whole of Scotland (including Orkney) 47 are in the counties of Banff and Moray. Most are situated in the upper reaches of the counties, especially along Speyside, a name synonymous with Scotch whisky the world over. Three distilleries have been built within the last two years, namely, the Glenkeith-Glenlivet at Keith, the Macduff near the town of Banff and the Tormore in Moray. There is also one distillery in Nairnshire and a few distilleries in Aberdeenshire, the Lochnagar in the parish of Crathie, the Glendronach in the parish of Forgue and two small ones at Kennethmont and Oldmeldrum, while in the neighbouring county of Kincardine there are distilleries at Fettercairn and Stonehaven.

Apart from Parkmore in Banffshire, which is engaged in malting only, all these distilleries produce 'single malt whiskies', some of which is bottled and sold as such under the name of the distillery—for example, Glenlivet and Glenfiddich in Banffshire and Glen Grant and Glen Rothes in Moray. But the bulk of the whisky is sold to blenders, whose aim is to produce a blended whisky with a distinctive flavour. Blending is a highly-skilled operation and the work of an expert, who has to discriminate between the different Scotch whiskies he may use to produce a perfect blend. Indeed a branded whisky may be a blend of over a dozen different malt and grain whiskies, the secret of the blend being closely guarded by its blender who sells it under a proprietary label. Blenders divide pot-still or malt whiskies into four classes, according to their geographical origin, namely: the Lowlands, the Island of Islay, Campbeltown and the Highlands, the last-named being the principal and largest area, stretching north from a line extending from Dundee on the east to Greenock on the west.

The barley used for malt or pot-still whisky must be of good colour and care exercised in its selection. It is estimated that between one-quarter and one-third of the barley grown locally is used by distillers, but the proportion is naturally determined by the weather. Imported barley comes from Denmark, Australia and California. On reaching the distillery, the barley is steeped in water for 40 to 60 hours or until the moisture has penetrated each grain, after which it is spread over the malting floor to germinate. During germination an even temperature must be maintained to regulate growth and so the grain must be frequently turned in hot weather but in cold only occasional turning is required. On reaching a certain stage, germination is stopped by drying the sprouted grain in a kiln over a peat fire. The malt then passes to the 'grist' mill, where it is bruised before being mixed with hot water, the resulting liquid after straining being known as the wort. This is fermented by yeast for about three days, which converts the sugar content into alcohol (or as it is called wash). After two distillations pure malt whisky is produced from this wash, which is run into casks, under the supervision of excise officers, to mature for several years.

All Highland pot-still whiskies have their own characteristics and unmistakable flavour. Some are light and mature quickly, while others are heavier and take longer to mature. During maturing, considerable losses by evaporation take place and stock figures for the industry are therefore always higher than actual gallonage. An excise allowance of 2 per cent. per annum is made for this loss, plus an additional 2 per cent. for whisky stored in butts and 3 per cent. for storage in hogsheads. After blending, whisky is again put into casks to ' marry ' for perhaps as long as a year and further losses through evaporation occur during this period. A finished blend stored in wooden casks will improve up to an age varying from 15 to 20 years, but once the product is bottled it undergoes no change. The intensive increase in production since 1945 has created a storage problem at the distilleries for, while whisky will mature elsewhere, it matures best in its native habitat. Distillers, therefore, prefer to keep it there and to overcome the problem of storage, many have had to extend existing warehouses or build additional bond-houses. For example, Glenlivet has increased its storage capacity since the war to allow for an additional 737,000 gallons, while Glen Grant in Moray has made provision for an additional 750,000 gallons.

Malt distilleries have on an average 42 periods of distilling yearly and generally cease production during summer months. This allows time for holidays to workers and also for general repairs and maintenance to be carried out at the distilleries. A distillery is not a large employer of labour. Some may have 50 on their payroll, but others no more than 20. The process of distillation has become more highly mechanised in recent years. To a large extent this has offset the present shorter working week. Besides those directly engaged, the industry gives employment to coopers, coppersmiths and transport workers, while distillery maintenance affords work to tradesmen in nearby towns and villages.

Granite

The North-East holds an important place in the granite industry, because of the large deposits of granite of high durability and beauty occurring within the area. Geological factors determine the extent of deposits, but in defining areas to be worked, economic considerations have to be taken into account. For example, it is uneconomic to work deposits too far removed from centres of population because of difficulties of transport and the heavy costs involved. Again, a quarry may contain excellent stone but be limited in quantity and therefore unprofitable to work, except for road material. The architectural and monumental branches of the industry demand considerable quantities of a given quality and shade; thus many small quarries in the North-East, as elsewhere, have been passed over or closed in favour of larger producing quarries.

The Aberdeenshire industry dates back to the eighteenth century, although granite was used in building long before this, notably in the medieval castles of Crathes and Drum on Deeside, and Midmar and Fraser on Donside, and in the fifteenth century St. Machar's Cathedral in Old Aberdeen. Before the

Union of Parliaments in 1707 there were probably a few granite buildings in Aberdeen itself, although most houses were constructed of wood or freestone. Among the earliest examples of granite public buildings are the Town House of Old Aberdeen, erected in 1721, and Robert Gordon's College, erected in 1732. The use of granite in the building of houses, however, did not become general until after a disastrous fire had laid waste a great part of the city in

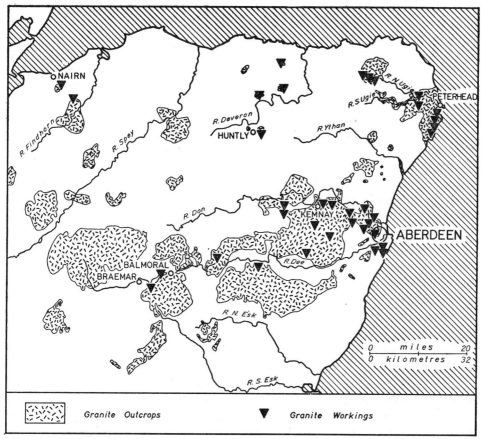

FIG. 19. Granite outcrops and quarries (open and closed). Aberdeenshire clearly dominated in the extraction of granite.

1741. By the end of the century it was being extensively employed, notably in Marischal Street, Queen Street and Union Street, an integral part of the last-named, Union Bridge, being built between 1803 and 1805 to a design of Thomas Fletcher approved by Thomas Telford, consulting engineer.

The drive for public health, involving the paving of streets, and the industrial revolution, which required improved harbours to handle the products of the new machine age, gave a great stimulus to the industry during the late eighteenth century. At first, sea-washed boulders and stones, cleared from fields to allow for more intensive cultivation, were exported from Aberdeen, but the increasing demands led to the opening of quarries in the vicinity of the city, the most famous being Rubislaw Quarry which was worked as early as 1741. In 1885, the Adamant Stone and Paving Company was founded at Bucksburn for the production of artificial stone for paving purposes. The basic materials used by this company, which is still in operation, are finely-crushed granite and Ferrocrete cement.

The new profession of civil engineering, headed by men like Telford and Rennie, quickly appreciated the value of granite for large constructional works, such as harbours, bridges and lighthouses. In 1801, when Telford surveyed the new harbour of Peterhead, he reported on the great mass of local granite 'very proper for wharfs, piers of harbours and bridges, and for forming tide walls', while Rennie himself went to Peterhead to secure large blocks when he was engaged on the construction of Southwark Bridge. Other public works constructed about this time of granite (although not all Aberdeen produced) were Portsmouth and Sheerness Docks, Waterloo and London Bridges and the famous Bell Rock Lighthouse.

The other main branch, the manufacture of monumental stone, dates back to about 1820, when Alexander MacDonald, a manufacturer in Aberdeen of paving-stones, chimney-pieces and headstones, succeeded in evolving a satisfactory method of polishing granite. According to tradition, MacDonald's interest was aroused when he had seen examples of Egyptian polished granite in the British Museum and after many experiments he succeeded in producing a satisfactory surface. In 1832, the first polished granite monument from his works was despatched to London and erected in Kensal Green Cemetery. Although the process he employed was very primitive and done entirely by hand, others soon followed his lead and the monumental branch was speedily established.

During this period of experiment and extension the chief quarry in the county was at Rubislaw, now within the city boundary. In 1858 the large Kemnay quarry was opened, which has produced silver-white granite for many famous buildings, the best known being Marischal College. In the vicinity of Peterhead several quarries were also worked, producing stone of a rich red colour, which, besides taking on a brilliant polish, is said to be the best weathering red granite. This granite was used for the columns of the London Stock Exchange, the polished pillars in Covent Garden, the Foreign Office, Australia House and for the decoration of many other important buildings.

The first requirement of a good quarry is a large supply of good quality stone, free from flaws and uniform in colour. For long, Rubislaw and Kemnay fulfilled this essential requirement, but in recent years Kemnay quarry has ceased to yield good stone and so the production of 'cube stone' for architectural work has had to be abandoned. But even in good quarries, as much as 90 per cent. is unsuitable for 'cube stone' on account of colour or cracks and this stone is usually crushed for use in concrete, road surfacing, and the like. Many smaller quarries operating in the nineteenth century have either been closed or limited to producing crushed granite for road metal. In the neighbourhood of Peterhead, where at one time some 20 were in operation, only one now remains, and many others in the county have also been closed.

Overlying the granite deposits of Aberdeenshire is a thick covering of exceedingly tough boulder clay, very costly to remove, and as the quality of the rock generally improves with depth quarries have tended to be developed downwards. Great depth involves heavy expense in raising stones to the surface. Rubislaw quarry, for instance, which has been worked for over 200 years, is conical in shape and 465 feet deep. Until the quarry was about 200 feet deep, horse-drawn carts carried the stones to the surface by a winding roadway. The first suspension cableway with a travelling carrier to be employed in granite quarrying was designed and erected by John Fyfe at his quarry at Kemnay in 1873. This was called a 'blondin', after the tight-rope walker of that name. Today there are two blondins at Rubislaw; the larger, lifting 20 tons, is used to carry large blocks from the quarry floor to the top. On reaching the surface the blocks are classified according to size and quality, and cut by pneumatic plug drills into cube stones for architectural and monumental work. The smaller blondin, for 10 tons, carries material to the crushing and screening plant, where it is reduced to sizes ranging from one-sixteenth to three-quarters of an inch.

Today operations at Kemnay are confined to handling crushed granite and the management has shown great enterprise in turning to good account the large output of this material. A concrete brick-making plant installed in 1940 to make bricks from granite dust, using cement as a binder, produces over 4 million bricks per annum, sufficient to build some 270 houses. Since coloured bricks were introduced a few years ago the market has been extended beyond Aberdeenshire and large supplies are sent regularly to Edinburgh, Glasgow and other places. About 1957, the firm of John Fyfe Ltd. also commenced the production of synthetic granite, commonly called 'Fyfe stone', for building purposes. This composition of granite chips and cement, which is subjected to extreme pressure so that the concrete is consolidated making the block impervious to damp, is less costly than granite and yet has appearance and wearing qualities similar to natural stone. Moreover, it is produced in large blocks which can be split to sizes required by builders. This stone has been in great demand by builders not only in Aberdeen but throughout Scotland and the market is rapidly expanding. Today production exceeds 10,000 square feet per week.

11

Aberdeen has also gained a reputation for the manufacture of dressed and polished stone for buildings and monuments. Indeed, the city itself is a monument to its craftsmen, and a striking advertisement of this branch of the industry. Its proximity to the quarries, from which until the present century almost all its raw material was derived, its well-established coasting services to the chief ports in the United Kingdom, and its ample supply of labour gave Aberdeen an assured position in granite manufacturing at an early date. Its workmen became noted for their craftsmanship, which was of immense importance to a trade, until recently so largely a handicraft. The combination of mechanisation and handicraft can readily be appreciated when one considers the processes involved in manufacturing. The raw material is rough-dressed stone. The first operation is to face the blocks, which used to be done by masons working with chisels or hammers, or with a machine, called a dunter or surfacer, operated by compressed air with an action comparable to that of a steam hammer. In most yards the process is now mechanised by using a frame saw. The next step is to cut the stone to the required size by diamond saw which to a large extent has replaced the carborundum saw although in its turn it is being ousted by the wire saw.

In the next process, polishing, there are three distinct steps. First, the face of a block is made level, by sanding with cast steel rings and iron grit; second, it is polished on the same machine by a revolving cast-iron ring with carborundum or emery until a glazed surface is obtained; and, third, the final bright polish is secured by using putty powder (oxide of tin) and wooden blocks faced with felt. The polished stone is then passed to the stone-cutting shed, where it is jointed by masons using pneumatic tools. It is here that skill plays a predominant part. If the stone is required for a tombstone or monument, the ends and mouldings are usually cut and polished entirely by hand.

Generally granite manufacturing is carried on by firms with no connection with the quarrying side of the industry, the chief exception being John Fyfe Ltd., which, in addition to operating Kemnay and several other quarries in the county, has its own manufacturing yard in Aberdeen. Altogether there were 32 granite manufacturers in the city in 1960, varying in size from the small firm, with a labour force of about 10 to 12 men, to the largest, with between 60 and 70. Since 1914, the number of firms has steadily declined, as will be seen from the following:

1914—71	1935—51
1920—60	1940—46
1925—57	1950—41
1930—51	1960—32

One reason for this decline is that the death of an employer has often been followed by the closing of the yard. There has also been a number of amalgamations or absorptions, and so the tendency has been to concentrate production into fewer and more efficient units.

But more important is the considerable increase in the amount of capital now required. The machine age in the granite industry commenced about the end of last century. Before 1900 steam power was being used to lift and move granite blocks but most cutting and polishing was done by hand.

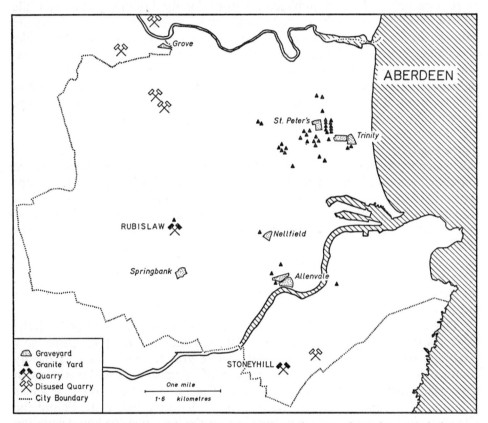

FIG. 20. The granite industry of Aberdeen city. The main area of granite yards is between Old Aberdeen and the commercial district of the city.

Pneumatic drills, imported from the United States and first demonstrated in Aberdeen in 1895, were followed by the use of sand blast, the electric polishing machine and, in the inter-war years, the carborundum saw. Since the end of the Second World War substantial economies have been achieved by the use of circular saws with diamond-tipped blades and, more recently, by the adoption of the wire saw, capable of cutting at the rate of 9 inches per hour as compared with the old rate of 1 inch. New equipment has increased output fourfold with a saving in labour, while in polishing some progress has also been made through mechanisation. The industry has in fact experienced more development in machines and in productive methods during the past ten years than in any other period of its history. Consequently the equipment of a yard today involves a capital outlay far beyond the capacity of the small man.

At one time the majority of the firms were engaged wholly in monumental work, and only a few on architectural work for the building industry, while one or two specialised in turned work, such as the production of granite rollers used in the manufacture of paper, paint or certain food-stuffs, like chocolate. But today the architectural section is the most important. Consequently the chief products of the yards are dressed stones for constructional purposes. These may be dressed granite blocks for large public buildings and bridges or polished slabs of one to two inches thick for frontages to buildings. Once solid granite blocks, polished on one side, were used for these purposes, but now with steel construction and reinforced concrete there has been an increasing demand for a facing material. Granite is particularly suitable for this, since it can be sawn into thin slabs while its weathering properties are unrivalled, especially in the atmospheric conditions of urban centres. Perhaps the largest single contract ever to come to Aberdeen was the provision of stone for a large block of offices at Knightsbridge, which is completely clad with granite. The monumental section, producing tombstones and other granite monuments, has declined in importance and is mainly confined to the small firms. It has been adversely affected by the growing practice of cremation. Nevertheless, the manufacture of tombstones is still very profitable, for the retail buyer is unlikely to haggle about the cost, and so sentiment rather than economics is an important factor in determining price.

The extension of Aberdeen in the post-war years has undermined the city's claim to be ' the granite city '. Brick, concrete and Fyfe stone now constitute the major building materials, while granite, when used, is mostly confined to frontages. In the construction of some municipal houses, as in Kincorth, extensive use has been made of Fyfe stone, but in other schemes they are brick built, with exteriors in facing-brick or rough cast. Before the war many of the quarries were engaged in producing stone for house building but today granite for this purpose is drawn almost entirely from Rubislaw.

The pull of quarries and availability of skill were for long dominant factors in determining the location of the manufacturing side of the industry, but during the present century certain influences have tended to its decentralisation. The market for manufactured granite is widely dispersed, with London and the industrial centres of England constituting the largest part of the home market. This has encouraged the development of manufacturing at other centres in the south. The importation of raw granite has also caused decentralisation, by giving manufacturers greater freedom in the selection of sites for their works, while the opening of quarries, such as Creetown and

Dalbeattie in Kirkcudbright, have encouraged manufacture in Galloway, Glasgow and Edinburgh. But despite these factors, the lead of Aberdeen is likely to remain in the foreseeable future.

Before 1900 local supplies of granite were being supplemented by imports, principally from Sweden and Finland, and these became a flood in the inter-war years.

Granite Imports into Aberdeen, 1930-1961
(Year to 30th September)

Year	Tons	Year	Tons	Year	Tons
1930	18,238	1939	9,497	1953	5,917
1931	11,574			1954	6,082
1932	14,434	1946	161	1955	5,003
1933	15,489	1947	259	1956	6,722
1934	14,458	1948	2,280	1957	7,212
1935	14,348	1949	5,769	1958	7,733
1936	12,333	1950	7,066	1959	8,014
1937	16,381	1951	6,616	1960	10,094
1938	16,392	1952	10,922	1961	11,522

Source: Aberdeen Harbour, Annual Reports & Abstracts of Accounts.

Just before the Second World War, Aberdeen received no less than 80 per cent. of her raw material for monumental and architectural work from these sources, largely because of the variety of colours, black, green, red and grey, the most common being black, which is said to harmonise well with stainless steel, iron and other metals used in modern building. Today the position is much the same. A certain quantity is also brought from quarries in Kirkcudbrightshire and the north of England.

But more serious has been the expansion of quarrying and manufacturing in countries hitherto supplied by firms in the city. At one time Aberdeen manufacturers and craftsmen held an unrivalled position in world markets for their products, but Canada, the United States and New Zealand, to mention only three, have been able to supply their own requirements since before the Second World War, a development which has had a serious effect on some North-East firms. For instance, Aberdeen's export trade with the United States, which amounted to 4,013 tons in 1909, fell to 569 tons in 1921 and by 1930 her exports to that country were nil. Exports to the British Empire also fell from 6,013 tons in 1909, to 1,410 tons in 1930 and to 224 tons in 1938. In addition to the expansion of manufacture abroad, however, tariff barriers were also a cause for the fall in exports. But Aberdeen's favoured position was also partly undermined in another direction. In the inter-war years foreign granite manufacturers were sending finished goods into the British home market, and this has been on the increase in recent years. Manufactured stone as well as rough stone are imported from South Africa, India, Belgium, Spain and other countries.

In the early days of granite importation to Aberdeen a variety of merchants engaged in the trade, although coal merchants predominated. In 1896 the manufacturers founded the Aberdeen Granite Supply Association to handle all imports. This association, originally a co-operative concern in which the manufacturers held shares, was able to effect many economies, especially in transport charges and in commercial organisation. But the tendency has been for the control of the association to become highly concentrated, so it is now a monopolistic body controlling the supply of both foreign and Rubislaw granite to Aberdeen manufacturers. It makes bulk purchases and keeps large stocks of every variety of granite at its depot and is thus of great assistance to manufacturers requiring a special quality or colour at short notice. The association also checks independent imports by refusing to supply firms which do not buy foreign supplies through its channels and is therefore in a strong position when selling in the home market. It supplies timber, putty powder and other materials required in manufacture.

The Aberdeen granite manufacturers have also their own association, a powerful body exercising both direct and indirect influence over the industry. Unless a manufacturer joins the association he finds himself without labour, for it has an agreement with the local trade union to employ union labour only, while the union, on its part, has agreed to work only for members of the association. The association has made many endeavours to limit competition and to bring agreement on prices among its members, but with little success, possibly because of the strong individualism of the trade.

Granite operatives in Aberdeen are organised in the Amalgamated Union of Building Trade Workers. The union, which is 100 per cent. strong in the city, has two sections, one covering workers in the yards and the other, building masons. The total number employed in the industry (including concrete products but excluding quarrying) at June 1960 was 1,793 (1,705 men and 88 women).

Shipbuilding and marine engineering

The shipbuilding industry of Aberdeen has a long and distinguished history, but perhaps the most exciting period in its career was from 1839 to 1869, during which time the port gained a world-wide reputation for the building of clippers.

The firm of Alexander Hall and Co., founded in 1790, was the pioneer and in 1845 built to the order of Jardine Mathieson and Co., the *Torrington*, the first British clipper to enter the China seas. At first she engaged in the opium trade but it was in the more reputable tea trade that she won fame. A few years later the *Chrysolite* was launched and on her maiden voyage in 1851 reached Hong Kong in 102 days. On her return journey with a cargo of tea she made a magnificent run, overtaking three crack American clippers and arriving in Liverpool 103 days after leaving China. But more famous was the *Cairngorm* (1,250 tons) which, it was claimed, equalled if not outclassed her American competitors. Among many other clippers built at Aberdeen was the *Thermopylae* (947 tons), launched from the yard of Hood and Co. in 1868 and claimed to be the fastest sailing ship in the world. By this time, however, Aberdeen shipbuilders had to contend with competition from builders on the Clyde, who were launching such famous clippers as the *Taeping*, and the *Cutty Sark*, the last-named being a worthy rival of Aberdeen's *Thermopylae*.

Clippers were not exclusively employed in the China tea trade. The firm of George Thomson and Co., founder of the Aberdeen White Star Line, owned a magnificent fleet built by Walter Hood and Co., which engaged in the wool trade of Australia, while another famous company, John T. Rennie and Sons, owners of the Aberdeen Line, sailed between London and Natal in 1854.

During these eventful years the most famous yard in Aberdeen was owned by Hall and Co. Among others at the port were John Duthie, Sons and Co., founded in 1815, and Walter Hood and Co. founded in 1839. The last-named shared with Hall and Co. the honour of producing the majority of the clippers which placed Aberdeen in the front rank of shipbuilding firms. But the clipper age was a short though glorious episode in the history of Aberdeen shipbuilding, the last to leave the slipway being the *Caliph*, launched in 1869. The Clyde, pioneer of marine engineering, was clearly more suited than Aberdeen for building iron ships. Furthermore, in 1869 the Suez Canal was opened and this was a great boon to steamers though not to sailing ships. By 1871 of Aberdeen's fleet of clippers only three remained in the tea trade, one being the *Thermopylae*. Her last tea voyage was made in 1878, but she remained in the service of her original owners, the Aberdeen White Star Line, until 1890, when she was sold to a Montreal firm for the rice trade between Rangoon and Vancouver. Later she was sold to the Portuguese Government and served as a training ship, under the name of *Pedro Nunes*, at the mouth of the Tagus, until 1912 when she was towed out to sea and sunk. So ended the *Thermopylae*, the pride and glory of Aberdeen clippers.

Long before this, however, Aberdeen had embarked on marine engineering and the building of steamers. The pioneer firm was Hall, Russell and Co., founded by James and William Hall of the shipbuilding firm of Alexander Hall and Co., who joined with Thomas Russell, a Glasgow engineer. Having acquired the premises of the Aberdeen Iron Works, which they largely rebuilt, they commenced the production of marine engines and boilers in 1864 and three years later expanded their business by building iron ships. Thus Aberdeen, despite her distance from coal and iron resources, embarked on a new phase of shipbuilding. At first the company built only small coasters, but in the closing years of the century seized the great opportunities offered with the introduction of steam trawling and steam drifting. Other ship-builders, like Hall and Co. and John Duthie, Sons and Co., also specialised in the construction of trawlers and drifters. The *North Star*, the first steam fishing vessel to be built in Aberdeen, was engined by Hall, Russell and Co. and launched from Duthie's yard in September 1883. Thereafter the pace was rapid and scores of trawlers were built not only for Aberdeen owners but for other ports both at home and abroad. Between 1882 and 1902 no fewer than 267 steam trawlers were launched from Aberdeen yards at an average cost of approximately £4,500. In addition, many passenger and cargo boats for the coasting trade were built. During the First World War when trawlers and drifters were used extensively for mine-sweeping, the industry rendered notable service to the country by building special types for the Admiralty. Aberdeen, being the nearest shipbuilding port to Scapa Flow, was also used by the Admiralty for repair work. Facilities for this type of work were greatly extended in 1917 by the founding of the Lewis yard on the south side of the river.

At the end of the war Aberdeen, like other shipbuilding centres, enjoyed a short boom, but this was followed by a long period of depression. In 1925 Duthie and Co.'s yard closed down, but the remaining three showed great enterprise and versatility in seeking new customers. The demand for trawlers and drifters at home was almost negligible and it was to foreign countries, which at this time were actively expanding their fishing fleets, that they turned their attention. During these years one firm built for France and Spain numerous large trawlers fitted for fishing in the North Atlantic and Arctic Oceans. Various coastal trading vessels and colliers were also built both for owners at home and abroad, one firm securing several orders for tugs, hopper barges, dredgers and similar vessels. With the Second World War activity increased, as the Admiralty and Ministry of War Transport made heavy calls on shipbuilders. A variety of craft, including tank landing craft, frigates, corvettes and mine sweepers, were built, amounting in all to 114, while thousands of repairs were carried out, many of a major nature.

The post-war years brought considerable work to the yards and this was matched by extensions and modernisation. Today there are three firms belonging to the port engaged in shipbuilding, namely Hall, Russell and Co., J. Lewis and Sons and A. Hall and Co. In 1942 Hall, Russell and Co. amalgamated with the Burntisland Shipping Co. of Fife, their combined facilities enabling them to develop a wider field of operation. Eleven years later Hall, Russell and Co. purchased the share capital of Alexander Hall and Co., resulting in co-ordination and increased efficiency. Each company, however, has retained to some extent its individual identity and goodwill with its many customers, although several of the production and technical depart-ments have been amalgamated. Hall and Co. specialised in the construction of tugs, trawlers, coasting vessels and other craft up to about 300 feet in length and in recent years has built several 3,000 I.H.P. tugs for the Admiralty, as well as a fast coasting vessel, the *St. Rognvald*, for the carriage of cargo and livestock, for the North of Scotland and Orkney and Shetland Steam Navigation Co., and two modern diesel trawlers for Aberdeen Motor Trawlers Ltd. After the war Hall, Russell and Co. embarked on a massive modernisation programme, including the installation of heavy lift cranes on the slipways, the building of new fabrication shops for welded construction and prefabrication, the introduction of flame-planing and cutting tables and welding equipment for over 150 welders.

Since the end of the war this yard, capable of building ships up to about 9,000 tons deadweight and of about 450 feet in overall length, has built a wide range of ships, the most distinctive and specialised being used for the carrying of bulk sugar. For example, five vessels, ranging from 5,300 tons to 6,500 tons, were launched recently for the carriage of bulk raw sugar from the West Indies to the Tate and Lyle refineries at Plaistow, one of 6,600 tons built to the order of the Colonial Sugar Refining Co. of Australia, and one of 7,100 tons for the Adelaide Steam Ship Co. of Australia for the carriage of raw sugar and molasses from Fiji to Australian ports. The firm has also built tankers, like the *Esso Preston*, specially designed for the carriage of liquid bitumen, as well as colliers for gas and electricity supply corporations. Among the smaller vessels, two are worthy of note, namely the *Bonavista* and the *Nonia*, for the Canadian National Railways. These all-welded vessels, although only 200 feet in length, have accommodation for over 100 passengers and a cargo of 850 tons and operate along the coast of Newfoundland. Many trawlers have been built both for local companies and for the Icelandic Government. One of the most interesting in this class is the diesel-electric trawler, *Sir William Hardie*, built for the Torry Research Station of the Department of Scientific and Industrial Research, which was the first of its type to be built in Great Britain.

The third firm, John Lewis and Sons Ltd., was founded in 1917 on the south of the Dee at Torry. Since the end of the Second World War considerable sums have been expended on re-equipping the yard and engine works. In the shipyard, large areas have been concreted, and diesel electric mobile cranes have been installed, as well as an oxy-acetylene flame planer and extensive electric welding equipment, while to keep abreast of modern engineering, the engine works has been equipped to build marine diesel engines. In the last ten years this firm has been extensively engaged in the modernisation of the trawler fleet; 82 trawlers have been built during this period, 50 being for Aberdeen and the remainder for home and foreign ports. Among vessels recently launched from the yard is the *Fairtry*, a fully refrigerated, stern-operating factory trawler of 2,500 tons gross, the first of such dimensions to be built in the world. It has been extensively copied and developed by the Russians, who now operate a large fleet of vessels of this type. Other interesting vessels built include the *Lammermuir*, a distant water diesel trawler, which at the time of her launching was the largest in the United Kingdom, the *Norango*, a large diesel yacht for United States ownership, and the *Droxford*, a deep sea salvage ship engaged on recovery of valuable cargoes from ships sunk in deep water.

Vessels built in Aberdeen, 1959-62

Year	Ships	Gross Tonnage
1959	18	31,545
1960	24	7,335
1961	23	14,486
1962	13	10,182

Source: The Glasgow Herald Trade Review.

At other ports in the North-East, boat-building is but a minor activity, although in the heyday of the steam drifter many of these fishing vessels were launched from the yards of Peterhead, Fraserburgh and ports along the Moray Firth. Since the end of the First World War Peterhead and Fraserburgh boat builders have turned their attention to the construction of dual-purpose motor vessels of 55-70 ft. length, for which their yards are well fitted. During the Second World War Fraserburgh yards built 5 motor mine sweepers of 140 ft., 22 of 120 ft. and 48 'liberty boats' of from 60 to 75 ft. In recent years some 100 dual-purpose boats have been built at this port and fitted with the latest type wireless, radio telephone and echo-sounding equipment. Of ports along the Moray Firth, Macduff has a small shipbuilding yard but its importance is eclipsed by Buckie, which has no less than 500 people engaged in boat-building and repairing.

In the whole region, the total number of people employed at June 1960 in shipbuilding and repairing was 3,099 and in marine engineering 955.

General engineering

General engineering is also of importance to the North-East. The initial impulse for much of the engineering activity in Aberdeen itself was created by the local needs of the city and surrounding district. For example, the presence of a vigorous and progressive agricultural industry resulted in a demand for agricultural implements, the granite industry stimulated the manufacture of polishing machines and later of steam derricks and other handling machinery, while the textile and paper industries also required machines.

The largest firm is John M. Henderson and Co., King Street, founded in 1866. Its large up-to-date works specialises in the design and manufacture of mechanical handling equipment for public works construction and industrial undertakings. Normally half the production is for export and the firm sends out its own experts to supervise installation of the equipment. Thus Henderson's products are to be found in practically every country in the world, including even equipment in some power stations behind the Iron Curtain. Aerial cable-ways, which are extensively used in quarries and dam and bridge construction, as well as in the construction of hydro-electric and water supply schemes both at home and abroad, are among the firm's main products. Cranes of all kinds are also produced for home and overseas markets. In short, the company has a world-wide reputation for the excellence and variety of its mechanical handling equipment.

But there are several other substantial engineering works in the city, well-known for the manufacture of their own special products. For instance, stone-working machinery, compressors, conveyors, quarry plant etc. are made by such firms as Wilson of Ashgrove Road, Barry, Henry and Cook, and George Cassie and Son, while the firm of Wm. McKinnon and Co., founded in 1790, has for long specialised in the manufacture of rice-milling and coffee machinery, the former being exported to Burma and other rice-growing countries, and the latter mainly to Central America, Jamaica and East and West Africa. Many smaller firms, like those associated with the granite industry, make cutting and polishing equipment, pneumatic tools and other stone-working machinery.

There are also a few engineering establishments in the county, the largest being the Consolidated Pneumatic Tool Co. at Fraserburgh. This is an American concern and the reason why an offshoot came to be sited at Fraserburgh makes an interesting story. In 1900 two English companies amalgamated to form the Consolidated Pneumatic Tool Co. which was later acquired by the Chicago Pneumatic Tool Co., itself formed by the amalgamation of two American concerns. J. B. Duntley, one of the American executives to play an active part in the merger, was a close associate of A. W. Maconochie, prospective member of Parliament for Aberdeenshire, and it was through this association that he became interested in the possibility of establishing a manufacturing enterprise in Scotland. In 1904 the building of the factory at Fraserburgh was commenced. At first only pneumatic drills were produced, but by the end of ten years production included a wide variety of tools. In the First World War, diesel-engine parts for the Royal Navy and bayonets for the Belgian army were produced but the main output was portable power-tools for the manufacture of munitions. In the post-war period, considerable expansion took place. Branches were established in South Africa, Australia, India and France, together with agencies in practically every capital city. During the Second World War the firm was once more heavily involved. In addition to its normal products, fuel pumps and booster controls for Rolls-Royce Merlin engines were manufactured. Two new factories were opened in Fraserburgh by taking over existing buildings for the production of Bofors guns, Howitzer-gun units and turret rings for Churchill tanks. At the peak some 2,400 people, more than 1,000 of them women, were employed at the three factories. Production was carried on under very trying conditions, for Fraserburgh, only 350 miles from German airfields in Norway, was subjected to frequent attacks.

When the war ended the company was faced with the problem of reconstruction and expansion to meet heavy demands for new equipment in all types of industry, both at home and abroad. In the immediate post-war years the factories turned to the manufacture of still larger compressors and extended their range of pneumatic tools. By 1947 it was necessary to extend the works and about this time the company took over the Tullos Works in Aberdeen, which had been built during war-time under a Government-assisted scheme for the defence programme. Today the products of C.P.T., as the company is called, comprise a wide variety of highly specialised articles, such as stationary air and gas compressors, portable air compressors, rock drills and contractors' plant, pneumatic portable power-tools, electric portable power-tools, heavy drilling equipment, known as Reich drills, and industrial tube cleaning equipment, called Lagonda tube cleaners. These are exported to all parts of the world, except the Americas and Japan, which are supplied by the parent company, Chicago Pneumatic. Recent orders include the provision of 1,000 electric coal drills for China, and air compressors and rock drills for part of the giant Indus Basin contract in Pakistan. The C.P.T. Company at Fraserburgh is thus of unusual interest. Its success emphasises the latent possibilities of sites in North-East Scotland for industrial production and the immense importance of initiative and enterprise, for the only advantages Fraserburgh possessed were adequate land for building and good quality labour.

Different in character is the Locomotive, Carriage and Wagon Works of British Railways at Inverurie, established in 1902 to serve the needs of the Great North of Scotland Railway Co. and later absorbed in 1923 by the London and North Eastern Railway Co. After this amalgamation the works dealt with repairs to rolling stock for the whole Scottish region, and when the entire railway system was nationalised in 1947 there was great anxiety lest the importance of the works would diminish with centralisation. But fortunately this did not happen. The works has recently been modernised to deal with new types of freight stock and to service and carry out major repairs to diesel locomotives. This has been of immense importance to Inverurie for the 'Loco Works' is a major source of employment. Approximately 600 people are engaged, though not all are drawn from Inverurie, some travelling daily from Aberdeen, as well as from Kemnay, Kintore and Oldmeldrum.

Much smaller than C.P.T. or the Locomotive Works at Inverurie, is Grays of Fetterangus, manufacturers of agricultural machinery. Founded by Eddie Thomas Youle Gray in 1929, this firm quickly established itself and is second to none as an example of enterprise and initiative. Its greatest expansion took place after the Second World War, the first major extension being completed in 1947, but so rapidly did business grow that further major extensions were made in 1955-6 and again in 1960. Today this establishment, situated in the heart of Buchan, has works so extensive that they dwarf the tiny village where they are sited. The employment roll totals 70. The main products include hydraulic loaders, silage forks, potato diggers, hammermills, fertiliser distributors, snow ploughs, saw-benches, transport boxes, land rollers, field gates and buckrakes, which are manufactured not only to supply the home market and Ireland, but also to satisfy an extensive foreign trade, especially with Germany. In April 1961 a sales office was opened in Euskirchen, some 18 miles from Cologne, and since then agencies have been established in Austria, North Italy, Holland, Belgium, Luxembourg, France and Switzerland.

The success of this firm emphasises the vital role of enterprise in the conduct of business. The partners, natives of Buchan, possess character and determination, inventiveness and courage and, in addition, know and care for their own district. The works, though far removed from sources of raw materials and from markets, competes successfully with other producers at home and abroad. With an extensive modern fleet of sales-service and delivery vehicles, distance is no handicap, and transport belonging to this enterprise is to be found on roads all over Britain.

Textiles

For many centuries the manufacture of textiles has held a substantial place in the economy of Aberdeen and other towns in the North-East. Prior to the Union of 1707, plaidings and fingrams figured among Aberdeen's main exports and later in the century woollen stockings, knitted by women throughout the county, were exported to London, the Low Countries and Germany. The manufacture of linen cloth and thread and cotton cloth was also extensively engaged in and was of considerable importance during this period. In the county, Huntly was well known for its linen manufacture, while Cullen, in the neighbouring county of Banff, had an extensive linen cloth and thread industry in the eighteenth century. In Moray spinning and weaving were also of some importance, especially around Elgin.

This group of textiles was affected by the industrial revolution before the end of the eighteenth century. In Aberdeenshire, the main centre of activity lay along the River Don between Woodside and Inverurie. Indeed, it might be said, here was the cradle of Aberdeen's industrial revolution. The first substantial linen mill was erected on the banks of the Don by Leys, Masson and Co. in 1797, on the site now occupied by Grandholm Mills. This firm entered the machine age by harnessing the water of the Don to drive its machinery. The flax mill was seven storeys high and the whole establishment, including a large bleachfield laid out beside the works, cost more than £100,000. About the same time another linen enterprise was established by John Maberley at Broadford in Aberdeen.

Cotton mills were also erected in and around Aberdeen. Through the influence of Richard Arkwright, Gordon, Barron and Co., who had previously been concerned in bleaching and printing, erected a mill in 1785 on the south bank of the Don at Woodside (now within the city boundary). This was followed by two others shortly afterwards, the Bannermill erected by Thomas Bannerman and Co., and one at Poynernook built by Forbes, Low and Co. By 1819 some 4,000 people were employed in the cotton mills of Aberdeen and district. An interesting feature of these textile firms was the overlapping of partners—as John R. Allan says, ' there was a small group of men central in the trade who could attract others in for longer or shorter times and with larger or smaller shares, and who had no difficulty in getting credit from the banks or the general public '.

Depression in the early eighteen-forties dealt a heavy blow at Aberdeen's textile industries. In the linen industry the Broadford works alone survived, while in the cotton industry one firm after another failed. After many vicissitudes Broadford is now successfully carried on by Richards Ltd. and is, in fact, the largest industrial establishment in the city, comprising the whole process of flax spinning and weaving and giving employment to some 1,200 people. The works produce the heavier types of linen used in the manufacture of hatch covers for shipping, tarpaulins for railways, covers for road lorries, artists' canvas, camp equipment, seed bags, chair canvas, fishing lines, shop blinds, tents, tennis strings and numerous other items. Flax canvas hose of great tensile strength and flexibility is the most important of these products and is in great demand both at home and abroad. Raw materials, flax and a smaller amount of soft hemp, are imported from Russia and the Baltic. The chief customers on the home market are shipping companies, British Railways, the Post Office, Royal Navy and the fire services, while abroad the main markets, which absorb some 45 per cent. of output, are found in South America, the United States and various countries within the Commonwealth. The only other works in the North-East concerned with flax manufacture is the small Craigview Mills at Inverbervie in Kincardineshire.

Some of the woollen mills were also drawn down in the depression of the 1840s, but the firm of J. & J. Crombie, which had a small mill at Cothal on the Don about ten miles from Aberdeen, was able to weather the storm. This firm had its origins in the nineteenth century. John Crombie, the founding father who had been brought up as a weaver, established a woollen mill, along with James Knowles, an Aberdeen merchant, at Cothal in 1805. In a short time the mill proved too small for their growing business, and in 1859 the partners purchased the linen mills at Grandholm of Leys, Masson and Co., who had gone bankrupt in the difficult years of the forties.

Today Grandholm is probably the largest woollen works in Scotland and has a name well known at home and abroad. It is a fully integrated establishment, where every operation is carried out, from the handling of the raw material to the production of the finished cloth. Raw materials include merino wools from South Africa, Australia and New Zealand, cheviot wool from Scotland, cashmere and camel hair from China, vicuna from the Andes, alpaca from South America and mohair from South Africa. These are manufactured into cloth for men's overcoats, sports jackets and suitings, while blankets are also made for sale locally. Grandholm or Crombie cloth is exported all over the world. (The story of this celebrated works is told by John R. Allan in *Crombies of Grandholm and Cothal, 1850-1960,* privately published, Aberdeen, 1960.)

Another textile firm in the city of Aberdeen is Harrott and Co., Rose Street, which manufactures gloves, hosiery and knitwear. Several others in Aberdeen engage in the manufacture of hosiery and woollen goods, the most important being Gordon and Co. at Glen Works, Spring Garden, and Kilgour and Walker at the Berryden Mills. This industry, which had almost disappeared before 1914, was greatly stimulated by the demand for knitted goods during the First World War, while in the inter-war years its reputation as a prosperous and important industry became firmly established. Woollen gloves are the main product but there is also a considerable demand for woollen stockings, jumpers and knitted suits. Since the end of the last war the firms concerned have had to carry out a considerable amount of modernisation in order to contend with keen competition from the south, especially from Leicester. Besides supplying the home market, goods are exported to Western Europe, Canada and South Africa.

Cloth manufacture is also carried on in the county of Aberdeen, as well as in Banffshire and Moray. Since 1854 Thomas Smith and Co. have carried on a woollen mill at Peterhead, which they purchased from Arbuthnott, Scott and Co., who went bankrupt. Their products, mainly Scotch tweeds, are renowned throughout the world. Another mill in the county, founded in the early nineteenth century at Huntly, has also gained a reputation for its cloth, both at home and abroad. Its buildings have been greatly enlarged and modernised and some 250 workers are now employed.

At Keith the woollen industry is carried on by two firms, G. & G. Kynoch Ltd. and Robert Laidlaw and Sons. The Isla Bank Mills (G. and G. Kynoch) is the larger and dates back to 1805. Until 1925 this firm also carried on an extensive manufacture of bone manure, which was sold to local farmers. At present between 300 and 350 people are employed by the company which provides houses for some of its employees. The Seafield

Mills (Robert Laidlaw and Sons) is a family business which was started on a small scale in 1901. In 1910 the mill employed only 14 people; by 1958 the number was 150. The bulk of raw material for both firms is imported from New Zealand, South Africa and Australia but a percentage of home-produced wool is also used. Approximately 75 per cent. of the products of the Isla Bank Mills and 60 per cent. of the Seafield Mills are sold in foreign markets.

There are two woollen mills in Elgin, which are among the largest employers of labour there. The larger, James Johnston and Co. (incorporated in 1943), was founded about 1797 by Alexander Johnston and employs approximately 220 people. Its products, over 70 per cent. of which are exported, consist mainly of luxury cloth, scarves and rugs, made largely from rarer wools, cashmere, vicuna and camel. The other mill, belonging to Reid and Welsh Ltd., was founded about 1875 by William Ramsay. The chief products in its early days were reversible travelling rugs but at a later date the manufacture of fancy check-back overcoating was developed. More recently an extensive export trade has been built up in travelling rugs, cashmere and fine saxony scarves and plaids, while the tweed side of the business has been extended to include fine twist cheviot and worsted suitings. Employees number about 100 persons. Taking the textiles as a whole 4,830 (1,559 men and 3,271 women) were employed in North-East Scotland at June 1960.

Paper

The paper industry is very important to Aberdeen and its immediate surroundings. There are five mills in the area. The Culter Paper Mill on the Culter Burn, less than half a mile from the River Dee into which it flows, is the only one on Deeside, the other four being on the River Don, namely, Donside Mill at Woodside (the only mill within the city boundary), Mugiemoss, a short distance up river from Woodside, Stoneywood at Bucks-burn and the Inverurie Mills, lying between Kintore and the town of Inverurie.

The Culter Mill, the first to be established in the area, was founded in 1751 by Bartholomew Smith, a paper maker from England, who leased the Culter estate for 114 years. Twenty years later a returned emigrant leased a site at Stoneywood on the Don for another mill. An abundant water supply was clearly the main reason for locating these mills in Aberdeenshire, but doubtless the presence of the linen industry, which at that time occupied an important place in the economy of both the city and county, had also some bearing on the selection of the sites. From the linen mills as well as from the general public, the paper works were able to obtain a plentiful supply of rags, then the main raw material used in paper-making.

These mills still occupy the same sites, although in the course of their history they have changed hands many times. The Culter Mill continued in the possession of the Smiths until 1819, but in the next few decades there were several changes before it was acquired, in 1856, by Alexander Pirie and Sons of the Stoneywood Mill. Nine years later, on the expiry of the original lease, the Culter Mills Paper Co. was formed. In 1883 this company came to an end and in January of the following year fresh Articles of Association were drawn up creating the second Culter Mills Paper Co. This date is significant since it was about this time that James Lawrence Geddes became associated with the company. Geddes was eventually made chairman of directors and his family have remained in control of the mill down to the present time. Meantime the Stoneywood Mill had passed through a period of varying fortunes and about 1800 came into the possession of Alexander Pirie, whose name the firm still bears.

Technical improvements, resulting in a greatly increased output, were carried out at both mills and this necessitated wider markets. The tide, however, was running in favour of paper-making, as Aberdeen itself, with its growing population, its university, its schools and its various printing-presses presented an expanding market. Thus the Culter and Stoneywood Mills went from strength to strength. Shortly after Geddes joined the Culter company the manufacture of coated paper was carried out at the mill, which was an epoch-making innovation. Though this new departure involved considerable risks the demand became so great that a completely new factory had to be built.

The Mugiemoss Mill, founded in 1796 by Charles Davidson, a partner with Charles Smith at Stoneywood, was the third to be established in the area. Since trade was growing so fast the two partners decided there was room for each to operate on his own account and, it is said, tossed a coin as to who should remain at Stoneywood. The senior partner Charles Smith won and elected to remain where he was and let Davidson move to the new site of Mugiemoss. The other two paper mills were founded in the nineteenth century, the Inverurie Works of Thomas Tait and Sons in 1860 and the Donside Mills of the Donside Paper Co. at Woodside in 1888.

Paper-making became firmly established during the twentieth century as one of Aberdeenshire's most important industries. The extent and nature of the markets both at home and abroad encouraged the mills to increase their productive capacity and to specialise in particular lines. The industry received a heavy blow, however, during the First World War. Many employees were called to the colours, but more serious was the curtailment of raw materials required for paper-making.

At the end of the war the industry directed its attention to modernisation and expansion to meet the insatiable demand for paper. The inter-war years, however, proved precarious, and paper-making, like other industries, was soon

12

engulfed in the great depression of the early thirties. By the time recovery had taken place, hopes were shattered by the outbreak of the Second World War, and raw material supplies were once more cut. At the end of hostilities the demand for paper was overwhelming and once the difficulties of adjustment to conditions of peace were overcome, the industry advanced rapidly on a basis of modernisation of equipment and expansion of research.

The chief raw materials required for this important industry are rags, esparto grass, and wood pulp from Scandinavia and North America. The proportions of these basic raw materials used at Stoneywood are about 15 per cent. each of rags and esparto grass and 70 per cent. of wood pulp. In addition, large quantities of China clay, alkali, lime, chlorine, rosin, size, alum, casein and other materials are used. Production of high-class paper involves many complex processes as well as a prodigious amount of water, which is first passed through a filtration plant and chemically treated to ensure purity. At Stoneywood, for instance, about 25 million gallons of water are used weekly.

The Stoneywood and Culter Mills have always been noted for the production of ' fine ' and speciality paper of high quality. Down to the Second World War the main orders were for ledgers, bonds, writing and printing papers, but in recent years there has been a radical change in the pattern of the market. Demand for ledger paper has been greatly reduced owing to mechanisation of office systems, resulting in an increased demand for tabulating card and index boards. Advertising in the form of catalogues and brochures has also led to an increased demand for coated paper, while the installation of photo-copying equipment in many offices has raised the demand for photo-copying papers. Orders for cheque paper have also increased since the war, a new requirement being a special cheque paper suitable for high speed automatic sorting, following mechanisation in banks. There has been a decrease in the demand for high-grade rag papers, probably because there is no longer the same need for permanency in records and cheaper grades of paper therefore suffice.

Today the chief products of the Stoneywood Mill are tabulating cards, esparto writing and printing papers, high-grade rag ledger and writing papers, index boards, coated art papers, high wet-strength papers for charts, tracing paper, base paper for blue prints, cheque papers and abrasive base papers. The main markets are Australia, New Zealand, South Africa, India, the Near and Middle East and, to an increasing extent, Europe. In 1960 the total output at the mill was 22,000 tons of paper and 7,500 tons of art paper.

The production of fine paper for purposes ranging from ordinary correspondence to sensitised cheque paper is also engaged in by T. Tait and Sons Ltd. at the Inverurie Mills, while C. Davidson and Sons Ltd. of the Mugiemoss Mills are mainly concerned with the manufacture of paper board, and top quality and specialised wrapping paper, but they also produce multi-wall paper sacks, paper bags, cartons and containers. The main raw materials used are waste paper, of which about 50,000 tons a year are collected mainly from Scottish local authorities, and wood pulp, of which about 12,000 tons per annum are imported from Scandinavia and Canada. The Donside Paper Co. is a large producer of newsprint and provides a considerable proportion of the paper required by the Scottish press. Printing and publishing have long been of great importance to Aberdeen. Today there are some 20 firms of varying size and much of the paper used is obtained locally. Pirie, Appleton and Co., now a subsidiary of the Wiggins, Teape Group, specialises in the manufacture of stationery at their Union Works close to the railway station. But Aberdeen and the North-East absorb only a small proportion of the output of the local mills; hence manufacturers have to seek markets in other parts of the country, as well as overseas, where competition is keen.

The manufacturers in this area have not been immune to the movement towards larger business units. The Stoneywood Works, for instance, became associated with the Wiggins, Teape Group in 1922, while the Donside Paper Co. was incorporated into the Inveresk group of paper mills in 1928. Because of its size and scale of production, the Stoneywood Mill has been chosen as the principal training centre, where courses for recruits, foremen, managers and office staff are conducted, to which students from all branches of the Wiggins, Teape Group are sent. There is also an important research department at the mill, subsidiary to the main research activities of the Group at Beaconsfield. This link with larger units has been a great advantage to local mills, which have been able as a consequence to specialise and draw on more extensive resources.

At June 1960, 4,117 (2,670 men and 1,447 women) were employed in the paper industry of the North-East. At Culter, the number of employees is about 600, about 100 of whom travel daily from Aberdeen. In 1888 the company built houses for workers and in 1915 further houses were built on four acres of ground purchased for this purpose. At the end of the Second World War a recreation ground for their work people was laid out. Stoneywood Mill employs about 1,540, of whom 60 per cent. travel from Aberdeen. The management has been particularly progressive in the provision of social facilities for its work-people. Mugiemoss employs over 900 people, a large number of whom live in the Woodside district of Aberdeen. The company owns 22 dwelling houses and a sports and recreation club at Mugiemoss.

Other industries

There are many industries other than those already mentioned. Some are represented by only one or two firms, while others are subsidiary to agriculture or the fishing industry, the two main economic activities of the North-East.

The Caledonian Milling Co., one of the largest milling concerns in Aberdeen, is such an enterprise. Indeed it is associated with both agriculture and fishing for, in addition to its main operation of milling, the firm has a factory for the production of white-fish meal, for which there is a big demand from farmers for the feeding of poultry, pigs and dairy cattle.

Scottish Agricultural Industries (now a subsidiary of I.C.I.) is another business closely identified with the two major industries. This company was formed in 1928 by the association of John Miller and Co. of Sandilands, the Aberdeen Commercial Co. and John Milne and Co. of Dyce. Miller and Co. were interested in the manufacture of fertilisers and were pioneers in the production of fish meal for the feeding of cattle and other livestock. Their chemical works at Sandilands was founded by John Miller of Glasgow more than 100 years ago, for the disposal of residual products of the gas works in Cotton Street. At first, sulphuric acid was purchased from the Broadford Linen Mills, which had a bleach and vitriol plant at Rubislaw, situated on the present site of the Aberdeen Grammar School playing fields. When this supply proved insufficient, Miller erected a small plant at Sandilands, not only to provide acid for the treatment of crude naphtha and the manufacture of sulphate of ammonia, but to dissolve bones for the production of bone meal. This marked the beginning of the fertiliser branch of the business. The production of fish meal at the works dates from the close of last century, when the expansion of the white fishing industry created the need for the disposal of offal.

Since 1928 great changes have been effected in the plant at Sandilands; increased emphasis has been laid on the production of sulphuric acid, superphosphates and granular compound fertilisers. In 1953 a sulphuric acid plant, with a capacity of 37,000 tons (expressed as 100 per cent. H_2SO_4) per annum, was brought into operation. The superphosphate plant has also been extended and now gives an annual production of 80,000 tons, while the compounding plant produces 41,000 tons of granular compounds annually. The fish-meal plant deals with 24 tons of fish offal per day, yielding 10·6 tons of fish meal, or an annual production of 3,500 tons. The Dyce Chemical Works, founded in 1869, is now integrated with the Sandilands Works. In 1946 a new plant was built at Dyce, which is concerned mainly with the manufacture of granular compound fertilisers (with superphosphates from Sandilands).

One firm concerned only with agriculture is Robert Lawson and Sons (Dyce) Ltd., bacon curers. The factory, established in 1934, is extensive and modern in its methods of production and provides employment for over 200, of whom slightly more than half travel daily from Aberdeen.

Associated with the fishing industry is Isaac Spencer and Co. (Abdn.) Ltd., founded early in the present century. This firm, among the pioneers in the production of cod-liver oil and halibut oil, both for medicinal and veterinary purposes, also manufactures paint for all uses, including a special paint suitable for fishing vessels. Another firm specialising in the manufacture of paint is Farquhar and Gill, a private concern with a history dating back to 1818. It has a well-equipped laboratory, where chemists are engaged on the investigation of new materials and techniques. With the changes that have taken place in building construction, such as the substitution of metal window frames for wooden ones, the firm has turned its attention to the production of steel-sash putty, which finds a ready market both at home and abroad.

The building industry is well represented. The largest and best known firm, Alexander Hall and Son, founded in 1880, has played a major part in the erection of public buildings and houses throughout the north of Scotland. Among the largest firms engaged in civil engineering and contracting is William Tawse Ltd. whose contracts have included Glencoe and Loch Ness roads, dams and power stations in the Highlands and numerous harbour and aerodrome works.

Many of the small burghs of the North-East have also become identified with their own industries. In the burgh of Turriff, the centre of a rich farming district, for instance, the main activities are milling and the manufacture and servicing of agricultural machinery. The largest firm is Hutcheon (Turriff) Ltd. which owes its origin to John Hutcheon, who began business as a hairdresser in a small thatched cottage in the High Street in 1841. Today the firm carries on the business of wholesale grocers, seedsmen, grain drying, storage and grass-seed merchants, and has an employment roll of over 100. To serve their rural customers they have numerous lorries on the road. Grass drying and milling are also carried on by the North of Scotland Milling Co., while four firms engage in agricultural engineering, one also manufacturing threshing machines. All do servicing and repair work and two act as distributors of Massey-Ferguson machinery and Fordson machinery.

The coastal burghs of Peterhead and Fraserburgh and Buckie have also industrial enterprises, several of which are of recent origin. In the inter-war years a weakness of Peterhead's economy became apparent, namely, its almost total dependence on the herring industry, which in turn was dependent on the Baltic markets for the sale of cured herring. Today the industries of the town are more diversified. Leading in this development are the manufacture of canned foods and the production of twist drills. The former was established by Crosse and Blackwell in 1920, when they took over a small family canning business, which they expanded and developed until now it is not only the largest cannery in Scotland, but the largest fish-canning factory in the United Kingdom. The firm, which is the chief purchaser of herring at Peterhead and Fraserburgh, is well known for the various herring packs it produces. During the war the Government contracts for food supplies for the armed forces resulted in a widening of the activities of Crosse and Blackwell. When hostilities ceased the company decided to maintain and develop these new products and today the factory produces, in addition to herring packs, a wide range of foods—soups, peas, beans, pickles, sauces, dried herbs and meat packs—which are sold on both the home and foreign markets. This new development has had beneficial effects on employment in Peterhead, for workers, hitherto engaged only on seasonal packing of herring, now find steady employment throughout the year.

Credit for the introduction of the other new industries to Peterhead, the production of twist drills and metal-cutting tools and the manufacture of gear boxes, must be given to two American firms, The Cleveland Twist Drill Co., Cleveland, Ohio, and Euclid (Great Britain) Ltd. In August 1957, Cleveland Twist Drill (Great Britain) Ltd., a subsidiary of the parent company in America, commenced production of twist drills and other cutting tools in a new factory at Peterhead, which was considerably extended two years later. Approximately 400 people are employed. For the most part, managerial and professional employees have been recruited from outside the actual burgh of Peterhead, although most are natives of the North-East. Of shop-level employees, however, only a small number, perhaps a dozen in all, have been hired from outside, so that the firm provides a substantial source of employment in the town. The major raw material, a high-speed steel alloy, is obtained from English, continental and Canadian suppliers. Roughly 40 per cent. of the works' output is sold in Britain, 30 per cent. in Europe, where a stock-room and sales office have been established in Amsterdam, and the balance in other export markets, primarily Canada, Central and South America and South Africa.

Euclid (Great Britain) Ltd. is also a subsidiary of an American company. Its main business, carried on at a large factory at Newhouse, Lanarkshire, is the production of earth-moving equipment. In 1951 the company took over a small concern in Peterhead which it had formerly employed as a sub-contractor, and today the Peterhead works of Euclid specialises in the production of gear boxes for their main manufacture, earth-moving equipment, giving employment to between 200 and 250 people.

Mention should also be made of Maconochie Brothers Ltd. of Fraserburgh, founded in 1887. This factory, which in its early days was concerned only with the canning of herring, produced during the two world wars the famous ' Maconochie rations '. Since the end of the Second World War, Maconochie Brothers Ltd. has become part of the H. S. Whiteside Group of companies and the management of the Fraserburgh factory now comes under British Fish Canners Ltd., also a member of the group. The process of absorption has been of advantage to the North-East, for the complete production of the British Fish Canners, formerly carried on at Dundee, Leeds and Whitstable, is now concentrated at Fraserburgh. This has involved considerable extension of the factory and complete mechanisation of all the processes involved in manufacture, from herring splitting and filleting to packing and vacuum sealing of the cans. The principal products of the factory are the well known ' Rob Roy ' range of canned fish and the 'Royal Twenties' brisling and herring, either fresh or in tomato sauce, approximately half being sold in the home market and the remainder exported, particularly to Australia, New Zealand, the U.S.A. and South Africa. The firm also produces its own tins and lids from Welsh tinplate. Approximately 450 are at present employed and this figure is likely to be increased to 500.

Buckie, like Peterhead, has made efforts to diversify her economy. The decline of the herring industry brought great hardship to this vigorous community until her fishermen turned to the use of dual-purpose boats, which could engage in herring or white fishing according to the season of the year. The high cost of transport has militated against the establishment of any new industry in this burgh, not only in transporting the finished article to market centres but also in importing the raw materials. Thus any new project coming to Buckie must be such that transport costs represent but a small part of the price of the finished product. A step in this direction was made in June 1956 by the establishment of a factory by the British Thomson Houston Co., for the production of small lamps for telephone switchboards, a project necessitating a high labour requirement but a small bulk of raw materials.

In addition to textiles (p. 176) and distilling (p. 154), Elgin has one or two other industries which may be noted. Three sawmills in the burgh give employment to approximatey 100. The largest, the Morayshire Sawmills erected in 1853, occupies 10 acres and is owned by A. G. and W. H. Riddoch of Rothiemay, who have extensive interests in timber in the North-East. Aerated water manufacture is carried on by three factories, two of which are locally owned, while the third is a subsidiary of an Aberdeen company. The oldest factory was established by John Ettles who originally intended running it as a sideline to his chemist's business, but so profitable was the enterprise that he decided to concentrate on it and disposed of his chemist's business in 1890. The purchaser was Robert Thomson, who, along with his son, devoted much of his leisure to perfecting the manufacture of an emulsion of cod-liver oil. This venture proved so successful that in 1926 they also disposed of the chemist's business and set up a factory for the manufacture of 'Thomson's Cod-Liver Oil Cream', a product now widely known in Britain, and to a limited extent abroad.

In the location of industry the pull of urban centres is strong, but there are exceptions. There are the industries which owe their origin and development to the enterprise of the villager. A typical example is the firm of W. A. Baxter and Sons, manufacturers of canned and bottled foodstuffs, in the Moray village of Fochabers. This enterprise originated in the village shop of Mrs. Margaret Baxter, who excelled in jam-making. Her fame soon spread from her own village to the surrounding countryside and among her customers was the Duke of Richmond and Gordon, whose castle stood on the outskirts of Fochabers. While he was entertaining shooting and fishing parties Mrs.

Baxter's preserves invariably graced his table, and it was not uncommon for guests to leave orders with her for regular supplies to be sent to them in the south. With the increase in business, her shop was unable to meet demands, because of its limited resources, and her son, W. A. Baxter, shortly before the First World War, built a factory close to the west bank of the River Spey on the main Fochabers-Elgin road. Since that date the business expanded so that a larger factory had to be erected and the original one is now scarcely sufficient to house the administrative offices. The firm has also greatly extended its range of products, which now include canned pheasant, grouse, haggis, soups, jams and marmalade. A speciality of the firm is vintage marmalade, which is matured for several years in whisky casks, while strawberries, raspberries and peaches are bottled in French cognac. It is not surprising, therefore, that the products of this enterprising firm have a high reputation both at home and overseas.

Another village enterprise is the bakery of John Smith and Sons at New Pitsligo in Aberdeenshire. This business is well known for its butter biscuits and shortbread, which find a market at home and abroad.

In the countryside the traditional work of miller and blacksmith has changed. The local meal mill is now largely a thing of the past. Changed habits in diet, centralisation of milling and the payment of farm servants' wages in cash, instead of part-payment in meal, have all contributed to the decline, especially in outlying areas. Larger mills still exist in urban areas and there are a few scattered throughout rural districts, but many of the latter are worked as one-man concerns, and even then, do not provide full employment for the miller. The blacksmith shop—'the smiddy'—is also rapidly disappearing and giving place to the engineering workshop for the repair of agricultural machines, while better transport facilities have had the effect of centralising these workshops in the burghs or main villages, where spare parts are stored and large repairs can be undertaken.

One industry which has shown a striking increase in all parts of the North-East since the end of the Second World War is tourism. This is not surprising, for the area offers to the tourist a wealth of contrasting scenes, ranging from the wild rugged beauty of the mountains to a coastline remarkable for its rock scenery, its fine stretches of sand and numerous old fishing villages, with their picturesque harbours and fishermen's houses standing in rows with their shoulders to the wind. The industry, of course, is seasonal, stretching from the end of May to the end of September, but during this period hotels and boarding-houses in Aberdeen, in the months of July and August, are filled to capacity. Deeside is a powerful magnet and there too the hotels do a thriving business throughout the summer. All round the coast, from Stonehaven to Fraserburgh and westwards along the Moray Firth to Nairn, the holiday season brings thousands of tourists, to enrich the whole economic life of the North-East.

Winter sports have assumed considerable importance in Scotland in recent years, and though the main centre of activity lies outside the North-East region, the impact of this new and expanding interest is felt in the hotels of Deeside and Speyside. The latter particularly has played a lively and constructive part in the development of winter sports in the Cairngorm Mountains. Through the initiative of hoteliers and prominent local people a fund was raised to make the slopes of Cairngorm more accessible to devotees of this sport. At a cost of over £120,000 a motor road was built from Glenmore to a height of some 2,000 feet on Cairngorm and last year a ski lift, costing some £36,000, was erected.

Communications

Aberdeen is the focal point of communications in North-East Scotland. It is the only large port in the area and its harbour serves a wide district extending far beyond the city boundaries, while a network of roads and railways radiating northwards, westwards and southwards, links the town to all centres throughout the country.

Towards the end of the eighteenth century, the great expansion of trade compelled the city authorities to carry out improvements on the harbour. At that time the River Dee, instead of following a single route to the sea, meandered through a number of channels, on what now comprises a large part of the harbour area. Moreover, material washed down river, together with sand carried by the tide from as far north as the mouth of the River Don, constantly silted up the sea channel. The major problems facing the port, therefore, were the controlling of the river within a single channel, the deepening of the harbour entrance and its protection from storms from the east, and from the movement of sand from the north. In 1770 Smeaton recommended the construction of the North Pier, extending to 1,200 feet, to prevent the influx of sand from the north, but this pier, completed in 1781, did not prove entirely satisfactory and the harbour bar remained dangerous to shipping. Telford was then consulted and in 1810 he recommended extending the pier by a further 900 feet. Six years later this work was completed, but in the following winter the pier was destroyed by storm. Later it was rebuilt with a slope towards the sea since when it has withstood any serious material damage.

Meantime a breakwater, extending to 800 feet, was built on the south side, which not only narrowed the mouth of the channel but afforded protection to the entrance from easterly storms. Nevertheless, one problem which has continued to exercise the harbour authorities has been the dredging of the navigation channel. Today two dredgers are constantly employed, at an annual cost of £45,000. The width of the channel is 110 ft. and the maximum depth at high water 32 ft., which limits the size of ships that can be accommodated.

Moreover, there is only one dock, namely the River Dee dock, providing a depth of 28 to 31 ft. In addition to the tidal harbour, comprising some 31 acres, there are, however, three main docks—the Albert Basin, given over to a large extent to trawlers and the Fish Market, and the wet docks of Victoria, the main trading section entering at St. Clement's dock gate, and the upper dock beyond the Regent Bridge. There is also a deep water berth at Point Law

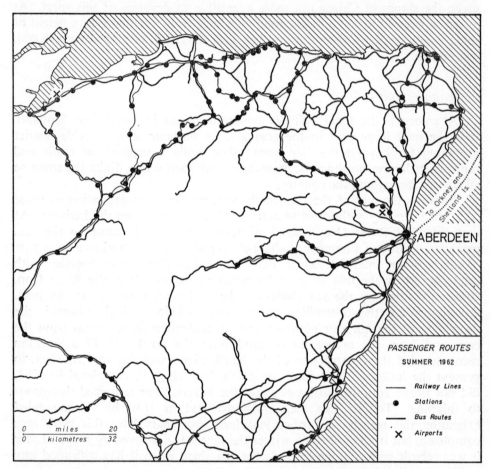

FIG. 21. Transport facilities. Public transport plays a vital part in the life of the North-East.

with a depth of $42\frac{3}{4}$ ft. at high water. The River Dee forms the southernmost part of the harbour and is used mainly to berth fishing vessels either requiring repair or taking in coal, ice and other stores. On the north side at Mearns Quay, there are facilities for the unloading of motor spirit and petroleum, and on the south side the Lewis shipbuilding yard (p. 169). The River Dee dock is mainly devoted to repairing and fitting out fishing vessels. There is also Torry harbour where small boats and pleasure craft are berthed. The quays, extending to 19,229 ft., are well provided with sheds, railway lines, and cranes.

The harbour was administered by the city authorities until 1829, when an independent body of harbour commissioners was established. This body, though large and unwieldy, continued in control without changing its essential character until 1960, when it was replaced by the Aberdeen Harbour Board, consisting of 15 members, 7 being elected by the harbour users, 4 appointed by Aberdeen Town Council, 2 by the Chamber of Commerce and 2 by the Scottish Trades Union Congress.

The trade of the port is naturally determined by the economic activities of Aberdeen and its environs. Coal and oil for both industry and domestic consumption are by far the largest imports. In the year ending 30th September, 1961, 275,186 tons of coal and 303,075 tons of oil were imported. Other imports included 73,642 tons of wood pulp and 17,581 tons of esparto grass for the paper industry, 33,898 tons of phosphates for the chemical industry, granite blocks of a total weight of 11,522 tons for the granite industry, and 57,975 tons of cement and 29,232 loads of wood for the building industry. In addition, 98,163 tons of white fish and 54,566 crans of herring were landed at the port. Wood and wood pulp came mostly from Finland, Norway, Sweden and North America, esparto grass from North Africa, phosphates from the Nauru Islands and North Africa, granite from Norway and Sweden, and fishing salt from Germany. The main exports from the port were oats (14,414 tons), fish meal (1,931 tons), superphosphates and other manures (4,176 tons), paper (2,582 tons), preserved provisions (3,976) and livestock.

The coastal trade of Aberdeen harbour overshadows foreign trade as can be seen from the table.

Statement of Trade, Port of Aberdeen, 1960-61

Type of vessel	Number	Net registered tonnage	Tonnage of goods imported	Tonnage of goods exported
Coastwise	1,786	781,745	778,415	155,507
Foreign	559	336,068	313,445	21,256
New vessels	20	4,091	—	—
White fishing	11,815	683,808	—	—
Herring fishing	582	28,005	—	—
Laid-up	241	23,431	—	—
Totals	15,003	1,857,148	1,091,860	176,763
Total tonnage of goods imported and exported			1,268,623	

Source: Aberdeen Harbour, Annual Report & Abstract of Accounts for year ended 30th September, 1961, p. 11.

The shipping industry has not escaped the movement towards amalgamation and the formation of larger units. At one time Aberdeen had quite a number of local shipping companies but most of these have now disappeared or have been absorbed in larger concerns. Coast Lines Ltd. has taken over many small coasting services throughout Scotland and those belonging to Aberdeen have not been exempt. The North of Scotland and Orkney and Shetland Co., recently absorbed in Coast Lines, carries on regular sailings from Aberdeen to Leith and to Orkney and Shetland. The coal trade is largely in the hands of Aberdeen coal merchants, but apart from these there are no local lines. So far as foreign trade is concerned, Aberdeen has regular sailings to ports on the Continent, as well as to the United States and to Canada.

Regular Steamship Lines at Aberdeen

Line	Nationality	To	Frequency of service
W. H. Muller	Dutch	Holland	Fortnightly
G. Gibson & Co.	British	Continent	Irregular
Chr. Salveson	British	Norway	Every 3 weeks
J. T. Salveson	British	Sweden	Irregular
Axel. Brostrum & Co.	Swedish	Sweden	Every 3 weeks
Monark Line	Swedish	Baltic	Every 3 weeks
Ellerman Wilson Line	British	U.S.A. & Canada	Every 3 weeks
Baltic Lloyd	Finnish	Finland	Irregular

Source: Aberdeen Harbour, The Official Handbook, p. 12.

In goods traffic to and from Aberdeen, railway and road transport also plays an important part. It is now more than a hundred years since Aberdeen was first linked by railway with the south and since the first through-line from the city to Inverness was opened to traffic. The Great North of Scotland Railway Co., formed in 1845, was the main company concerned in the development of railways in the counties of Aberdeen, Banff and Moray, although it had a strong rival in the Highland Railway, which was responsible for linking Inverness to Perth and thus providing a more direct line south from the Highland capital. On some lines, however, the Great North and the Highland agreed on through working agreements. For instance, on the Inverness to Aberdeen line, the Great North had a working arrangement with the Inverness and Aberdeen Junction Company, which had constructed the section of the railway from Nairn to Keith. This latter company amalgamated with the Inverness and Perth Railway in 1865, under the title of the Highland Railway.

In addition to the Great North and the Highland there were several small companies to which credit must be given for connecting the principal centres in the various counties with the main north-south railway lines. Although these small companies were nominally independent, they were to a large extent financed and ultimately absorbed by the Great North, or the Highland. After the First World War the Scottish railways were divided into two groups under the Railway Act of 1921, the London and North-Eastern Railway and the London, Midland and Scottish Railway. The Great North was merged in the L.N.E.R. and the Highland in the L.M.&S.R. In 1948, private ownership of the railways came to an end, when they were nationalised under the title of British Railways.

Since the Second World War the railways have had to contend with ever-increasing competition from the road, both in passenger and goods traffic. Consequently, they have had to curtail or withdraw services on some branch lines. Nevertheless the railways are still responsible for a considerable amount of goods traffic into and out of Aberdeen.

Livestock Forwarded from & Received at Kittybrewster Station

	Forwarded				
	1948	*1949*	*1950*	*1955*	*1960*
Cattle & calves	12,294	9,818	10,340	13,325	10,944
Sheep & lambs	28,705	25,121	23,055	26,450	30,740
Pigs	2,472	2,322	1,858	1,980	4,225
Horses	560	148	208	145	121
Total head	44,031	37,409	35,641	41,900	46,030
	Received				
	1948	*1949*	*1950*	*1955*	*1960*
Cattle & calves	38,772	42,536	44,117	25,370	20,945
Sheep & lambs	81,545	72,228	88,877	12,450	10,831
Pigs	1,064	1,229	2,346	325	108
Horses	163	35	149	63	34
Total head	121,544	116,028	135,489	38,208	31,918

Source: British Railways (Aberdeen District).

The main goods station is at Guild Street, whence six special trains are run daily with consignments of fish to markets in the south and if landings are heavy this number is increased. Kittybrewster station, adjacent to the marts, is mainly concerned with the transport of livestock. The other industries of the area also make heavy claims on railway transport. The tables list the main raw materials and manufactured articles passing through this station.

Aberdeen Guild Street Goods Station
Traffic Received in Tons

Commodity	1947	1948	1949	1950	1955	1960
Grain	44,303	55,577	48,274	42,351	25,500	17,580
Paper-making materials*a*	44,015	51,078	41,240	42,681	12,000	6,250
Manures, Phosphates, etc.*a*	39,907	21,646	19,438	21,078	24,100	23,500
Iron and steel	28,801	22,063	19,819	12,389	14,500	12,849
Sulphuric acid*a*	22,530	18,605	17,586	7,571	—	—
Bricks	14,212	2,423	2,975	1,156	1,200	1,405
Oils	12,446	16,479	16,472	17,029	8,500	7,393
Fruit and vegetables	11,220	7,443	4,107	3,899	3,750	2,033
Plastic pipes, sand tubes, fireclay	9,218	5,642	4,897	5,232	1,300	817
Timber	9,200	6,074	5,648	5,513	3,200	1,590
Ale	6,287	5,972	4,514	4,968	4,825	4,796
Granite	4,658	3,383	1,634	1,099	300	120
Preserves and provisions	4,562	3,475	4,007	3,252	4,210	3,306
Paper (manufactured)	2,375	1,608	758	429	625	679
Meat	4,131	2,764	1,360	2,905	430	301
Sugar	4,059	3,664	3,511	3,513	520	132
Scrap	3,368	6,552	4,595	2,779	—	—
Butter, fats, etc.	3,154	3,482	2,916	2,855	300	250
Bitumen tar, etc.	3,102	1,505	438	207	—	—
Salt	2,082	1,158	1,191	623	120	42
Slates	2,068	4,114	3,410	3,315	150	80
Pyrites*a*	2,000	862	2,135	—	—	—
Ropes, tow, flax	1,782	1,580	1,087	1,230	426	348
Hardware	1,127	863	410	194	350	300
Machinery	890	595	540	261	310	210
Cement	—	—	—	—	—	5,767
Tinplate	—	—	—	—	—	862

Note: *a* Includes quantities from suburban stations.

Source: British Railways (Aberdeen District).

Many of the roads in the North-East date from the period of the turnpike trusts, namely, the last quarter of the eighteenth century and the early years of the nineteenth. The numerous former toll-houses still in existence are relics of that age. The system of building and maintaining roads from revenue derived from assessments and turnpike tolls, as well as from statute labour, did achieve some success, particularly on the main highways, but with the advent of the railways it soon became apparent that new measures of management would be necessary if road traffic was to compete with the railways and existing lines of communication were to be preserved. In 1878, the whole road administration in Scotland was completely reorganised by the passing of the Roads and Bridges (Scotland) Act, under which the numerous small trusts were replaced by one general trust for each county. The administration of a county trust was assigned to County Road Trustees, whose

Aberdeen Guild Street Goods Station
Forwarded Traffic in Tons

Commodity	1947	1948	1949	1950	1955	1960
Grain	70,047[a]	30,035	24,253	40,882[a]	7,289	20,349
Paper (manufactured)	25,912	32,316	25,566	31,724	3,630	7,629
Manures[b]	25,202	33,533	47,822	31,029	7,679	3,656
Meat	10,898	7,667	9,124	13,757	10,691	12,777
Potatoes	8,836	2,527	1,187	2,904	1,871	399
Scrap-iron and steel	7,263	7,081	9,315	7,826	7,379	9,470
Preserves and provisions	6,767	5,665	6,030	4,551	2,594	1,980
Seeds	4,538	19,906	24,517	—	—	—
Creosote	4,534	5,310	5,438	5,218	1,219	—
Granite	3,758	3,604	2,885	1,982	1,339	1,870
Timber	3,709	6,548	5,966	5,277	2,177	1,013
Boxes, barrels and staves	3,640	3,309	4,007	—[c]	444	494
Paper-making material	3,323	1,303	745	—[c]	12,129	6,297
Coke	3,344	3,576	475	—[c]	—	—
Pyrites[b]	2,379	—	—	—	605	11,373
Skins, hides	2,041	2,223	2,333	1,572	749	432
Iron and steel	1,547	1,043	1,720	1,688	543	801
Boxes (fish), new	1,524	1,400	221	—[c]	2,540	1,030
Coal tar pitch	1,471	584	488	111	—	8,365
Machinery	1,242	329	318	1,513	645	235
Scrap, other metals	1,088	928	247	—[c]	Included above	
Wines, spirits	760	572	797	1,126	1,799	563
Textiles[b]	554	516	772	896	1,522	2,006
Vegetables	362	303	37	143	184	75
Straw	253	—	—	—	—	—
Fish (frozen)	—	—	—	—	896	3,910

Notes: [a] Includes seed grain.
   [b] Includes quantities from suburban stations.
   [c] Not available.

Source: British Railways (Aberdeen District).

number included Commissioners of Supply and representatives of rural parishes elected by ratepayers and by Town Councils of small burghs. Eleven years later, under the Local Government (Scotland) Act of 1889, County Councils assumed full authority for the management of roads within their own county.

Since the County Councils took over administration the standard in the North-East has been steadily raised. The County Councils have been active in their administration and maintenance, because of the increase in the volume of traffic, especially since the Second World War. A century ago the main turnpike roads were almost totally eclipsed by the competition of the railways, but now the railways are having to face competition from the road. Railway passenger traffic, especially for short journeys, has declined in favour of bus travel, which is not only cheaper but can be more convenient.

There has also been an increase in goods traffic by road, which has many advantages over the railway, especially in agricultural areas. By road, farmers can get delivery of livestock and other commodities direct to their farms, and in like manner, livestock can be transported to marts, grain to granaries and other products to centres of disposal, without the loss of time incurred by collection from, or delivery to, a railway station which in some cases may be several miles distant.

In addition to British Road Services, the largest operators, there are 261 A and B licence holders in the city and county of Aberdeen. The largest firm has 107 vehicles and there are two with 60 each. The majority have 5 or fewer vehicles with 131 firms having only one vehicle.

It is impossible to provide statistics on the amounts of freight carried by road. The main outward traffic from Aberdeen consists of paper, grain, milk and eggs and other agricultural produce, while the main inward traffic consists of foodstuffs (including fruit), waste-paper, building materials and agricultural supplies.

The total employed in rail and road transport and communications at June 1960 in the counties of Aberdeen, Banff, Moray and Nairn was 7,762 (6,825 men and 937 women); of this number 3,145 were employed on rail haulage (excluding workers in locomotive workshops and in carriage and wagon repairing), 2,533 in road passenger transport and 2,084 in general road haulage.

POPULATION CHANGES

UNFORTUNATELY for the preparation of a contemporary view of the population situation in the North-East of Scotland only the *Preliminary Report on the Sixteenth Census of Scotland* has as yet been published and so parish details are unavailable as also is material for a study of age composition. The latest material available is that for the 1951 Census which, with the changes due to the passage of time, is now largely historical.

Population Statistics, 1951

	Kin-cardine-shire	Aber-deenshire excluding city	Aberdeen city	Banff-shire	Moray	Nairn
Males	13,561	70,055	83,636	23,808	24,695	4,057
Females	14,321	74,745	99,093	26,340	23,523	4,662
Population per 100 acres	11	12	1,742	12	16	8
Population in burghs	8,766	41,395	—	28,453	24,154	4,700
Under 15 years of age:						
Males per cent.	26·6	28·2	25·7	29·6	23·6	26·6
Females per cent.	23·7	25·3	21·1	25·2	23·7	23·4
Birthplaces:						
Scotland	26,359	139.073	172,087	48,439	42,706	8,053
England	880	3,476	7,040	1,069	4,130	400
Wales	48	143	247	56	186	23
Ireland	91	313	809	121	308	24
Alien	208	682	608	139	296	88
Percentage born in county	44·2	74·2	65·5	69·9	56·6	47·4
Gaelic speakers	76	335	454	146	268	140
Persons per room:						
1861	1·55	1·65	1·54	1·66	1·41	1·53
1951	0·84	0·89	1·04	0·86	0·85	0·77

Source: Report on the Fifteenth Census of Scotland, Tables 1, 4, 12, 16, 17 and 20.

Figure 22 shows the changes since Webster's enumeration just over two centuries ago. With the exception of Moray every county, with Aberdeenshire excluding the city, shows a population total rising to a peak in the latter part of the nineteenth century and a decline 1951-61. This last decline is proportionately greatest in Banffshire with 7½ per cent. but absolutely is largest in Aberdeenshire. The sector of Aberdeen which fell within the county of Aberdeen lost population in the last intercensal period but this was marked by the increase in the southern sector which was part of Kincardineshire.

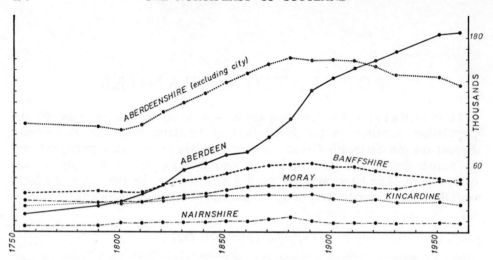

FIG. 22.   Graph of population changes, 1755-1961. Sources: Old Statistical Account and
Report on the Fifteenth Census of Scotland, 1951, Table 3 and Preliminary Report on the
Sixteenth Census of Scotland, 1961.

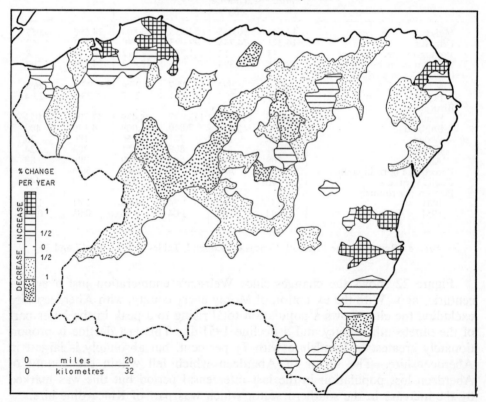

FIG. 23.   Parish population change, 1931-51. Source: Report on the Fifteenth Census of
Scotland, 1951, Table 1.

Within the region the counties showed marked difference of population changes in the intercensal period 1931-51. Figure 23 shows the change by parishes with average percentage change per year for this period. The greater part of the area has a neutral position with plus or minus $\frac{1}{2}$ per cent. per year over the period 1931-51. Increases occur largely in the areas associated with the burghs or the city of Aberdeen. The city shows a peripheral increase coinciding with the greater freedom of movement brought by the private motor car and by the extension of the urban bus routes into new housing areas. The great increase near Kinloss and Lossiemouth is a result of the influx of personnel for the R.A.F. and Fleet Air Arm bases in this district comparatively free of fog. The Deveron Valley and the interfluve between the upper Don and the Upper Spey forms a belt of heavier depopulation with the greatest declines in the upland parishes of Clatt and of Cabrach. The coastal parish of Dunnottar in Kincardineshire also shows a substantial decline which may be attributed to the shift of population from the older part of Stonehaven in this parish to the Fetteresso parish sector of the burgh.

Burghs in the region have shown a general increase with the exception of Speymouth, the Banffshire coast, Aberchirder, Aberlour, and Inverbervie. The change for the years 1931-51 is shown in Figure 24. In the decade 1951-61 all the burghs of Aberdeenshire, except Fraserburgh and Inverurie, showed decreases, as also did all those of Banffshire except Dufftown and Macduff. In the other counties all burghs showed increases in this period except Banchory and Laurencekirk in Kincardineshire and Burghead and Rothes in Moray. In this period the burghal parts of the counties, which include most of the larger agglomerations showed a net increase of 326 persons but the only increases of population in the small burghs were in Moray and Nairn. The increases of 1,347 for Elgin and 908 for Lossiemouth, due to the military air stations, were the only substantial increases and indeed these two small burghs had a combined increase in the decade 1951-61 which exceeded the net loss of all the other burghs in the region.

Depopulation is becoming a serious problem in the region. As the rural population declines so the smaller schools are being closed (see Figs. 27-29) and this accentuates the rural decline. A reduced population in areas with considerable distances between the nucleations makes more difficult the provision of modern services. Districts such as Tomintoul are isolated and in winter residents can become acutely aware of their isolation when trying to maintain contacts with the outer world. At the re-rating appeals Tomintoul residents won their appeal against some of the higher assessments partly on the ground of reduced site value with the isolation in winter.

Population totals mean very little in themselves and age-composition is of more significance. When the full Report on the 1961 Census appears it will be of interest to see whether the upland districts of the counties have a population disproportionately older than the lowland districts. As the Table

on page 193 shows, Aberdeen City and Moray had in 1951 markedly fewer
children under 15 years of age compared with the counties of Aberdeenshire
and Banffshire, suggesting that these counties may still to some degree be a
source of migrants to the urban areas. This same Table, giving the main

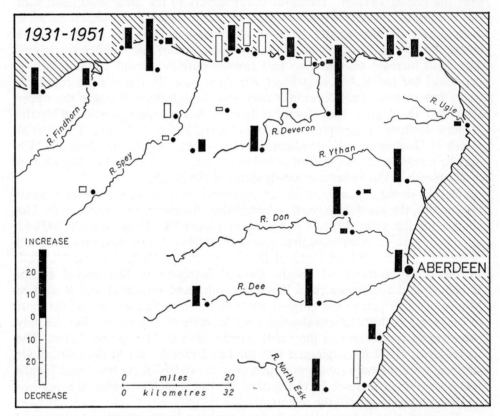

FIG. 24. Percentage change of population of urban areas, 1931-51. Source: as Fig. 23.

birthplaces of residents in 1951, raises questions as to the cause of the great
immigration into the counties of Kincardine and Nairn which resulted in less
than half the population resident in 1951 being born in the county of residence.

The Table also shows the average number of persons per room for 1951
compared with that in 1861 from which it is seen that the room density is
greatest in the city and least in Nairnshire but for all areas there has been a
marked improvement in the last hundred years.

LOCAL DIALECTS

THE stranger in Aberdeen for the first time will see much to arrest his attention but his ears too will be assailed to his at least temporary bewilderment by the speech of the people—a strong, clear, deliberate somewhat high-pitched utterance that may at first seem to have only a distant affinity to English, though of course there will be many recognisably English words in it. The listener will hear plenty of *ah*'s, *eh*'s, *ee*'s and *f*'s in odd places which will eventually make a pattern for him, for like all dialects it conforms to a system of sounds and one too with a long history and pedigree.

The problem for the purpose of this article is in fact to know just how far back to go, for one obvious feature of life in the North-East of Scotland is its deep-rootedness in its past. In speech indeed we can go further back than we can understand for there are monoliths scattered about Aberdeenshire and Kincardineshire with inscriptions in the old Ogam alphabet of Irish origin which can be transliterated only with some difficulty and interpreted hardly at all. It is wisest to call this language with the historians Pictish from the name of the confederated tribes who inhabited this part of Scotland in the first five or six centuries of our era, and leave it at that. We know that these amalgamated in the course of the next few centuries with the Scots proper who came from Ireland and brought their Gaelic language with them and started giving names to the places where they settled with their rudimentary ploughs and flocks of cattle and sheep. So we get those geographical terms familiar to Scotland such as *glen, loch, bog, craig, strath,* and the actual place-names themselves, of which nearly 90 per cent. in the North-East are of Gaelic origin, a clear indication of the widespread and enduring nature of the Pictish-Scottish settlement. Hence the Gaelic speaker has the advantage in extrapolating the meaning from the hill-names, *Bennachie,* unmistakably ' the mountain of the breast ', *Lochnagar,* ' the loch of the rocks ', *Cairngorm,* the blue cairn ', *Mormond,* ' the big hill '. The towns too are fairly simple, *Braemar,* ' the uplands of Mar ', *Kintore,* ' the head of the hill ', *Inverurie,* ' the confluence of the Urie ' (with the Don), *Ellon,* ' the island ', though *Aberdeen* itself, ' the mouth of the Don ', is a little more difficult to explain on Gaelic principles. Probably it should be ascribed to Pictish.

There are, however, place-names which are much more intelligible to the uninitiated, like Stonehaven, Peterhead, Fraserburgh, Huntly, due to another linguistic element which began to operate in the North-East in the twelfth century. The Norman Conquest and the consequent establishment of the feudal system in Scotland as well as in England gradually imposed a new pattern on the countryside—the French-speaking baron in the castle, the

English-speaking overseer or steward who had followed in his wake, sat down and spread themselves over the land among the Gaelic peasantry, for the most part peaceably, and there followed the usual intermarriage and mingling of speech as well as blood. In addition, in the new Norman burghs the Scottish kings had been encouraging manufactures and had been importing Flemish weavers and artisans with their Dutch speech to process the wool, skins and flax of the countryside. By the fourteenth century English, which had been established as Anglo-Saxon in the Lothians since about 600 A.D., had triumphed throughout the Lowlands of Scotland and the undulating plains of the North-East. In the Highlands of course Gaelic persisted until the old Celtic system was broken up finally and forcibly after the '45, and indeed was spoken by a few old people round Braemar till the period of the Second World War.

So the speech of the North-East is a fusion of several elements still traceable in the place-names and the ordinary vocabulary of the people. Besides the generally-used words from Gaelic mentioned above, one or two more peculiar to the North-East are still in current use, e.g. *connach* (to waste, spoil, destroy), *shargar* (the weakling in a litter), *eeshan* (a chicken), used as a pet-name for a child, *greeshoch* (the red embers of a fire), *etnach* (juniper), *prann* (to beat). To the Dutch influence it owes even more common words like *cran* (a tap), with its diminutive *crannie*, which has come to mean the little finger, *cweet* (the ankle), *dubs* (puddles, mud), *begeck* (an unpleasant surprise), and, perhaps the commonest of all, *loon*, the ordinary Aberdeen word for a boy.

By far the greater part of the vocabulary of this part of Scotland is, however, derived from the speech of the North of England which had worked its way up with the Feudal system in the eleventh and twelfth centuries. This speech was itself a composite based primarily on Old English or Anglo-Saxon but with a large admixture of French and Scandinavian words brought in by the Danes and Norwegians who had first raided as Vikings and later peaceably settled in the Northern counties. It is to this Scandinavian influence that we owe distinctions between, for instance, English *church, chest, bridge, ridge, brow* (of a hill), *own, hang, straw* and Scots *kirk, kist, brig, rig, brae, ain, hing, strae,* and such common words as *gar* (to cause or compel), *big* (to build), *blae* (livid), *eident* (industrious), *ferlie* (a noteworthy sight), *flit* (to move house), *gowk* (the cuckoo, a fool), *kilt, low* (a flame), *rowan* (the mountain ash), *til* (to), *tyne* (to lose), *maun* (must), *rowp* (an auction sale), *rug* (to pull, tug). And of course the Norman Conquest had added its own huge quota to the Anglo-Saxon that it replaced in England as the speech of government and the ruling classes for nearly three centuries until English reasserted itself, but a very different English from the English of King Alfred and King Edward the Confessor. About these last elements, overwhelmingly preponderant as they are, little need be said since between them they provide the thousands of words common to Scots and English, which make the two speeches by and large mutually intelligible. Contrary to a common assertion, the Auld Alliance contracted by France and Scotland in the late thirteenth century for mutual help against England, gave relatively few words to Scots though some are interesting or important, like *fash* (to bother), *fiar* (market price of grain), *Hogmanay*, *barley* (a truce in games), *bajan* (a freshman at Aberdeen University) and *Bon-Accord* (the motto of Aberdeen itself).

What in fact creates the real difficulties in understanding lies chiefly in the differences in the development of the Anglo-Saxon vowels between the North and the South. What was once a long *ah* has become in standard English a long *oh* sound, but in Scots a long *eh,* and so we get the correspondences go, *gae;* so, *sae;* more, *mair;* both, *baith;* home, *hame;* stone, *stane;* and so on; where the original sound was *oh,* English has turned this into *ooh* while Scots modified it into a sound like French *u* or German *ü,* usually written *ui* and so poor, *puir;* moon, *muin;* school, *schuil;* good, *guid;* and where the Anglo-Saxon said *ooh,* the Southron says *ow* but the Scot keeps the *ooh* sound as it was, as in down, *doon;* cow, *coo;* proud, *prood.*

Then of course there are obvious consonantal differences between an English and a Scots speaker, the strongly trilled *r*; and the guttural persisting in *nicht, lauch;* and in *wh-* in why, where, whale, etc.

It is largely on the geographical distribution of these various sounds that the area of North-East Scottish speech and its sub-dialects is delimited. The test words are *stane,* i.e. an original *ah* before *n, muin, wha, white.* A glance at the map will explain the situation best. To the west of the continuous black line, the 'Highland' line, Scots was never the native speech. Gaelic held sway, as has been said, until the breakdown of the old clan system after the Jacobite risings, but has now been so eroded by school English that in effect only this English remains west of the line, with its distinctive pleasant-sounding *r* pronounced with the tip of the tongue turned upwards and back, instead of being trilled against the teeth as in the Lowlands. The southern boundary of our speech area is marked on the map by a broken line and it runs roughly north from Dundee to the Devil's Elbow at the top of Glenshee. Outside it in the counties of Angus, Perth and Fife speakers have a system of twelve vowels, the largest repertory of vowels in Scots, while inside the boundary the vowel system is reduced to eleven and, as one goes further north into Kincardineshire, ultimately to ten. South of the line the key words follow the general Scots pattern of *stane, muin, wha, white.* Northwards, however, *stane* becomes *steen,* and *wha* becomes *fa,* i.e. in relative pronouns and adverbs only. Hence the rhyme:

> ' By *fa, far, fat* and *fan,*
> Ye can tell a Farfar man.'

These features continue till just south of Stonehaven when we cross another sub-dialect boundary running along the dotted line from the coast westwards along the watershed of the Dee and the Esks to meet the first line

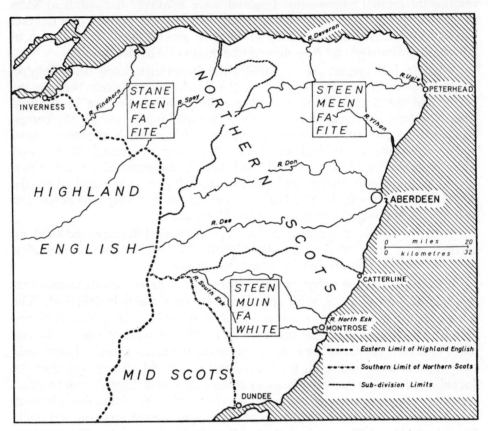

FIG. 25. Dialect districts.

at the top of Glen Shee. Inside this line *muin* now becomes *meen* and the *f* is extended to all words beginning with *wh-* (except *wheel*), hence *fite*, *fussle* (whistle), *furl* (whirl), *fuskie* (whisky), etc. Here is the most populous and most characteristic area of North-East Scots, including Aberdeen itself, the district from which a not inconsiderable regional literature has been produced from the middle of the eighteenth century to the present day, the poems of Skinner, Ross and Charles Murray, and the novels of George MacDonald, William Alexander and Lewis Grassic Gibbon, and which is most conservative in keeping its vocabulary and idiom. It reaches to the Spey and includes the whole of Aberdeenshire and the Banffshire coast. Inland, however, towards the west, Upper Banffshire, and Morayshire, the *ee* sounds drop away, *steen* returns to *stane, meen* is still *meen,* but *peer* is *pyoor,* and so to Nairn where the Highland speech of Inverness begins to take over. There are incidentally two small enclaves of Scots speech on the other side of the Moray Firth, at the old fishing-towns of Avoch and Cromarty, which speak a Scots dialect with marked peculiarities, including the dropping of *h* at the beginning of words and also the *f* in *fa, far,* etc. This may well represent an earlier form of Moray Firth Scots still surviving and indeed all the fishing communities in the North-East seem to preserve earlier and archaic speech forms and usages.

The following passage from William Alexander's *Johnny Gibb of Gushet-neuk,* written in 1871, gives a good idea of North-East Scots of a hundred years ago, when a farmer's wife consults the local schoolmaster about her son's education:

'Keep me, Maister Tawse! ye've sic a heid o' leernin yersel'. I dinna believe but ye cud mak' up a prent buik an' ye war to try. But mithnin he dee wi' the less coontin?'

'No; certainly not; he maun hae Mathematics confeerin.'

'An' that be the gate o' 't, the seener he's begun the better, I wud think, to nae loss time. Cudna ye begin 'im at ance wi' a bit lesson? 'Leern ear', leern fair ', they say, an' Benjie's a gran' scholar o' 's size. He wud bleck 's breeder that's twa year aul'er nor him, ony day.'

'Aweel, lat me see,' said Mr Tawse, ' I'll see if I can get anither ane or twa, an' try them wi' the Rudiments—ye may jist get a Ruddiman i' the meanwhile, or we see.'

'That's the buik that they get the Laitin oot o', is't?'

'No, no; jist the grammar—the rules o' the language.'

'It cudna be deen wuntin, cud it? I dinna care about owre muckle o' that gremmar, 's ye ca't.

'Care or no care, it's quite indispensable; an' it's utter nonsense to speak o' wuntin 't.'

While only older folk in rural districts would probably now speak exactly like this, it would still be intelligible to any native, though he might be stumped with *confeerin* (to match) and perhaps *bleck* (to outshine, beat), and would rather say *grammar* and *Latin.*

Despite the overwhelming pressure of school, university, radio, cinema, and the social rat-race, which have made serious inroads on the richness of the old speech, it still manages to exist probably better than in most other parts of Scotland, perhaps because the area of its currency is to a fairly large degree geographically separate and socially and economically self-contained. It is still reasonably adequate to express the basic requirements of a community with its roots firmly fixed in the land (and the sea) and with most of the traits, good and bad, of the countryman, given to cautious understatement as ' it's nae that ill ' for ' it's very good ', to proverbial wisdom, ' Keep your ain fish-guts til your ain sea-maws,' to an ingrained conservatism in ' Changes is lichtsome—and feels is fond o' them ', to irony, ' If aa stories are true, that een's nae lee ', to sarcasm in the hundreds of contemptuous terms for fools, knaves, weaklings and so on, *gype, gowk, moniment, ablach, snyte, smatchet, gabbysnarrach, hurb,* often conveyed, as in *mannie,* simply by the use of the diminutive, which is characteristic for its frequency and nuances of the North-East; in *bairnie* and *loonie* on the other hand, it connotes tenderness and affection, sometimes friendliness and familiarity, as when a farmer is called by the name of his farm, e.g. *Loanie,* meaning the farmer of *Loanhead* or the like; and the idea of smallness or insignificance can be intensified up to fivefold as in *a little wee bit housockie.*

So the speech reflects the people, superficially somewhat grim, blunt, sardonic and non-committal, and yet beneath the surface durable, self-reliant and sentimental in the better sense of the word. Perhaps the best one-word epithet for them is the motto they chose for their own local regiment, the Gordon Highlanders, the old Scots participle *Bydand*, 'standing firm '.

LOCAL GOVERNMENT IN SCOTLAND

THE principal instruments of Local Government in Scotland are Town Councils which exercise jurisdiction in Burghs, and County Councils which exercise jurisdiction in what are termed ' Landward ' areas.

In Scotland a town or populous place is designated a burgh when the inhabitants have acquired the right to appoint a local corporation responsible for the administration of some or all of the functions of local government. Originally burghs were established by Royal Charter and were classed either as Royal Burghs or as Burghs of Barony or Regality according as the burgh lands were held directly under the Crown or under one of the great feudal lords. The burgh may, accordingly, be said to have been in origin a feature of the feudal system.

The council of a chartered burgh was appointed in some cases in virtue of express provisions embodied in the Charter, and in other cases was elected to office according to procedure resting upon local custom or usage. At a fairly early stage of the history of Scotland, however, legislation did go some way towards providing a common form of constitution for burgh councils.

Down to the year 1707 a total of seventy Royal Burghs had been set up in Scotland, but since that year no new Royal Burgh has been constituted. It is not known with certainty how many Burghs of Barony or Regality were established, but it is known that some of these were little more than hamlets and the powers conferred by some of the earlier Charters must have fallen into disuse. Burghs of this class were established subsequent to the year 1707, but no such burgh has come into existence since 1833.

With the growth of the population of the country, particularly during the later eighteenth and early nineteenth centuries, many communities grew up wherein the inhabitants had little or no effective voice in the management of local affairs. These communities ranked merely as populous places within the county of which they formed a part.

The movement for Parliamentary reform which produced the first Reform Bill served also to throw into relief the aspirations towards local autonomy which were entertained in many of the new industrial communities. In the year 1832, the reform of the system of Parliamentary legislation had conferred upon a number of towns the right to return or to contribute to return a member of Parliament. In the following year, the Parliamentary Burghs Act prescribed for these towns the mode of election of magistrates and councillors and conferred upon the Council so elected substantially the same powers as had previously been possessed in Royal Burghs. The burghs affected by this Act were subsequently known as Parliamentary Burghs and included the more important Burghs of Barony and Regality. In the same year, the Royal Burghs Act of 1833 made provision for the election of the magistrates and council of Royal Burghs and regulated the number of office-bearers.

In the case of Burghs of Barony or Regality which had not been given the right to contribute to the return of members of Parliament, the election of local councils continued, subsequent to the year 1833, to be regulated by the prior law and the existence of two separate administrative codes led to a considerable measure of confusion.

In the year 1833, Royal Burghs and Burghs of Barony and Regality were given the right to establish a system of police and to adopt resolutions enabling them to undertake the paving, cleansing, lighting and watching of the burgh and also to undertake the supply of water. These powers were subsequently extended so as to apply to the class of Parliamentary Burghs established in 1833, but were exercised by the council as police commissioners, in which capacity they were deemed to be in theory a body separate and distinct from the town council.

In the year 1850, provision was made upon a general and uniform basis for the establishment in Scotland of burghs of yet another class. An Act of that year enabled the inhabitants of a populous place to form the community into a burgh in which magistrates and police commissioners could then be elected to undertake the administration of the police and other functions previously made available to the councils of the existing burghs. The community was then termed a Police Burgh. The provisions of the Act of 1850 were amplified and extended by the General Police (Scotland) Act, 1862, and this Act, in turn, was superseded by the Burgh Police (Scotland) Act, 1892. By the last-mentioned Act the general code regulating the election of magistrates and councillors was at length applied to those Burghs of Barony or Regality which had not in 1833 become Parliamentary Burghs.

In conjunction with the Town Councils (Scotland) Act of 1900 the Act of 1892 abolished the need to distinguish between the proceedings of a town council when acting in their capacity of police commissioners and their proceedings when acting as local authority either under statute or in the exercise of powers derived from inveterate custom. At the same time magistrates and commissioners of Police Burghs were invested with many of the powers previously available only to the councils of chartered or Parliamentary Burghs. As an obvious corollary such magistrates and commissioners were given the right to use the designation of 'town council'. These Acts made available a general code of law for the management of local affairs in all the burghs in Scotland excepting only the four cities of Glasgow, Edinburgh, Aberdeen and Dundee, and the burgh of Greenock. In the latter five burghs the system of administration was dependent on local private acts.

Recent legislation and, in particular, the Local Government (Scotland) Acts of 1929, 1947 and 1948 have now virtually abolished all remaining differences in the powers possessed by individual burgh councils which resulted from the original character or status of the burgh.

County Councils in Scotland are in relation to most of their functions the creation of Statute and are of much more recent growth than Town Councils. They owe their origin in the main to an Act of 1899 and since that date the policy of the Government has been to invest County Councils with powers which are virtually identical with those exercised by the Town Councils of the

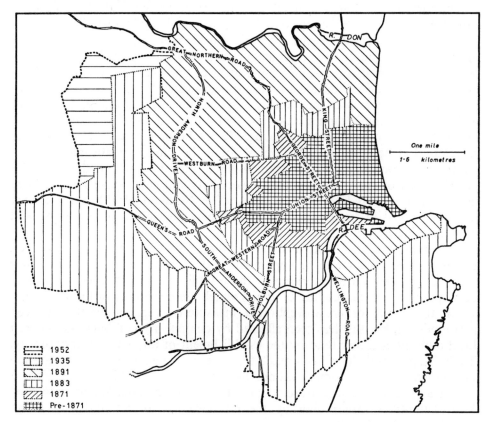

FIG. 26. Changes in the boundaries of Aberdeen City, 1871-1952.

four Scottish Cities or by the Town Council of what is termed in England a County Borough. The County Council, however, may decide to provide services which are local in character in relation to a defined and limited area. This is an important advantage in that the County Council can adjust part of its services to local needs and to a considerable degree can ensure that the cost of a particular service is met by the area which benefits from it.

Burghs in Scotland now fall into three broad classes. The cities of Glasgow, Edinburgh, Aberdeen, and Dundee are counties of cities. They do not form, territorially, a portion of any county and they enjoy the fullest measure of local autonomy. Burghs having a population in excess of 20,000 but not being counties of cities are considered to form part of the territory of the county in which each is situated, and while the burgh council is responsible for the administration of most of the functions of a local authority the county council exercises, within the burgh, the duties of local education authority. Where the population of the burgh is less than 20,000 the powers of the burgh council are further restricted and the authority, within the burgh, of the county council is correspondingly increased.

During the period of the Second World War there was established throughout the country an emergency system of administration which was related to territorial regions; and subsequent to the war there was a considerable body of opinion that local administration should similarly be related to regions. This view was strenuously opposed by all local authorities and, while it has become clear since the war that the functions of local government are to be the subject of radical change, it has become equally clear that the structure and basis of organisation is not to be fundamentally altered.

In many burghs the local council had, prior to 1948, undertaken the responsibility of providing supplies of electricity and gas. These services have now been transferred to State control. The National Health Services Act has also served to transfer to the State the responsibility of providing and administering hospitals and has thus closed a whole chapter in the history of local administration. Notwithstanding these immense changes, however, burgh councils continue to be appointed on the former territorial basis. They continue to hold office according to the established pattern and continue to be responsible for the conduct of affairs which are essentially of local concern.

In the sphere of fire-prevention a measure of regionalisation has been accomplished, but this has been effected by compulsory combination between local authorities rather than by the establishment of any new super-authority. Tentative proposals have been made for effecting a measure of regionalisation in relation to police administration, but in the case of this service, also, it would appear that changes are to be effected by combination of individual local authorities rather than by the establishment of an authority of an entirely new description.

Civic affairs in the City of Aberdeen are the responsibility of a popularly elected Council having corporate status. In terms of statute, the Council is designated ' The Corporation of the City of Aberdeen.'

The City is divided into twelve wards and each ward returns three members to the Corporation. Members hold office, in normal circumstances, for a term of three years and retire in rotation. An election is held each year to return one-third of the members.

In addition to the popularly elected members, the Corporation includes the holder for the time being of the ancient office of Dean of Guild. The

Dean of Guild is appointed annually by those residents in the City who have been admitted as Burgesses of Guild.

The Chairman of the Corporation is designated Lord Provost and holds office for a period of three years from the date of his appointment as such. During his term of office he does not retire in ordinary course as a Councillor, notwithstanding that a period of more than three years may have elapsed since the date of his last election.

Six members of the Council are appointed to hold the office of Baillie, and those members discharge judicial and administrative duties as Magistrates. The Corporation also appoint one of their number to be City Treasurer, an honorary office, the holder of which by inveterate custom is charged with the duty of exercising general supervision over the financial affairs of the Corporation. Like the Lord Provost, he holds office for three years, and he is the Chairman of the Finance Committee.

The Corporation are responsible for the administration of such services as those related to education, housing, water supply, and public transport. They are also responsible for the policing of the City, the maintenance of roads and streets, the public cleansing and lighting services, and for the discharge of many other duties which are too numerous to mention. Much the greater part of the work of the Corporation is carried out through the medium of Committees. With some exceptions, each of the Standing Committees includes at least one representative from each of the twelve wards of the City and the Committees in turn appoint Sub-Committees responsible for dealing in detail with some particular aspect of the duties of the full Committee. Committees meet according to a regular cycle, and at the end of each cycle the full Corporation is presented with a printed record of the decisions of each Committee. This record embodied in Minutes of Council forms the basis and warrant for the whole of their administrative actings.

In many respects the business management of the affairs of the City is regulated by public general statutes, but, in addition, the Corporation have been invested with special powers by virtue of local Acts. Local legislation was formerly comprised in a total of forty-one Acts extending over a period from 1862 to 1934, but in the years 1936 to 1940 the Corporation promoted four successive consolidating statutes amending, co-ordinating and integrating the previous unwieldy administrative code.

The pattern of administration in Counties follows fairly closely the scheme enforced in the City. To some extent, however, the functions of the County Council are administered by local district committees popularly elected for the administration of functions entrusted to them by the County Council.

The County Council is popularly elected on much the same basis as the Town Council but all of the members demit office at three-yearly intervals so that an election is held every three years in the County rather than annually as in a Burgh. No doubt this distinction is in part at least attributable to the difficulties of communication and travel which as recently as last century tended to increase the complexity of the arrangements for a local election in a County.

SCHOOLS

THROUGHOUT rural Scotland the education of the laity did not begin to any appreciable extent till after the Reformation. In the burghs conditions were more favourable. While there is little evidence that there was much educational activity in the North-East generally before the seventeenth century, schooling in a limited field was to be had in early times in the burghs. Banff had its grammar school as far back as 1544; Elgin Academy, though the present structure dates from 1886, has traditions stretching back to the thirteenth century. In early days Aberdeen had its song school, linked with the burgh church (there is a record of the appointment of a master to it in 1475), and its grammar school, which was in existence before 1418; and there is evidence from early times of a school linked to the Cathedral in Old Aberdeen (to it in 1262 a new *rector scholarum de Aberdene* was appointed), and of a grammar school, which is shown in James Gordon's Map of 1661 within the precincts of King's College.

Education in Scotland on a national scale owes its inception to John Knox, whose declaration that every parish should have its school and schoolmaster must have seemed revolutionary and quixotic to most of his contemporaries. In 1616, nevertheless, an Order in Council, ratified by Parliament in 1633, made this proposal legal. The heritors of the parishes, upon whom the obligation to provide the school was laid, showed no eagerness to obey the law, and it was not till after 1696 that the parochial school became a common adjunct to rural life. Aberdeen County was fairly enterprising; as early as 1650, of its 83 parishes 23, at the lowest computation, were or had been supplied with a school.[1] Economic distress, the apathy of the people, the lack of suitable premises and the poor remuneration offered to the schoolmaster, all made progress slow and intermittent.

King's College and Marischal College—the two universities founded within a mile of each other—had considerable influence on educational advance in the North-East. It was well towards the end of the eighteenth century before the area had its full quota of schools, but by then the two colleges had roused a desire for education not to be found in less fortunate regions, and later opened their gates wide to welcome even the most humble into the academic fold. At one time throughout Scotland the graduate in arts was not uncommon in the parish school, but for many generations before the passing of the Education Act of 1872 he had largely disappeared save in the North-East, where this class of teacher, of high intellectual attainments, continued to flourish. It aroused no surprise when a crofter's son from Aberdeenshire or Banffshire, taught by a devoted Classical scholar, entered

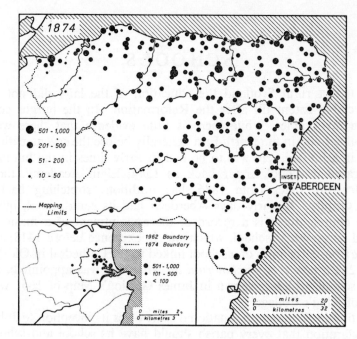

FIG. 27. School roll, 1874. Source: Annual Report of the Board
of Education for Scotland.

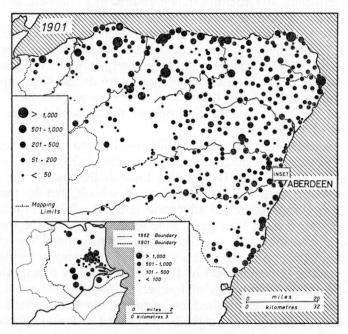

FIG. 28. School roll, 1901. Source: Annual Report of the
Scottish Education Department.

King's or Marischal to begin a distinguished career. The Counties of Aberdeen, Banff and Moray were fortunate in the nineteenth century in that, by a generous endowment (the Dick Bequest), the parish schoolmaster who submitted himself with success to a stiff examination in Latin, Greek and Mathematics was rewarded with a substantial increase to his salary. Another endowment (the Milne Bequest) also supplemented in Aberdeenshire the master's income and provided free education for the poor. In 1875, 85 per cent. of the teachers in the North-East were masters of arts, while elsewhere not one in 50 was a graduate.[2]

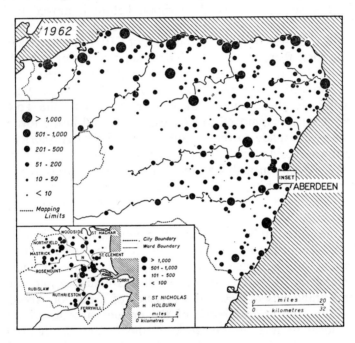

FIG. 29. School roll, 1962. Source: MS. returns supplied by
Directors of Education.

In the City of Aberdeen the demand for higher education was satisfied for a long time by the Grammar School, and, later, Robert Gordon's College. In 1607 the magistrates instituted a school for instruction in writing, arithmetic and book-keeping, and another in 1672 in English grammar. More appeared in course of time, and in 1833 there were 37 schools, having 3,664 pupils, of whom 1,118 were girls.[3] This for an estimated population of some 50,000 is meagre by modern standards, but not in relation to the general lack of schools throughout the country at the time.

Today in Aberdeen City the Local Authority provides schooling for some 30,000 in a system, comprehensive and diverse, and incorporating all that is new and best for the development, both intellectual and physical, of the pupils. Old schools have been reconditioned and extended, and the new ones, notably Torry, Hilton, Powis, Kaimhill and Northfield, rank among the most up-to-date in the country. Under its control the Authority has 44 primary, 12 secondary, and 3 senior secondary schools, two of which have primary departments. Of these the oldest in the burgh is the Grammar School (for pupils from 5 to 18), which can trace its descent from before 1418, the year of the appointment of John Homyll as *magister scholarum*. For centuries it stood on the Schoolhill, and a plaque on the wall of Gray's School of Art indicates its last site in that neighbourhood before it moved to its present building in Skene Street, a handsome structure in Scottish baronial style. The best-known of the Grammar pupils is Lord Byron, who received part of his early education there in 1795-98. The other two senior secondary schools are the co-educational Aberdeen Academy in Belmont Street, and the High School for Girls (with a primary department) in Albyn Place. This developed from an earlier ' English School ' taken over in 1874 by the Town Council. In 1893 the school was removed to its present site, and in the forties considerable additions were made to the buildings. The Local Authority established in 1945 Tertowie Residential School in a beautiful mansion-house nine miles from the city. Open throughout the year it houses pupils from secondary schools in groups of thirty, and each of these for a period of two weeks gains some experience of communal living and some first-hand knowledge of the countryside.

Outwith the Authority's control are fee-paying schools. The oldest of these is a boys' day school for pupils from 5 to 18 (with, however, one boarding-house for about 50), the successor of a Hospital, handsomely endowed by an Aberdeen merchant, Robert Gordon, for the maintenance and education ' of the sons and grandsons of decayed Burgesses of Guild of Aberdeen '. The original building, the central block of the present structure, is an excellent example in local granite of the work of the famous Edinburgh architect, William Adam. The three bays, into which the front is divided, with the middle one recessed and the other two raised to form pediments, the moulded main doorway with hood cornice, and the well-proportioned leaded spire, are all distinctive and attractive features. The Hospital was opened in 1750 and was carried on mainly in accordance with the founder's wishes till 1881, when it was converted into the present college, with bursaries and foundations for a number in lieu of the maintenance provided by the original endowment. The other main ' independent ' schools in the city, with the date of foundation are: St. Margaret's School for Girls (1846), Albyn School for Girls (1867), and the Convent of the Sacred Heart Senior Secondary School (1897).

In the rural areas of the North-East changes have been made necessary in recent years by the shifting population, etc. The general movement has been towards a very gradual centralisation of schools. In Aberdeenshire 45 primary schools have been closed since 1945, and some secondary departments have been discontinued. In Banffshire 39 primary schools have been closed since 1948, and in Moray & Nairn 7 since 1958. Ample provision remains, however, for the school population in these counties. Aberdeenshire provides for 24,600 pupils in 132 primary and 58 secondary schools (6 of these senior), Banffshire for over 8,400 pupils in 30 primary and 23 secondary (7 of them senior), and Moray & Nairn for 13,000 pupils in 51 primary and 9 secondary (5 of them senior). The senior secondary schools in the smaller burghs are, academically, held in high esteem. In open competition the best of these county schools frequently challenge with success the best in Aberdeen City. No hidebound traditions fetter the advance of education in the area; in experimental work and in variety of curricula the schools satisfy the varying needs of the time. The introduction in 1962 of a new Fourth Year Certificate of the Scottish Education Department entailed considerable alterations in the curricula of a number of secondary schools, with the aim of giving as many pupils as possible the opportunity of gaining the Certificate.

Throughout the North-East the demands of the School Health Service are carried out punctiliously. Moreover, for the instruction of children mentally or physically handicapped special schools (or classes) with trained staff are provided—in Aberdeen (at Beechwood School), Inverurie, Banff, Elgin, etc. For the deaf there is, in Aberdeen, Linksfield School, which is in the nature of a regional centre, since children from the county attend it, a hostel being provided for their accommodation. The speech-therapist and the psychologist, with knowledge and experience, are at hand to help to cure or alleviate a physical or nervous disorder, and to encourage the backward child to make progress. Nor does the North-East fall behind other regions in its playing-fields, holiday camps, tours abroad, and so on—all indeed that will help to bring to maturity a generation of healthy and intelligent children.

In recent years many old school buildings have been enlarged and new ones constructed to accommodate more class-rooms, laboratories, etc. Additions or improvements have been made, for example, in Aberdeen Grammar School, Gordon's College, Peterhead Academy, Banff Academy, etc. A new Fraserburgh Academy was officially opened in September, 1962, and in the near future there will be a new Mackie Academy (a well-known senior secondary school in Stonehaven), and a new Aberdeen Academy. Gordon's College envisages the completion within a year or two of a large four-storied block within the grounds, to house modern laboratories, workshops, and art rooms.

Without destroying the old liberal tradition in the schools in the North-East, every effort is made to satisfy the demand for scientific and technical training. While senior schools in general provide the normal courses in Science (Chemistry, Physics, Biology), in Technical, and in Art Studies, the small burgh at times pushes its way to the forefront by some feature of specialisation. In recent years there has been a great development in technical training in Banff Academy. Inverurie Academy, in the heart of a farming community, has three biology specialists on its staff, and has developed a comprehensive rural science course, with all kinds of experimental facilities. The study of botany plays an important part also in Banchory Academy (in Kincardineshire), with practical and laboratory work in garden science, and a pool for the study of pond flora and fauna. Peterhead Academy has a first-class Art Department, with an electric kiln for pottery-making. These are but examples of the initiative and enterprise widespread in the area.

Aberdeen is the focal point of an extensive region, and it gives the opportunity to both city and county pupil of post-secondary training. With a Trades College (to be replaced in 1963 by a new Technical College), a Commercial College, and a Pre-Nursing College, the Authority provides pre-vocational courses to trades and professions of every kind, including (essential in Aberdeen) every section of the trawling industry. Well may those who control education in Aberdeen and the North-East claim that they fully satisfy the needs of the young from the early years in the nursery school to the stage when the individual is equipped to enter a trade or profession, a university or technical college, there to continue his or her education on a solid and secure foundation.

SELECTED REFERENCES

1. SIMPSON, IAN J., *Education in Aberdeenshire before 1872*, London, 1947.
2. WATT, WILLIAM, *A History of Aberdeen and Banff*, Edinburgh, 1900.
3. WILSON, JAMES H., *The Bon-Accord Repository*, Aberdeen, 1842.

ABERDEEN UNIVERSITY

THE University of Aberdeen owes its origin to three famous persons. Of these the one rightly regarded as its founder was the great and good William Elphinstone, Bishop of Aberdeen from 1483-1514—statesman, diplomat, high-minded Christian and patron of many good causes, one of the wisest and finest prelates that the medieval church in our country produced. It was his idea to found a *Studium Generale* in Old Aberdeen, in order to cater specially for the needs of young men north of the Mounth—for whom facilities to acquire the higher learning were then available only in the existing universities of St. Andrews (founded in 1411) and Glasgow (founded in 1450).

The second person whom we revere as one of our founders was the gallant and unfortunate King James IV of Scotland. His support of the application to the Holy See was required, as also his assistance in providing land and revenues for the proposed university.

The third founder was the Pope. Medieval universities were part and parcel of the general framework of Latin Christendom. A degree was a *facultas ubique docendi*: so that a student who had graduated in any university within Catholic Christendom was free to teach or to undertake further study in all. As a result of the application submitted to him by Bishop Elphinstone, with the support of the King, Pope Alexander VI (otherwise, and less happily, known to history as Rodrigo Borgia) issued, on the 10th February, 1495, a Papal Bull authorising the establishment of a University in Old Aberdeen. This Bull, which is still preserved in the University Library, provides for a *Studium Generale* in the ' renowned City of Old Aberdeen ': a university complete in all its faculties—theology, law, medicine and arts.

Pursuant to the Papal Bull, the College of St. Mary of the Nativity—known almost from its foundation as King's College in honour of its Royal patron—was formally constituted on 17th September, 1505. A stone on our ancient Chapel records the commencement of its building on 2nd April, 1500: and the work was completed in the year of incorporation of King's College.

When in the middle of the sixteenth century the Reformation struggle broke out in Scotland, King's College for long remained, openly or secretly, loyal to the ancient faith. In this attitude the College authorities could rely on the powerful support of the Earl of Huntly, the leader of the Counter-Reformation in the north. It was probably to some extent with the idea of setting up a Protestant rival to King's College that George Keith, the 5th Earl Marischal, a leader of the Reformation Party, on the 2nd April, 1593, founded in the New Town a second University—known ever since as Marischal

College. From the outset the new foundation was devised, strictly and expressly, as an organ of the Reformed Church.

It should be noted that Marischal College was in no sense merely another College within the University of Aberdeen, like the various Colleges of Oxford and Cambridge. It was nothing less than a separate University, likewise complete in all Faculties, and with power to grant a degree in any of them.

The provision of two Universities within little more than a long mile of each other, in a region sparsely populated and poor in natural resources, and competing with each other for staff, students and endowments, was bound to result in a rivalry seldom generous and too often downright hostile. Repeated attempts were made to negotiate a union. Of these the first and most promising was the proposed ' Caroline University' in 1641—an enlightened project unfortunately brought to ruin by the Civil War. It was not until an Act of Parliament was passed in 1858 that, two years later, what was known as the ' Fusion' was carried out in the teeth of much local hostility, particularly on the part of Marischal College. In this way the University of Aberdeen, as now constituted, took origin in 1860.

King's College and Marischal College have both retained their identity, though no longer as collegiate establishments but simply as teaching centres. In 1860 it was decided that in the united University the Faculties of Arts and Divinity should be housed at King's College and those of Law and Medicine, with the classes in Science (which was not at that time a Faculty) at Marischal College. Since then, and particularly since the beginning of this century, the University has undergone a process of continuous expansion. Soon after the ' Fusion' new and enlarged buildings were provided at King's College. At the end of the century, Marischal College underwent a very large extension, which was opened in 1906 by King Edward VII. Since the First World War, however, it has been found that even the present huge pile of buildings there was completely inadequate for the voracious demands of modern science and medicine. The result has been the successive transference of scientific departments to Old Aberdeen—a process still in the full-tide of fulfilment—as well as the building of a new Medical School close to the Royal Infirmary on the western outskirts of the town. This building was opened by Lord Dawson of Penn on the 28th September, 1938—the day before the Munich settlement. Although little more than a score of years old, our Medical Building is already inadequate, and large extensions are planned.

In Old Aberdeen, besides the original (and now greatly extended) buildings at King's College, there are now the departments of Botany, Forestry, Chemistry, Geography, Psychology and Education and the Faculty of Law. A large building for the Natural Philosophy Department has just been completed, and it is planned that within the next ten or twenty years other great scientific departments will be brought across from Marischal College to the Old Town.

All the four Scottish Universities may be said to possess each its own peculiar *ethos*. For Aberdeen it may justly be claimed that more than any of the others it has retained a distinctive provincial background. As envisaged by its Founder, it still exists primarily to serve the needs of students from Scotland north of the Mounth. Nevertheless it has always been happy to welcome within its halls students coming from ' a' the airts ', and particularly from the former British Dominions and present members of the Commonwealth. At present the total number of students is somewhat over 2,000—a large proportion of whom still come from northern Scotland. Under the urgent pressure of Governmental policy, however, the University is now faced with expanding to a total student population of 4,500. This prospect is not viewed without misgiving. At the moment it may perhaps fairly be said that Aberdeen University is the most Scottish of the Scottish Universities. But it is obvious that the extra students envisaged in the Government plan are not going to come from our own ' province '. Young men and women of the requisite calibre are just not there in anything like the prescribed numbers. Our huge new intake of students will be drawn from south of the Mounth, from the members of the British Commonwealth and from foreign countries. The danger thereby involved to our own native, deeply rooted, and highly cherished traditions and standards, to the essential Scottishness of our University, is too obvious to need labouring. Nevertheless, experience shows that national character, particularly Scottish national character, is one of the toughest and hardiest of growths. Upon the whole, therefore, there is no need for undue alarm.

One thing at all events is certain, that all through its history the University of Aberdeen, though profoundly conscious of its deep roots in its own native soil, has never been narrowly parochial. Half a century ago one of the greatest of our Principals[1] set the matter forth in the following eloquent sentences; and what he said then remains as relevant to our conditions of today:

' Our University today has a history second to no other of the land in the weight of its traditions and the brilliant variety of its examples. Her founders planned her on more liberal lines than any other Scottish school of the time, and if the realisation of their ideals was delayed for centuries by the comparative scantiness of her resources, she found a moral compensation for this in the close touch which she has always maintained with the popular life about her, and in those energies and habits of hard work, which were fostered alike by the poverty of her students, and by the

[1] Sir George Adam Smith in the first number (published November, 1913) of *The Aberdeen University Review*.

invigorating climate in which she is set. We are not more proud of the eminent benefactors who have judged our University worthy of the use of their wealth, than we are of the longer list of humble men and women whose devotion to her of the thrift of their laborious and unselfish lives has been by far the noblest tribute to her power and will to serve the common people of this part of the Kingdom. How she has discharged her trust is to be measured by that unceasing supply of recruits whom she has trained for the services of the Commonwealth and Empire, and by the large proportion of those who, from the lowliest origins, have risen by the help of her hand to the first places in their professions: who have governed provinces, administered the national justice and led armies, who have explored new territories and widened the bounds of science, who have been the leaders in the practice of medicine and surgery, who have been pioneers in education and founders or presidents of colleges and universities, or who have influenced philosophy and inspired religion.'

While it is an essential part of a university that it should provide instruction covering the whole field of human knowledge, its geographical position has naturally imposed upon Aberdeen University a certain amount of specialisation in the biological sciences, including agriculture, fisheries and forestry. Close relations are established with the North of Scotland College of Agriculture, with the Macaulay Institute for Research in Soil Science (*vide inf.* p. 223) and with the Rowett Institute for Research in Animal Nutrition (*inf.* p. 221). The University itself maintains an out-station for zoological research at Newburgh near the mouth of the Ythan, as well as an agricultural estate at Tillycorthie in the same district. An important enterprise has been the recent acquisition of Tarradale House in Easter Ross. Under the aegis of the Geography Department, this is now being actively developed as a centre of field studies, which it is hoped will be utilised by other British universities.

In the outward and visible aspect of her buildings the University of Aberdeen offers much of interest to the student of academic architecture. King's College still retains its medieval Chapel, with the famous Crown tower, tracery in the flamboyant style revealing French influence, and the finest oaken choir stalls still remaining in Scotland. Owing to the fact that King's College remained so long openly or secretly attached to the ancient faith, the shock of the Reformation was cushioned; hence the Chapel escaped the violent destruction that took place elsewhere at that time in Scotland. In the same way, the local preference for Episcopacy saved it from ill-treatment during the Puritan period. The result is that, as the late Dr. Eeles remarked, King's College Chapel preserves to this day the arrangements of a medieval collegiate church more completely than any college chapel in Oxford or Cambridge.

In marked contrast, Marischal College frontage and the Mitchell Tower stand conspicuous as striking examples of the Gothic Revival. Given its premises, the great Perpendicular front, designed by the late Dr. Marshall Mackenzie, deserves recognition as an outstanding example of what may be called scenic architecture.

In the more recent buildings, however, the University has wisely broken clear from the Gothic tradition. When it was opened, the new medical building at Foresterhill, designed on frankly modernistic lines, was regarded as the last word in academic functional architecture. The new Chemistry building in the Old Town, the Natural Philosophy building recently completed and the new Science Library, upon which work is now in progress, all in different ways exemplify the need to design large modern research or technical institutions in a style in keeping with their internal functional needs.

The University buildings now existing or in future to be set up in Old Aberdeen will be assured of a peerless setting. By a most happy chance the ancient Episcopal Burgh of Barony has escaped the process of modernisation which has almost entirely denuded the New Town of its traditional architecture. The Old Town thus retains much of the atmosphere of dignified leisure that marked the eighteenth century. Many buildings of this date still survive, together with fine old precinct walls, while the venerable Cathedral and the Old Town House remind us of the ancient consequence of the Aulton. In spite of the encroachments which time, and not least the expansion of the University, have inevitably brought about, the Old Town may still be said to be enclosed by, or to include within its precincts, spacious bird-haunted lawns and umbrageous trees. It has been one of the great satisfactions of the University that, since the First World War, the policy has been pursued of purchasing these old properties as opportunity offered, and reconditioning them so as to preserve their ancient character. In this task the University has firmly refused to turn ' the Aulton ' into a suburb of academes. Every effort is being made to preserve the delightfully mixed population of the Old Town with its small shopkeepers and craftsmen. In these days of ever-rising costs the burden has been a severe one; but thanks to the generous assistance of the McRobert Trustees its continuance is now assured.

Relations between Town and Gown have always been extremely happy in Aberdeen. A notable proof of this was recently furnished when the University's building programme compelled us reluctantly to agree to the sacrifice of one of the two large playing fields at King's College. In this dilemma the Town stepped in and with remarkable generosity handed over as a gift to the University, under certain conditions readily accepted, the fine demesne of Seaton, stretching along the south bank of the Don. In this way Town as well as Gown will gain; and there is every prospect that within the next generation Old Aberdeen will develop into a *ville universitaire* equalled only by St. Andrews.

Research Units

Although in this *Scientific Survey* no account is given of the research being carried out in the various Departments of the University, it is proper to accord brief mention to the various Research Units wholly maintained within these Departments by various public bodies.

The Agricultural Research Council maintains, under the Direction of Dr. D. J. Finney, F.R.S., a Unit of Statistics attached to the University Department of Statistics. This Unit has responsibility for providing advice on statistical problems to agricultural research institutions and colleges throughout Scotland. The staff also undertake research on statistical problems of a more theoretical character that bear upon agriculture. Within the same Department there has recently been sponsored by the Scottish Hospitals Endowments Research Trust a Research Group in Biometric Medicine which, maintaining close touch with medical workers, will choose its own research projects with emphasis on their relevance to medical research rather than to statistical theory.

The Medical Research Council's Obstetric Medicine Research Unit, which is under the honorary direction of Sir Dugald Baird, Professor of Obstetrics and Gynaecology, was established in 1954 to continue work which had previously been undertaken by temporary research staff. It consists of four main divisions which undertake, respectively, research in the epidemiology, the sociology, the physiology, and the clinical aspects of human reproduction and family life. For the purposes of clinical and physiological investigation it has eight beds in the Aberdeen Maternity Hospital, together with associated laboratories. To members of the British Association it may well be of interest as an example of teamwork in the advancement of knowledge of human biology.

In the Department of Natural History the Nature Conservancy maintains a Unit of Grouse and Moorland Ecology. This Unit, under the direction of Professor V. C. Wynne-Edwards and with Dr. C. H. Gimingham of the Department of Botany as botanical consultant, was established in 1960 in direct succession to the Grouse Enquiry financed by the Scottish Landowners' Federation. The main field-centre is at Kerloch, an 8,000-acre grouse moor retained for experimental purposes near Banchory. The Unit's primary concern is the fundamental relationship between a herbivorous population of red grouse and their staple food-resource, ling heather.

On page 225 reference is made to the newly established Fisheries Biochemical Research Unit within the University Department of Biochemistry.

RESEARCH INSTITUTES

ONE of the outstanding attractions of the University of Aberdeen is its proximity to the snow fields of the Cairngorms; to devotees of biological sciences and arts an equally cogent consideration is its close links with the famous institutions at Bucksburn, Craigiebuckler and Torry—all within three miles of the centre of the city and the University.

Although it is over fifty years since the Development Commission launched its scheme for the foundation of a number of independent research institutions it may be as well to indicate briefly the origin of these bodies, since to-day, perhaps more than ever, is it of importance to be able to point to examples of the highly successful result of the combination of 'private enterprise' with imaginative guidance and financial assistance by organs of the state. A further point of interest is the recognition that, though each institution was intended to specialise in a single branch of agriculture, the most likely method of achieving success within each specialised field would be to concentrate a number of workers with very diverse talents and training in one institution, where the continuity already demonstrated at Rothamsted in respect of fertility could be assured. These institutions were indeed to be the fulfilment of Bacon's dream in the *New Atlantis*—the enlarging of the bounds of human empire—and of Thomas Sprat's description of the aim of the Royal Society —'a business of time, a steady, a lasting, a popular, an uninterrupted work'.

In the year following the first move by the Development Commission (1911) a Joint Committee representing the North of Scotland College of Agriculture and the University of Aberdeen appointed Dr. J. B. Orr to start work on the problems of animal nutrition. Through the initiative of Dr. (now Lord) Boyd Orr the original scheme was raised to a scale far beyond anything contemplated by the Committee, but though work was started on a building at Craibstone progress was halted by the outbreak of war in 1914. Dr. Orr, happily surviving ordeal by battle, returned in 1919 and soon to be assisted by additional staff began those nutritional studies that enabled the British people twenty years later to survive ordeal by rationing. The following year he was able to move from temporary accommodation in the basement of Marischal College to the new building at Craibstone, where research was continued for two years. Meanwhile various circumstances had arisen that had made it desirable to establish the Institute on a separate site, and through the generosity of the late Dr. John Quiller Rowett the main building of the Rowett Research Institute (as it was thenceforth to be called) was erected at Bridgefoot, Bucksburn, and opened in 1922 by H.M. Queen Mary. In 1948 a third floor of laboratories was added without any interruption of the work of the Institute.

By the time (1945) when Sir John Boyd Orr handed over the Institute to the present Director, Dr. D. P. Cuthbertson, there had been added at various times the Duthie Experimental Farm, the Reid Library and Strathcona House. The Farm of 500 acres developed by means of a benefaction of the late Mr. J. Duthie Webster to commemorate his uncle William Duthie of Collynie, a famous Shorthorn breeder, was at first run as a self-contained economic unit but the growing demands of the Institute in recent years have led to its incorporation as a research service department.

The Reid Library, founded and to a considerable extent developed through the generosity of the late Dr. Walter Reid, is housed in a building that accommodates not only the extensive library but also the administrative offices of the Institute and the Commonwealth Bureau of Animal Nutrition. The proximity of the Bureau with its great range of periodicals is of inestimable value to the research staff, whose work is made lighter, as is that of their colleagues throughout the world, by its quarterly publication of *Nutrition Abstracts and Reviews* and by its Technical Reviews.

From an early date the increasing number of workers from overseas made the provision of a residential and collegiate centre highly desirable. The need had been met since 1932 by a handsome building, about half the original cost of which was borne by the late Lord Strathcona. This was subsequently extended.

The basic financial responsibility for the Institute rests with the Department of Agriculture for Scotland, which with the Agricultural Research Council also maintains an over-all supervision of the research programme submitted by the Director through the Governing Body. Nevertheless numerous projects are undertaken with financial assistance from other official bodies and occasionally benefactions are received from industry.

Though the annual *Collected Papers* display a wide range of research activities it is probably true to say that the branch that has won for the Institute world-wide recognition is the detailed study of every aspect of digestion, absorption and metabolism in the ruminant. The growing recognition of the part played by micro-organisms—both bacteria and protozoa—in the gut has transformed this inner environment into a veritable microcosm in which the most diverse scientific talents and techniques find scope for discoveries often of the most fundamental importance to progress in our understanding of the processes of nutrition. To the industry this gives promise—already in part fulfilled—of considerable economies in the management of rations in relation to more rapid marketing. The development of this field has taken place since Dr. Cuthbertson became Director and has been accompanied by a great expansion of both staff and buildings. During the same period the Rowett achieved a unique distinction among non-academic institutions in Great Britain when in 1952 Dr. R. L. M. Synge, F.R.S., Head of the Department of Biochemistry, shared with Dr. A. J. P. Martin, F.R.S., then of the Medical

Research Council, the Nobel Prize for Chemistry in respect of their development of the powerful technique of partition chromatography.

Whereas the greater part of the work of the Rowett can be carried on in the laboratories and experimental farm at Bucksburn, the Macaulay Institute for Soil Research had its origin in a pioneer project in the Isle of Lewis and continues to range far and wide for the raw material of its endeavour. The War of 1914-18 had revealed the vulnerability of a densely populated country dependent for its existence on a very high proportion of imported foodstuffs. This applied strictly only to England; but what Scotland (and Wales) gained in respect of a sparse population was offset by a much higher proportion of land covered by infertile ' acid ' peat. In the knowledge that similar land in Northern Europe had been brought into cultivation by scientific management Mr. T. B. Macaulay, President of the Sun Life Office of Canada, set on foot an investigation to discover whether the Isle of Lewis, the land of his fathers, could be so improved. By 1929 improvement was so marked that he decided to assist in the foundation of a permanent institute to extend the investigation to the whole of Scotland. Thus in the following year the mansion house of Craigiebuckler, within fifty acres of grounds, was transformed into the Macaulay Institute for Soil Research under the direction of Dr. (now Sir) William Ogg, who had been mainly responsible for the work on Lewis.

The work of the Institute now comprises two main aspects: the systematic soil survey of Scotland mainly on a scale of 2·5 inches to 1 mile; and research to ' obtain from field, pot, greenhouse and laboratory studies of soil and plants information of value in the maintenance and improvement of soil fertility from the standpoint of both crop production and animal requirement '. But behind this utilitarian rubric there lies a wealth of scientific activity of the most varied kind. The use of arc, spark, and flame spectroscopy for the estimation of elements—especially trace elements—in soils and plants grown upon them is now of long standing; but to anyone nurtured in the tedious precipitation methods the ' rapid determination of gypsum and calcite ' by analysis of the thermal diagrams of the field samples may come as something of a shock.

Every problem is attacked on the broadest front: mobilisation of phosphate by the Department of Soil Fertility aided by the microbiologist and soil mineralogist. The absence of a Department of Ecology is an indication not of any failure to take a synoptic view, but of the reverse: in the problem of peat ecology for instance the superficial ' behaviour ' of *Calluna* is studied in conjunction with inter-specific balance, ion-exchange mineral analysis, and ' tracer ' following of rooting habits; and the Hill Farming Research Association has provided data in respect of rainfall, run-off, and water table.

Climate, elevation, exposure and soil conditions are the main factors to be considered in studies of soil productivity. In such studies it is necessary therefore to carry out experiments on different soils in their natural environ-ments. The Institute has done this successfully by enlisting the aid of com-mercial farmers in the carrying out of large scale investigations of fertility involving thousands of plots carrying a variety of crops on different soil types.

An important part of the Institute's work is that connected with the special problems of forest soils, where the analysis of samples of pine needles furnished by the Forestry Commission has demonstrated the threat of potash deficiency, for instance, on recently afforested peat. So highly do the Com-mission value this co-operation that they furnish an annual grant towards the expenses of the Institute.

The Forestry Commission is only one of the large number of institutions that forward samples for analysis and expert advice. If not from China to Peru at least from Iran (FAO) to British Guiana they come; and of course from most of the other Research Institutes and Colleges of Agriculture in Scotland. Even the most modest horticulturalist may submit samples through the local horticultural advisory officer.

The Institute is governed by a Council of Management consisting of representatives of the Department of Agriculture for Scotland, the University of Aberdeen, the three Scottish Colleges of Agriculture, and a few co-opted members. The planning and general supervision of research are decentralised to small committees. The Agricultural Research Council maintains intimate contact with the Institute by means of a ' visiting group ' every six years. These visits (the most recent of which occurred in 1960), far from being mere formalities, are greatly appreciated by the individual departments whose schemes of research receive careful scrutiny and constructive comment.

In 1958 the volume of advisory work in addition to survey and research had rendered the existing accommodation highly inconvenient in plan and inadequate in extent. A two-phase building programme was therefore sanctioned whereby the work of the Institute could continue unabated. The first phase was completed early in 1961, the second should be finished some considerable time before the visit of the British Association. The removal of the greater part of the laboratory suite from the original mansion house will allow of the latter being furnished eventually as staff rooms and as short-term accommodation for some of the workers who come from all parts of the world to perfect their knowledge of some aspect of the field in which the Institute has become a recognised authority.

From the moorland peat of a small island to a prominent place in the coming struggle to make fertile the waste places of the earth—that is the measure of thirty years' enlightened endeavour. And to those who may raise the cry of ' not by bread alone ' the Institute may point out the uncovenanted benefits of greater understanding of the tempo and mode of evolution from primitive settlement to mechanised farming. For by pollen analysis, carbon dating, and profile analysis of quaternary deposits the good earth has yielded up a story not only of its own weathering but of the manner of the men who shaped its course to their own ends.

To most of the denizens of the Deep South Aberdeen spells fish. Though this *Survey* will have shown that this is an over-simplification, ' the fishing ' is still a dominant interest along the coast of the North-East. It is not surprising then that in Aberdeen are situated the Marine Laboratory of the Scottish Department of Agriculture and Fisheries, and the Torry Research Station maintained by the Department of Scientific and Industrial Research. The former, under its Director, Dr. C. E. Lucas, is responsible for research into all those problems that arise in connection with catching the fish; the latter's problem starts from the moment the fish has been removed from the sea. By research planned and executed over a long period of years, and fortunately already well advanced during the period of food shortage in the war, fish preserved for weeks or even months by the methods developed at the Torry can be of better flavour and texture than ' fresh ' fish after a day or two in transit. This was achieved by bacteriological and biochemical studies combined with physico-chemical and histological investigation of the effects of low temperature and ice crystals on the muscle fibre and fluids of the fish. For the improvement of flavour and keeping quality of kippered herring and smoked haddock (the Arbroath ' smokie ' variety is a delicacy too little known South of the Border) at the mass production level, the problem was to design plant conforming to the demand of smooth gaseous flow analogous to that of ' matched impedance ' in loud speakers. More recently chemical investigation has been applied to the separation of those constituents of the smoke responsible for flavour and sterilisation respectively. Since 1958 Dr. G. A. Reay, Director of the Torry and of the Humber Laboratory has been assisted by a small Steering Committee whose policy has been to ensure ' support for basic research . . . and the closest possible contact with the practical problems of the industry '.

In this year of the visit of the British Association to Aberdeen, it may be possible to see the first fruits of the arrangements recently concluded between the Development Commission and the University for the creation of a Fisheries Biochemical Research Unit within the University Department of Biochemistry. Though staffed by members of the University it will be separately housed near the Marine Laboratory and the Torry Research Station. Under its own Director, who it is expected will be a Reader in the University, the Unit will be mainly concerned with fundamental research into the chemical structure and interactions of such substances as the mucus of the neuromast system which are especially characteristic of the living fish.

15

TECHNICAL EDUCATION

In the County areas of the North-East, even before the Education Act of 1872 provided for a national system of education, there had been sporadic but interesting experiments in technical education. These, as one might expect, had been mainly concerned with agriculture and fishing. The first recorded evening school in Aberdeenshire was held at Monymusk about 1792, when the parish schoolmaster taught 'either in the evenings or at by-hours on week days and stormy days when servants could attend'. It is probable, however, that the education in this and other similar evening schools was aimed at making good deficiencies in general education. However, ' vocational' instruction appears about the same period, as when, for example, the schoolmaster of the Academy of Udny advertised classes in land surveying and book-keeping. In 1807, navigation was taught at Newburgh, and between 1830 and 1840 land surveying was offered at Kemnay and Tornaveen and navigation at Fraserburgh, St. Combs, Belhelvie and Slains. Instruction in non-academic subjects was given in the ' academies' which began to appear in the region about the middle of the nineteenth century and which were originally founded in opposition to the established burgh schools, thought by some to be too much under the influence of the Church and to offer too exclusively a classical education.

In the City of Aberdeen, technical education had a different genesis. Although some earlier attempts had been made, its origin is clearly in the founding of a Mechanics' Institute in 1824. In 1818 the Aberdeen Academy, with classes in art, technical and literary subjects, was opened and in that same year the Institution for teaching the deaf and dumb was founded. The promoters of the last named (which is the only one of those early institutes still in existence) were also instrumental in organising the Mechanics' Institute in Aberdeen. The Mechanics' Institute movement sprang from the thirst for knowledge by the artisans of the new industrial towns. It started in Glasgow and Institutes were opened there and in Edinburgh, Greenock, Manchester, Birmingham and London. The Aberdeen Institute first organised public lectures on philosophic, technical and scientific subjects. In the early years as many as 500 tickets would be sold for some lectures and, in addition, many free places were allocated to apprentices, but, by 1828, the enthusiasm had evaporated and no lectures were given at all, although the Institute library continued to function. In the early 1830s the Institute was moribund, but in 1835, under the Secretaryship of Alexander Bain, interest revived and a building fund of £270 was gathered, but no suitable site was found for a permanent home. In 1844, by strenuous efforts, the funds were increased to

£1,500 and a site was found in Market Street, adjoining Adelphi Lane. The foundation stone was laid on 13th August, 1845, and the building designed by Archibald Simpson and William Ramage was completed in time for the winter session of 1848-49.

In the 1840s efforts were partly diverted into the fashionable staging of exhibitions, while organised courses in music, elocution and drawing replaced public lectures. In 1842 the Town Council was associated with the Committee of the Mechanics' Institute in discussing the establishment of a branch of the Government School of Design but it was not until 1853 that a School of Art was opened. The Institute was dissatisfied with the extent of this provision and now argued for a School of Science. On the occasion of a visit of inspection in 1854, Dr. Kilgour, the President of the Institute, expounded this view to the representatives of the Art Department of the Board of Trade, who were sufficiently impressed to approve a scheme for a ' School of Science and Art for the Operative Classes of Aberdeen ' as an experiment for one year to test the extent to which the workers would avail themselves of such opportunities. Aberdeen was selected because of its exceptional facilities for carrying out the scheme, and so far from being abandoned in 1855—the contingency allowed for by the Board—its success led to the establishment of Schools of Science and Art as part of the British system of education.

In 1856, the Committee of the Mechanics' Institute, the Council of the School of Science and Art and the Town Council proposed an English, Trade and Navigation School. Special importance was to be assigned to technical and mechanical draughtsmanship for shipbuilding, engineering and other industry in the City as well as to navigation. In 1857 the first Technical School was opened but in 1858 the local shipowners, unwilling to be associated with the Mechanics' Institute, withdrew the School of Navigation and put it under the local Marine Board.

The Education Act of 1872 gave the School Boards power to set up evening schools in a limited range of subjects and a few Boards established classes in general subjects and in shorthand and book-keeping. It was, however, with the publication of the Continuation Class Code in 1901 that the pattern of further education began to emerge more definitely. Two main divisions of evening classes were recognised—those, the beginning of our modern pre-apprenticeship classes, which provided elementary instruction in special subjects, especially such as might be of use to young people preparing for a particular trade, occupation or profession, and those, roughly equivalent to our present vocational courses which, being normally of three years' duration and providing an approved minimum of instruction each year, were intended to fit students for the intelligent practice of particular crafts, industries or occupations. Enrolments were remarkably high—probably because at that time many pupils were granted exemption from compulsory attendance at day school on condition that they attended continuation classes regularly up to the age of 16. By the Education Act of 1908 School Boards had to provide continuation classes for the further instruction of young persons above the age of 14 in the crafts and industries practised in their areas. This Act brought about a considerable expansion of provision through-out the region, with continuation classes in nearly every parish.

In the meantime, developments went on apace in the City. The Mechanics' Institute, like such Institutes everywhere, was chronically short of funds, and after the Endowed Institution Act of 1878 the Directors suggested that there ought to be an endowed institution in the City with schools for science and art training in day and evening classes, a museum and picture gallery and a free lending and reference library. This view coincided largely with the opinions of the Governors of Robert Gordon's Hospital who saw in the same Act a means of ' transforming the " monastic " system of boarding and educating inmates into an open college with day and evening classes '. The Mechanics' Institute then made proposals to the Town Council but the latter took no action. In 1881 a Provisional Order was made under the Endowed Institution Act changing the name of Robert Gordon's Hospital to Robert Gordon's Colleges and empowered the Governors to convert the Hospital buildings into a day college and to carry on evening classes in primary, secondary, mechanical, physical and other subjects ' with power to combine with the Managers, Trustees, or Directors of any Mechanics' Institute, or Scientific or Technical College or School in Aberdeen or elsewhere '. This Order came into force on 1st August, 1881, and four days later came formally before the Directors of the Mechanics' Institute. They were prepared to divest themselves of all their property on condition that their Library was taken over and maintained by the Town Council under the Public Libraries Act. The Town Council was reluctant to take on this commitment, but in 1883 Mr. John Gray announced that he proposed to erect, at his own expense, an Art School, thus enabling the Mechanics' Institute to offer their building as well as their books to the Town as a library. Finally, in March 1884, following a large public meeting in St. Katherine's Hall and a petition to the Lord Provost a meeting of householders was called which voted overwhelm-ingly for the ' adoption ' of the library.

The Mechanics' Institute now vanished; its classes had been taken over in 1881 by the School Board and transferred in 1882 to Robert Gordon's Colleges; its building became the Public Library; the School of Art was transferred to Mr. Gray's new building in 1885 and placed under the jurisdiction of Robert Gordon's Colleges. Robert Gordon's Technical College became, and has remained, the apex of the structure of technical education in the North-East; it is associated on the one hand with the University, particularly in various branches of engineering, and on the other with the Education Authorities' technical colleges and centres. The latter, with certain excep-tions, provide courses for craftsmen and for technicians up to Ordinary

National Certificate level, while Robert Gordon's Technical College provides Higher National Certificate and Diploma courses.

In the City, the School Board provision of continuation classes had developed in much the same way as in the county areas, although more over-shadowed by the other growths described, and it was during the period between the transfer of responsibility for educational provision from the *ad hoc* Education Authority to County Councils in 1929 and the end of the Second World War that the classes organised by the Education Committee were affiliated to Robert Gordon's Technical College. This altered the status of these classes from being simply local arrangements to being part of the National Certificate courses organised in the College, permitting students to continue to higher studies.

Since 1946 the trend has been for Aberdeen to become increasingly the regional centre for technical education with local centres in the counties providing junior courses in evening classes, many of which prepare students for the more advanced courses in the City. Elgin, Keith, Banff and other towns have commercial courses, engineering craft courses and Ordinary National Certificate engineering courses. The only centre with a more than local catchment area is the residential Pre-Nursing College at Elgin, which draws students from the whole north of Scotland.

In addition there are many examples of courses particularly associated with local industry. Perhaps the most interesting of these is the Basic Catering Course of the City and Guilds of London Institute in Elgin Girls' Technical School; this course was founded in 1906, the first of its kind in Scotland, and the girls find ready employment in local hotels and catering establishments. Elgin Further Education Centre has courses for electrical engineering apprentices employed by the Hydro-Electric Board, and courses in chemistry for the distilling industry; Lossiemouth, Banff and Peterhead have courses in navigation for the fishing fleets; and at several centres evening courses in agriculture and farm machinery are provided in co-operation with the North of Scotland College of Agriculture.

In general, however, all full-time and day release classes as well as many of the evening classes are provided in the City for students from the whole region and indeed far beyond. Aberdeen Education Committee has three main Further Education Colleges—the Technical College, for which a new building is almost completed in the Gallowgate; the Commercial College, at present in temporary premises while the new College is being built in Holburn Street; and the Pre-Nursing College. The Technical College provides pre-vocational courses in Engineering, Building, Hairdressing, Fish Processing, and Fishing and Seamanship as well as a very extensive range of day release, block release and evening classes for practically every trade and industry carried on in the area, including papermaking, trawling, cookery for fishermen, trawler diesel engineering, laboratory technicians' work, dental technique, monumental masonry, cinema operation and textiles. The Commercial College has departments of general studies, professional studies, office arts, retail trades work, with pre-vocational courses for office work and retail trades, and day release, block release and evening classes in a great variety of commercial, professional, retail and other courses. The Pre-Nursing College offers one- and two-year courses for girls leaving school at 15 or 16 intending to enter nurse training; provides day release courses for Nursery Nurse trainees; and has a one-year course for more mature students who are training to be Houseparents in residential homes for children.

It is interesting to note that very little of the City's further education is conducted on a private basis, but one well established example is the Wireless College in Albyn Terrace. This institution meets the needs of young men wishing to become radio operators in the Merchant Navy or in the fishing fleet.

The North of Scotland College of Agriculture is affiliated at one end of its range of courses to the University, and at the other assists the County Education Authorities in the provision of part-time courses in crop and animal husbandry, farm machinery, farm organisation and management, poultry farming, beekeeping, and horticulture. It also provides in Craibstone Junior College nine-month full-time courses of a practical nature for boys and girls of 15 years who will be engaged in the practical work of farming or running a farmhouse, while for more advanced students there are two-year full-time Diploma courses in agriculture and in dairying.

Robert Gordon's Technical College, as a Central Institution, has a diversity of higher provision to meet the needs of the North-East with its schools of Navigation, Electrical, Mechanical, Naval and Civil Engineering, Building, Architecture, Art, Domestic Science and Management Studies leading to qualifications of equivalent standard in these fields to Higher National Certificates, Higher National Diplomas and University Degrees. With such a diversity of provision, it is obvious that the College has to provide a very wide range of evening, day release, block release and full-time courses to meet the varied needs of its students and this is done not only in the central group of buildings on Schoolhill (and special mention should be made of the excellent Electrical Engineering wing recently opened there) but also in new buildings provided in recent years on the outskirts of the City, notably the new School of Domestic Science on Anderson Drive and the lovely Scott Sutherland School of Architecture at Garthdee.

ABERDEEN COLLEGE OF EDUCATION

FOR long the training of teachers like so much else in Scottish education was undertaken by the Church but in 1905 by a Minute of the Committee of Council on Education this responsibility was transferred to the State. Provincial Committees were then set up in the four Scottish University centres, the Aberdeen Provincial Committee taking over in 1907 the Colleges of the Free Church and of the Church of Scotland. To accommodate the students of both church colleges it was soon evident that a new ' Training Centre ' was required but it was not until 1919 that the Aberdeen Training Centre, occupying the site of the former Free Church Training College and adjoining properties, was opened and except for internal adaptations it stands today substantially as it did over forty years ago.

Meantime radical changes in education had made the training regulations obsolete in form if not in spirit and a comprehensive revision of the whole system was overdue. Nevertheless it was not until 1958 after a period of nearly thirty years that a new set of regulations appeared covering even then only the administrative aspects of training. Already the very numerous amendments to these regulations make them difficult to follow, so much so that the Secretary of State now contemplates their re-issue in consolidated form.

Administratively the most conspicuous results have been the replacement of the former Provincial Committees by new governing bodies and the change of title from Training Centres to Colleges of Education. The former, it is noted, will give the Colleges a greater autonomy, and the latter reflects more adequately the nature and scope of the work. What in fact may be the effect of these and other changes it is premature to say nor is it easy to distinguish what is real from what is illusory but the function of the Colleges remains unaffected by mere change in nomenclature or administration. This function is primarily to train teachers and thus our Colleges are essentially Teacher Training Colleges, correctly so described. As such they seek to fulfil their task in three main ways: first (in order of importance), by affording ample opportunity for practice-teaching under skilled supervision including regular demonstration lessons; second, by extending and enriching the general education of those who require it; and third, by providing a variety of courses for teachers in service to keep them abreast of recent developments in content and methods of instruction.

The Aberdeen College accommodates some 700 men and women students in all categories and has a staff of nearly fifty lecturers. It is probable that in this decade the student population will rise to a maximum of about 850 and the staffing establishment to about seventy-five. The trend of development is towards smaller sections for student instruction, increased use of seminars and tutorials, wider choice for students of optional subjects, and, in general, greater flexibility in the training curriculum. Doubtless the Wheatley Committee, whose chief remit is to consider certificates of competency to teach, will report also on these matters, and when their recommendations have been received the final revision of Teachers' Training Regulation will begin. By that time, however, many of the developments already envisaged will have been realised.

LOCAL SCIENTIFIC SOCIETIES

FIRST in order of time, the ABERDEEN PHILOSOPHICAL SOCIETY was founded in 1758. It was a small but select body, for it apparently never had more than sixteen members all told; but nearly all were men well known in their day, and some, such as Thomas Reid and James Beattie, had a European reputation. The Society flourished for about fifteen years until 1773, when its activities seem to have ceased. At some meetings members took it in turn to deliver a short discourse which was followed by a general discussion; at others a topic or ' question ' selected at a previous meeting was introduced by the member who proposed it, and then discussed by the others in turn. The Minute Book, now in the University Library, contains lists of members, the rules and accounts of the Society, brief minutes of the meetings, and a complete list of all the ' questions ', with the names of the members who proposed them and the dates on which they were discussed. Abstracts of the questions and of the subsequent discussions were apparently entered in a special book, and reports of certain selected discourses in another; unfortunately neither of these books appears to have survived. The Society was revived in 1840 and from this date printed records exist up to 1939, when the outbreak of war brought an end to its activities. For the first thirty years these records consist only of lists of members, names of speakers and titles of papers, but from 1872 they contain full reports of selected papers. The printed records are supplemented by the Minute Books of the Society, in six volumes, which have been deposited in the University Library; they contain brief summaries of many of the earlier papers.

More nearly ' scientific ' in its activities was the GORDON'S MILL FARMING CLUB founded in 1758. This consisted of a small group of men, not more than fifteen in all, who were mostly university professors, or farmers and country lairds from the district round Aberdeen. They met regularly over a period of several years to discuss matters of common interest, and fortunately a complete record of all their meetings, with full reports of papers and discussions, has been preserved in the Minute Book of the Club now housed in the University Library. These records are of considerable interest, for they reveal the progressive views held by many of the farmers and landed proprietors of the day and the comparatively advanced state of agricultural practice in the North-East at this period of the eighteenth century. Selections from this Minute Book, edited by Mr. J. H. Smith of Aberdeen University, were published in 1962 as a University Study.

The ABERDEEN MEDICO-CHIRURGICAL SOCIETY had its beginnings in 1789 and has proved the most viable of all the local societies. There exists a great

233

deal of largely unpublished manuscript material, which, being of interest primarily to the medical historian, calls for no detailed comment here.

There has been since 1845 a succession of not fewer than four Natural History Societies centred mainly on Aberdeen. The surviving society is now known as the NORTHERN NATURALISTS' CLUB (founded in 1886 as the Aberdeen Working Men's Natural History and Scientific Society); it has recently absorbed the Aberdeen Natural History and Antiquarian Society. Some of the records of these societies are preserved in the University Library. Other Societies still flourishing in the North-East include the BUCHAN CLUB (founded 1887), the DEESIDE FIELD CLUB (founded 1920) and the BANFFSHIRE FIELD CLUB (founded 1880).

An ABERDEEN AND NORTH OF SCOTLAND ZOOLOGICAL SOCIETY was formed early in 1962 with Professor V. C. Wynne-Edwards as President. In close co-operation with the Town Council and with Mr. Peter Scott, Rector of the University, as adviser, the Society hopes to open a Zoological Garden by 1964. In addition, the Society proposes to support schools in the teaching of biology and to arouse interest in the local fauna and its preservation.

THE MUSEUMS

THE visitor to the British Association Meeting who is interested in museums and their contents will find much of interest within the City of Aberdeen but little else in the North-East of Scotland and that only by travelling considerable distances. The pattern of museum development in the North-East of Scotland has been determined by geographical factors. The City of Aberdeen contains within its boundaries only half per cent. of the total area of the counties of Aberdeen, Banff, Moray and Nairn, but 43 per cent. of their population. Peterhead, the burgh next in size of population to Aberdeen, has only one-fifteenth of its population; only two other places exceed 10,000. The small size of the burghs, and the scattered population and high proportion of mountain or moorland within the counties, have resulted in rateable values too low to provide adequate support to museums. Yet even in the small centres of population, there are museums which, in size and diversity of interest, reflect a North-East characteristic.

The principal export of the region has been men. Missionaries and merchants, soldiers and administrators, have gone to other corners of the world, restoring the balance of trade to some extent by sending back the plants they studied, the skulls and skins of the animals they shot, the tropical birds and insects they collected, and the weapons, utensils and ritual objects of the peoples of other faiths whom they sought to convert. Eventually, many of such objects found their way into a museum, a fact which explains the heterogeneous character of some of the smaller museums within the area, and why the Anthropological Museum at Marischal College contains within its one room and small annex such a wealth and diversity of interest. Though small, when set against the riches of Oxbridge, this University collection must take first place.

Successive Professors of Anatomy have interpreted broadly the dictum that the proper study of mankind is man and have been pioneers in pre-historic archaeology and anthropology. To Marischal College came most of the archaeological finds from the North-East of Scotland which did not find their way to the National Museum of Antiquities in Edinburgh, and unique objects from other parts of the world, including examples from Oceania. There are important Egyptological collections and study collections of coins. At present a side room houses the St Ninian's Isle Treasure found by a party of Aberdeen University geography students in 1958 while on archaeological field-work. The treasure, pronounced the greatest find of its kind in Scotland, is well displayed with explanatory material.

For teaching purposes several departments at Marischal College have developed museums. That in the Natural History Department has achieved considerable size and importance due to the enlightened interest of holders of the chair, not least among whom was Professor Ritchie, himself one time a museum keeper at the Royal Scottish Museum. Both the Anthropological and Natural History Museums are open to the public.

The civic museum in Aberdeen is principally an art gallery with large and important collections of paintings and sculpture which particularly serve to illustrate the art of Scotland and the development of modern art from the middle of the nineteenth century. The Macdonald Bequest has enabled the Gallery, more comprehensively than most, to reflect the changes of taste during the present century. The collection of early English watercolours is representative and a notable feature is the recently opened James McBey Memorial Print Room and Art Library. Special exhibitions are constantly being held. Within the building is a small regional museum, first opened in 1936, which is designed to illustrate the life and environment of the people of the North-East of Scotland. So long as it is housed within this one room its aim—to illustrate local geology, botany, zoology and archaeology and to show the development of the various industries upon which Aberdeen and the North-East depends—cannot be realised; at present the room contains only a token of what such a regional museum should be.

Provost Skene's House, a seventeenth century town house opposite Marischal College, which was restored and opened to the public in 1953 as a period house and museum of local history and social domestic life, is also under the control of the Art Gallery Committee of the Town Council. Of particular interest within the House are its early seventeenth century painted ceiling containing New Testament illustrations and devotional symbolism, a small room with painted panelling of the mid-eighteenth century and several ceilings of decorated plasterwork. Also in Aberdeen is the Regimental Museum of the Gordon Highlanders, now housed in the new Regimental Headquarters at St. Luke's, Viewfield Road, on the outskirts of the City.

The Museum at Peterhead occupies four rooms in the public library building. Two of them contain portraits and landscapes of local interest, which are occasionally stored to allow of temporary exhibitions being held. Antiquities, coins, birds and other natural history specimens are to be seen in the other rooms, with ship models and other objects related to two maritime enterprises in which Peterhead has taken a leading part: the whaling industry in the nineteenth century, and fishing.

Collections of considerable interest are to be seen in Elgin and Forres. Until recently both had the character of small general museums, packed to the doors and ceilings with a great diversity of objects. The Falconer Museum at Forres is still a 'cabinet of curiosities', almost surrealist in its association of objects and far from scientific in its arrangement. Though it may cause the modern museum man to wonder, it remains a testimony to the capacity of a heterogeneous collection to excite that response in an Admass Society. At Elgin, although the Museum is rich in local Old Red Sandstone fish fossils and ecclesiastical relics, the interest tended to be concentrated upon its massive mammalian skulls, and its shrunken human one. The collections have recently been completely re-organised. Elgin has become predominantly a local museum, with attractive displays designed to appeal to both the mind and the eye, to stimulate the curiosity and to enlarge the local knowledge of the people of Elgin and visitors to the Burgh—a tribute to the inspiration and financial assistance of the Joint Committee of the Museums Association and the Carnegie United Kingdom Trust, and the freely given expert help of the great national institutions in Edinburgh.

The Carnegie Trust have also been active in carrying out a re-organisation scheme at the museum of Banff and it is understood that they will be shortly giving assistance to Inverurie to improve the one-room museum which is to be found within its library building.

THE HIGHLAND FOLK MUSEUM
AT KINGUSSIE

In 1954 the Pilgrim Trust bought the house and collections of Dr. I. F. Grant and gave them to the four Scottish Universities. During the seven summer seasons since then the museum has been trebled in size and in scope by gifts, by the purchase of neighbouring buildings and land, and by the erection of a large building which houses a representative agricultural collection.

The aim of the Scottish Universities is to make this a comprehensive and permanent collection in the Highlands of all things Highland of the past which will appeal to students and visitors of all nationalities. Pending the time when funds and donations have accumulated to build other and varied dwellings there is on view in the old shooting lodge, in the new farm building, and in Churchill (the neighbouring house given by the Lady MacRobert Douneside Foundation) a fine collection of Highland antiquities. An island-type Black House with a little clack mill beside it are also furnished and on view in the fields below the buildings.

In 1961, through the continued generosity of the Douneside Trust, the museum was able to buy the Church Hall opposite the entrance gate making possible storage while other buildings were being arranged and enlarged. This hall will be of great use in the future as exhibition space and for various other purposes.

The collections are partly on loan but are being steadily increased by gift and by purchase. Each year in October all exhibits are put in store, and in the following April a different show is arranged, thus ensuring that all articles used are twice handled and cleaned every year. All repairs and treatments are seen to during the winter so that a fresh and varied selection is ready each May. New exhibits can then be introduced among old friends and articles under treatment can be given a rest while under observation.

The site of the Museum at Kingussie in the heart of Badenoch looks across the Spey to Ruthven and the great range of the Cairngorms. Half across Scotland and due west of Aberdeen it is midway between the Moray Firth at Nairn and Fort William in the West.

Attendances at the Museum have risen from 2,500 adults in 1955 to over 9,500 in 1961, plus large numbers of children either with their parents or in school parties. These school groups have come from as far as Southampton and South Wales. Adults of all nationalities have visited the Museum from Europe, America, and the Commonwealth.

The Committee of Management responsible for the development of the Museum is composed of representatives of the four Scottish Universities, the Scottish Museums, and the Scottish Tourist Board. The first Chairman was Sir Thomas Taylor, late Principal of Aberdeen University. Any enquiries about visits by parties should be addressed to Mr. Davidson, the Curator, who will be pleased to welcome all visitors. The Museum is open 1st May to 30th September, Monday to Saturday 10-1 and 2-5. Admission for adults, 1/-; children free if accompanied by someone in charge.

SCIENTISTS OF THE REGION

THE sketch that follows is intended to deal with the human aspects of scientific culture in the North-East. This culture has been promoted no less by scientists who have come from other regions than by those who have sprung from its own bleak but not ungenerous soil. Some of the former like JAMES CLERK MAXWELL have in the course of a few years' sojourn played a vital part in its development. By contrast some of the latter like DAVID GREGORY have left its borders before they were old enough to have any recognisable influence upon its growth; but it would be rash to assume that their later influence bore no marks of the folk from which they sprang or the schools and universities where they learnt to tread the paths of learning. An attempt will therefore be made to bring to the notice of visiting members of the British Association the names of those who from the earliest times down to the present day (only saving the blushes of those who still labour in the cause of science!) have contributed in any notable way to this culture. Many worthy names (especially in the latter days) must perforce be omitted. And since the corresponding article of 1934 (to which the writer is greatly indebted) can still be consulted, many of the pioneers will here receive but passing mention in order that those who were still alive at the time of the earlier survey may now receive their rightful recognition.

Though the Bull of Erection of the University of Aberdeen (to be known almost from the beginning also as King's College) contained provision for a Faculty of Medicine, there is no convincing evidence of any activity that could be called 'scientific' until near the end of the sixteenth century. In 1568, however, there was printed in Edinburgh *Ane Breve Descriptioun of the Pest quhair in the Causis Signis and sum speciall Preservatioun and care thairof are contenit*, by Gilbert Skene, third Mediciner of King's College: hardly a work of scientific medicine, but temperate and critical to a degree not attained by many of his more famous continental contemporaries. Less than ten years later JAMES CHEYNE (d. 1602) was writing text books for his students in the newly founded University of Douai of such a character as to prove that he recognised the necessity for individual practical work as a basis for fruitful study of astronomy: he records the result of his own efforts to measure the latitude of Old Aberdeen when a student of King's College. Before the end of the century there flourished the first progenitor of the hereditary genius transmitted during nearly three centuries in the 'Academic Gregories'. The first and greatest GREGORY was JAMES, F.R.S. (b. 1638), inventor of the first reflecting telescope and a mathematician able to hold his own in discussions with both Newton and Huygens. But such has been the wall-eyed prejudice in favour of patrilinear descent of genius that it is not generally mentioned that the origin of the 'Gregorian' talent for mathematics was established in the family of James's mother. Herself noted for this talent when it was rare indeed for a woman to be able to demonstrate such a gift, she was a daughter of DAVID ANDERSON, a worthy representative of that class of 'mathematical practitioners' who were the equivalent of the modern engineer, and closely related to ALEXANDER ANDERSON. The last-named, who described himself as 'Abredonensis', passed most of his life in Paris, where he edited some post-humously printed works of his friend François Viète, the greatest algebraist before Descartes, and left one or two small but elegant works of his own.

JAMES GREGORY's brother, DAVID, Librarian of Marischal College and University, Laird of Kinnordy, and described by James as 'in Mathematicis non parum versatus' had an even greater son, DAVID, to whom reference will be made later.

Roughly contemporary with the Andersons was DUNCAN LIDDEL, born in Aberdeen in 1561, Master of Arts of King's College and Rostock, Doctor of Medicine of Helmstadt. An engaging polymath rather than a creative genius he nevertheless was probably the first to master, and to teach at Rostock, Frankfurt-on-Oder and Helmstadt the Ptolemaic, Copernican and Tychonic systems of the world. He died too soon (1613) to pronounce on the astounding revelations of Galileo's *Nuncius Sidereus* or Kepler's *Astronomia nova*. His influence on science in the North-East can not be gauged, since it took the form of the endowment of the second Chair of Mathematics in Great Britain (Henry Savile's at Oxford was the first) and six bursaries, both at Marischal College; to which university he also left his splendid library. The union of this with the library of THOMAS READ put Marischal College well ahead of the older King's and probably of any institution in Scotland, despite the fact that King's received part of the library of ALEXANDER READ, Thomas's brother. Both were doctors of medicine but Alexander Read continued to profess it. He wrote one of the earliest text books of anatomy on the Vesalian model, lectured to the College of Surgeons of London and showed by his annotations that he had carefully studied Harvey's recently published *De Motu Cordis*.

Liddel's literary executor was PATRICK DUN (d. 1699), who would find no place in this record but for the fact that the diploma (1607) declaring him Doctor of Medicine of the University of Basel signed by Felix Plater, one of the founders of that famous school of anatomy, hangs in the University Library. A near contemporary of Dun at Basel was JAMES CARGILL (thesis—1594), the first recorded Scottish botanist, pupil of Caspar Bauhin, who recorded his gratitude to Cargill for the gift of specimens. A more notable botanist of this period, ROBERT MORISON (1620-83), after graduating at Marischal College in 1638, acted for some time as Joint Keeper of the gardens of the Duke of Orleans at Blois. Charles II, perhaps recalling that Morison had been wounded in his father's cause at the battle near the Brig o' Dee, made him his personal physician and superintendent of the Royal Gardens. But his greatest service to botany was made as first Danvers Professor of Botany at Oxford, where he is said to have lectured in the Physic Garden at a table covered with specimens. Tournefort praised him highly for having brought order into the still somewhat confused classification of plants (he clarified the distinction between *genus* and *species* and used dichotomous keys), but regretted his egotistical failure to give credit to others. Robert is not to be confused with THOMAS MORE(I)SON (c. 1558 - c. 1603), author of a book contesting the Paracelsian theory of the origin of metals. Two followers (a century after the master's death) of Paracelsus were MATTHEW MACKAILE senior (d. 1696), whose works on mineral waters are not without interest for the student of the origins of ' scientific ' chemistry; and, of greater renown, WILLIAM DAVIDSON (c. 1593 - c. 1670). After graduating at the recently founded Marischal College Davidson (or d'Avissone, as he liked to call himself!) became successively Professor of Chemistry and Superintendent of the Jardin du Roi in Paris and later personal physician to the Royal House of Poland. He was almost certainly the first British native to hold an official ' Chair ' of Chemistry, a subject that he taught in such a way as to excite the admiration of John Evelyn and Thomas Hobbes, who both ' sat under him ' in Paris. *Philosophia pyrotechnica* is his best known book.

In 1661 was born DAVID GREGORY, F.R.S., nephew of James. After a short spell in Marischal College he went to graduate at Edinburgh where he became Professor of Mathematics at the age of 23. Three years later Newton's *Principia* was published and before the year was out the young professor had commenced his running commentary on this immortal work and certainly before 1691 was expounding the new ' philosophy ' to his students. In that year he left to become Savilian Professor of Astronomy at Oxford. He has generally been regarded and with justice as an astronomer who never made an observation. But a man of whom his referee, Sir Isaac Newton, wrote, ' I do account him . . . in mathematiques a great artist ' is not lightly to be ignored. As scholar (first definitive Greek text of Euclid's Στοιχεια), expositor (first advanced textbook of astronomy and geometrical optics on Newtonian lines), innovator (one of the first to handle Newtonian ' fluxions ' with ease and effectiveness), he served his generation in a manner surpassed only by Edmund Halley. His critical *Notae* (a contemporary transcript was discovered among the GREGORY MSS. gifted to the University by Sir Ian Forbes-Leith of Fyvie) played a part in the preparation of the second edition of the *Principia*, which has only recently been fully recognised. His son, DAVID, became Dean of Christ Church and first Regius Professor of Modern History.

David Gregory died in 1708; nine years later two young men were according to a then not uncommon custom undergoing ten days' examination (one of the examiners being Charles Gregory of St. Andrews), in competition for the Liddel Chair of Mathematics in Marischal College. The successful candidate was COLIN MACLAURIN, F.R.S. (1698-1746), who two years later took the MS. of his *Geometria Organica* to London, where a second time Newton was induced to testify to the mathematical virtuosity of one who had sojourned in Aberdeen. 'Sojourned', alas, is all that may be claimed for MacLaurin: from Argyll and the philosophic rigour of Robert Simson's geometry class he came, and to the Edinburgh Chair in 1725 he went, leaving no very clearly attested mark on Aberdeen except the record of a rebuke for having too long neglected the duties of his chair.

Not the least of MacLaurin's services to science was the writing of an admirable *Account of Sir Isaac Newton's Philosophical Discoveries*. This work, however, belonging rather to the *haute vulgarisation*, there was room for an exposition at a more popular level. The demand for such works two centuries ago comparable to that for 'popular science' today is shown by the appearance of three such books on astronomy and mechanics whose editions totalled twelve within a span of twenty years. The author was JAMES FERGUSON, F.R.S., born (1710) in the parish of Rothiemay, Banffshire, to parents so poor that his formal schooling was limited to three months at Keith Grammar School. But so lively was his native wit that during his leisure hours as a shepherd he studied from books the movements of the heavenly bodies and mastered the craft of representing them by means of mechanical models. Yet it was as a portrait painter that he gained sufficient notice by people of substance to be given the means of study in Edinburgh. Unable to support himself on an adequate scale he removed to London in the hope of finding a market for the products of his two skills; but it was his mechanical bent, allied to a mastery of exposition both in writing and in public lectures, that brought him fame and a measure of wealth. For this happy issue the granting of an annuity by that far-seeing monarch George III may have been decisive.

Two other sons of the North-East, ALEXANDER MALCOLM and WILLIAM TRAILL, made important contributions to the extension of mathematical education necessary for the appreciation of the 'mathematical philosophy'. The former's treatise on Arithmetic was described by De Morgan as 'one of the most extensive and erudite books of the eighteenth century'; the latter published in 1778 *Elements of Algebra for the use of Schools and Universities*.

So far in our survey we have taken account of medical men only in so far as they have gained distinction in fields related to those within the province of the British Association, and this in general must remain our principle of selection. But of one physician of the eighteenth century an exception must be made: this was JOHN GREGORIE, F.R.S. (1724-73), as he usually signed himself in the books now standing in the Gregory Collection in the University Library. He was a grandson of the great James, and after a period of practice in London he became successively Mediciner at King's College (1756), and Professor of the Practice of Physic at Edinburgh (1766). Though it is mainly as the 'source' of some of the finest scientific works of the seventeenth and eighteenth centuries in our library that he gains a place in this gallery of scientific worthies it might perhaps be claimed that in his lectures on the *Duties and Qualities of a Physician* he was doing some pioneering thinking on the relation of fundamental sciences to clinical practice, and his *Comparative view of the State and Faculties of Man with those of the Animal World* stood in a similar relation to modern comparative psychology.

Likewise to the physician and surgeon, SIR WILLIAM FORDYCE, F.R.S. (1724-92), must be accorded a welcome for his scientific foresight in endowing a lectureship at Marischal College ' recommending an examination of the soil of all Earths, Minerals, and Metals found in the county of Aberdeen in the beds of Rivers Rocks and that are likely to be of public use '. This might have been the first British foundation for Agricultural Chemistry, but the vitality of two legatees having a prior claim on the ' liferent' postponed its implementation for nearly fifty years. After the fusion of the two universities it was merged in the present Strathcona-Fordyce Chair of Agriculture. Sir William's nephew, GEORGE FORDYCE, F.R.S. (1736-1802), has a direct claim to our notice in that he not only carried the spirit of William Cullen's chemistry teaching to London but also carried out what may be the earliest demonstration of the thermo-regulatory office of the sweat glands: he (and later Sir Charles Blagden) were able to remain for some minutes without serious discomfort in a room the air of which was so hot as to be cooking a steak!

Fire may suggest firearms, ' improved ' in an epoch-making manner by ALEXANDER J. FORSYTH (1769-1843), minister of Belhelvie, near Aberdeen: this was the invention of the percussion lock and the replacement of the ancient flint and steel by fulminate of mercury. He succeeded in establishing the value of his invention by experiments in the Tower of London in 1806. A memorial tablet was placed there in 1929 and a replica in King's College in 1931.

Before the close of the eighteenth century a move was made in Aberdeen towards the establishment of a Medical School providing systematic instruction in the sciences ancillary to the practice of medicine which at that time was learned at the Infirmary. Although only eighteen, young (Sir) JAMES MCGRIGOR (d. 1858) was from the first the leading figure in the formation in 1789 of an active group who in 1811 took the title of the Aberdeen Medico-Chirurgical Society. From the Peninsula, in the intervals of converting the Duke of Wellington to his scheme for the reorganisation of army medical services, he continued by advice and generous gifts to ensure the survival of the group. He became the first Director-General of Army Medical Services in 1815; his portrait by Dyce hangs in the Court Room of Marischal College, where he graduated in Arts in 1788. About the same time ALEXANDER GORDON (1752-99) was demonstrating in the Infirmary the necessity for cleanliness in the prevention of puerperal fever—a lesson lost on the medical profession until after Semmelweiss had lost his reason in the vain attempt to convert his Viennese colleagues.

In the class of 1787-91 at Marischal College was one of the most famous of her sons, though owing presumably to his early journeys to the ends of the earth this connection with Aberdeen seems little known. ROBERT BROWN, F.R.S. (1773-1858) was born at Montrose. Though probably one of the greatest systematic botanists of all time, to the majority of scientists he is known merely as an adjective attached to the perpetual motion of minute particles, observed almost casually by him in a preparation of pollen grains and now universally regarded as the most direct evidence for the molecular-kinetic theory of matter.

The turn of the century is not marked by the presence in the University of any men eminent in natural science, but in 1805 was born at Braemar JOHN LAMONT, who as Johann von Lamont became Professor of Astronomy in Munich. Since he left Scotland for Germany at the age of twelve his distinguished career calls for no comment here.

It may have been noticed that in an age that witnessed the activities further south of Cullen, Black, Rutherford and Hope, there were in our region no names familiar to the chemist. GEORGE FORDYCE's knowledge and teaching were of a quality to command such notice but they were exercised wholly in London. By 1840, however, both universities were to include among their teachers chemists of undoubted merit. Neither indeed was a native of the North-East, but whereas THOMAS CLARK (1801-67) was born in Ayr, WILLIAM GREGORY, F.R.S. (1803-58), though born in Edinburgh, was the grandson of John mentioned above. Clark, Professor of Chemistry at Marischal College from 1833, gave his name to the method of softening 'temporarily' hard water with lime. Gregory, Mediciner at King's College from 1839, found there insufficient scope for the chemistry he had learnt from Liebig at Giessen; so despite the pleasant 'manse' built for him opposite King's College (still standing, though somewhat marred by additions) he moved on to Edinburgh, where he virtually founded the teaching of organic chemistry in Great Britain. To chemists it is unnecessary to comment on the fact that his text-book on organic chemistry was translated into German. One other shadowy figure has been brought to light—or half light—within the last year. In 1765 a WILLIAM CRUIKSHANK graduated at King's College; was he the CRUIKSHANK whose pioneering experiments in electrochemistry, rivalling Davy's in importance, have until recently been attributed to the contemporary surgeon, William Cumberland Cruickshank?

In the same decade as Clark and Gregory was born JAMES NICOL (1810-79) who while Professor of Natural History at Marischal College challenged at the Aberdeen Meeting of the British Association in 1859 Murchison's theory of the origin of the Highland schists. At the time no one was convinced; but posterity upheld his interpretation. Two of his contemporaries were JAMES

D. FORBES, F.R.S. (1809-68) and ALLEN THOMSON, F.R.S. (1809-84). Forbes had
but a vicarious association with Aberdeen as a formative influence in the
scientific life of Aberdeen's greatest ' associate ', James Clerk Maxwell; but
being generally reckoned as one of the founders of the British Association
(though only twenty-two at the time) he could hardly be omitted. Thomson
was Professor of Anatomy at Marischal College 1839-41; but it was mainly
in Edinburgh that as extramural teacher and Professor of Anatomy he gained
great reputation—a reputation that for some inexplicable reason seems hardly
to have survived into this century, which is all the more remarkable since
d'Arcy Power regarded him as the ' first great *biological* teacher before
Huxley '.

In the year that Thomson left the anatomy chair at Marischal College
WILLIAM MacGILLIVRAY (1796-1852) was appointed to that of Natural History.
Born at Old Aberdeen and graduating at King's College he is generally
regarded as the greatest naturalist of North-Eastern stock and nurture. With
ten years of experience as Servitor of the Museum of the Royal College of
Surgeons of Edinburgh he was able to make great progress in the creation of
the Zoological Museum still housed at Marischal College. His *History of
British Birds* is one of the great foundation works in the subject, and of no
less importance are the systematic descriptions attached to Audubon's *Ornitho-
logical Biographies*. Before MacGillivray the most notable natural historians
had been those without academic connections: GEORGE LOW (1747-95), who
accompanied Sir Joseph Banks to the Orkneys in 1772, and THOMAS EDWARD
(1814-86), a man of exceptional talents, who in the process of accumulating
a large collection, discovered twenty new species of sessile-eyed crustacea;
he became Curator of the Museum in the Banff Institute. Also concerned
with beasts, but from the agricultural angle, were JAMES CLARK (1734-1806),
a pioneer in ' scientific ' veterinary surgery, and WILLIAM MCCOMBIE (1805-80),
of international renown in cattle breeding without benefit of genetics.

Of the many notable additions to natural knowledge made by country
doctors, ministers, schoolmasters, etc., space allows only of the mention of
Dr. WILLIAM MACKIE (1856-1908), whose discovery of the fossil-bearing peat
bog at Rhynie made possible the later epoch-making researches of Kidston
and Lang on *Rhynia*, the earliest plant of which there is definite evidence.

Almost a century after he had ceased to work within the walls of Marischal
College, the University of Aberdeen erected a memorial to the greatest name
upon their roll. In the relief set upon the walls of the Picture Gallery the artist
(Mr. C. d'O. Pilkington Jackson) has with great sensitivity caught that
harmony of impish wit and high resolve that characterised the young Professor
of Natural Philosophy, JAMES CLERK MAXWELL, F.R.S. (1831-79). Nurtured in
Forbes's laboratory and Kelland's mathematical class, with his philosophical
insight deepened in the Logic Class of the oft-maligned Sir William Hamilton,
he was placed second wrangler and bracketed with the Senior Wrangler for

the Smith's Prize at Cambridge. He remained only four years at Marischal College, but despite an unquestioned devotion to the interests of his pupils, some of whom must have been of rather intractable stuff, his genius was such as to enable him to compose the magnificent demonstration of the particulate structure of Saturn's Rings—a problem involving an immense amount of arithmetical drudgery as well as the foreshadowing of those special methods of the probability calculus that enabled him to establish with far greater rigour than hitherto the fundamental equation of statistical thermo-dynamics. This more spectacular later achievement, first announced at the Aberdeen Meeting in 1859,* and that of the dynamical theory of the electromagnetic field, have tended to divert attention from the earlier; and especially from the fact that it was carried through in Aberdeen aided by a 'very neat model' of his theoretical ring, 'a credit to Aberdeen workmen'.

During the latter part of his stay in Aberdeen Maxwell was a somewhat amused spectator of the not very elevating squabbles between the 'unionists' (of the two *universities*) and the 'fusionists', in whose plan all academic posts would be cast into the melting pot without distinction of collegiate vested interest. It was a near run thing but the fusionists triumphed and Maxwell was one of the victims. There is, however, no doubt about the justice of the decision: Professor DAVID THOMSON (1817-80) of King's College had indeed published little; but he was an accomplished teacher who had served the University long and wisely in the difficult years of Scottish university reform.

So Maxwell went off to King's College, London, but not before his teaching had made a deep impression on at least one young man who was to attain to eminence in science. This was (Sir) DAVID GILL, F.R.S. (1843-1914), who took advantage of the phenomenally successful 'extra-mural' mathematical coaching of DAVID RENNET and the lectures of both professors of natural philosophy. After graduation Gill studied chronometry at Besançon to enable him to take his place in the long established family business in Aberdeen. But an invitation by James Ludovic Lindsay, Earl of Crawford and Balcarres, F.R.S. (1847-1913), to act as Superintendent of his newly constructed observatory at Dunecht set his feet on the ladder that led to the post of H.M. Astronomer at the Cape and the Presidency of the British Association (1907).

Born in the same year as David Gill was (Sir) DAVID FERRIER, F.R.S. (d. 1928), who after graduating in the 'new' university in 1863 completed his education in Edinburgh. But though it was in London that the greater part of his life was passed, the microscope with which he carried out his almost fabulous researches on the anatomy and physiology of the brain is to be seen in the Library of Marischal College.

* At the same meeting Lord Kelvin actually *measured* the earth's electrostatic gradient on the Links. One cannot avoid regretting the passing of the adventurous spontaneity of the Heroic Age of the British Association, when the Secretaries might sit up half the night preparing the programme for the following day.

Among the professors of the new University of Aberdeen were GEORGE DICKIE, F.R.S. (1812-82), first Professor of Botany, author of the *Flora Aberdonensis* (1838) and *Botanists' Guide to the Counties of Aberdeen, Banff and Kincardine* (1860), and ALEXANDER BAIN (1818-1903) who, though Professor of Logic and English, gained international renown as one of the pioneers who recognised the necessity for a *science* of psychology based on experience and controlled by experiment.

Likewise among the students to graduate soon after the fusion were two who took advantage of the new dispensation of graduation in Medicine without prior graduation in Arts. (Sir) ALEXANDER OGSTON (1849-1929) became Regius Professor of Surgery in 1882 and played a leading part in extending the use of Lister's antiseptic spray. This was based on sound bacteriological knowledge evidenced by his discovery and naming (for which he obtained credit only in Germany) of the *Staphylococcus pyogenes aureus.* His work on the stone circles of Cromar may appear a little amateurish by modern standards but was a striking achievement for a busy surgeon, soldier and administrator. His fellow student, (Sir) PATRICK MANSON, F.R.S. (1844-1922), has good claims to that much abused term, ' father ' of Tropical Medicine; what is beyond doubt is his ' fathering ' of the idea in the mind of Ronald Ross that the mosquito played an essential part in the transmission of malaria. In the same tradition were Sir WILLIAM J. R. SIMPSON and WILLIAM BULLOCH, F.R.S. (1863-1941). The former was the first Medical Officer of Health for Calcutta, and was notable for his contributions to the conquest of plague; the latter gave his name to the Bulloch jar for the cultivation of anaerobic micro-organisms and was famous for his studies of serology and haemophilia. Nor were they the last distinguished men to go forth from the North-East to battle with unseen foes: schooled at Banff Academy and graduating first in Arts and finally (1902) in the recently introduced ' combined ' degree of B.Sc. and M.B.,Ch.B., (Sir) JOHN C. D. LEDINGHAM, F.R.S. (1875-1944), became Director of the Lister Institute in London and is well known for his development of the National Collection of Type Cultures.

In the space that remains it will be necessary to restrict our notice to those who have made their mark on the world of science, though this involves the omission of some of the professors of the ' new ' University, without whose devoted and often inspired teaching science might have been much the poorer. And in respect of this relatively recent past it seems proper to review these names according to subjects, though the education and achievements of several of them happily transcended the narrowly spaced frontiers with which our future culture is threatened!

Botany

The three distinguished botanists we have to consider had much in common: all were Aberdeen graduates; all were systematists in the ' classical ' style, proving their abilities in studies of tropical flora; all were elected Fellows of the Royal Society. But whereas J. W. H. TRAIL (1851-1919) had laid the basis of his future work (by a masterly collection while acting as medical adviser to an expedition to the Amazon) before he became Professor of Botany at the age of twenty-six, Sir GEORGE KING (1840-1909) and Sir DAVID PRAIN (1857-1944) spent a considerable part of their lives in India. The former was the first Superintendent of the Royal Botanic Garden at Calcutta and pioneer in the economic extraction of quinine: the latter followed King at Calcutta but became Director of Kew in 1905.

Chemistry

In contrast to the three botanists the careers of the chemists, THOMAS CARNELLEY (1852-90), FRANCIS R. JAPP, F.R.S. (1848-1925), and FREDERICK SODDY, F.R.S. (1877-1956), had hardly anything in common. Graduates of different universities and with widely different interests within the field of chemistry, they left diverse impressions on the University of Aberdeen. Carnelley's liberal and far-seeing views on the importance of chemistry, both as an independent discipline and as a factor of growing importance in technological change, have been widely praised; but his equally important contribution to chemical knowledge is little known. Yet Mendeléeff thought that his two volumes of *Physico-Chemical Constants* placed him in the front rank of those whose work had extended the application of the Periodic System. Japp, on the other hand, has been described as existing in an Olympian detachment from mundane affairs. And, just as William Gregory had brought some of the atmosphere of Giessen to Scotland, so Japp planted the seeds of the more mature organic chemistry he had collected at Heidelberg (Bunsen) and Bonn (Kekulé). Though Carnelley rated research as high as the dissemination of knowledge it was Japp who established the first research school in chemistry at Aberdeen.

Of the peculiar genius of Frederick Soddy it is in the writer's opinion too soon to make any final assessment. When he succeeded Japp in 1914 he had already completed the work for which the world of science will always remember him with admiration—the chemical demonstration of the existence of isotopic elements—and for which together with his distinguished contribution to the work initiated by Rutherford in Montreal and Ramsay in London he was in 1921 elected the first English-born Nobel Laureate in Chemistry. Dr. J. A. Cranston, Soddy's colleague in both Glasgow and Aberdeen, believed that the outbreak of war in 1914 was for him a shattering experience: thereafter his life was passed in an atmosphere of controversy amounting at times to acrimony; his major intellectual concern was with the social relations of science and the problem of power implicit in these. His pioneer studies of real wealth and its relation to credit and exchange, by most of his colleagues regarded as an unfortunate aberration, may conceivably be looked back upon by historians of the future as of more far-reaching and unique significance—however faulty in detail—than his work as a radiochemist.

Physics

Most distinguished of the early professors of Natural Philosophy in the new University was CHARLES NIVEN, F.R.S. (1845-1923), born at Peterhead into a family of outstanding mathematical talent: four of the sons became Wranglers (Charles being Senior in 1867) and his brother, (Sir) William (who edited Maxwell's *Collected Works*), also F.R.S. After an early career marked by distinguished contributions to the theory of wave motion and the propagation of heat and electricity Charles was probably the unfortunate victim of the new dispensation which gave the Professors of Natural Philosophy little time for original work.

Although an astronomical observatory has been associated with one or other of the Departments of Natural Philosophy since 1780 and from almost the beginning had been equipped with meteorological instruments, it was not till the early decades of the present century that its most distinguished contribution to science was made in the form of the well known cloud studies made by GEORGE AUBOURNE CLARKE (1879-1949).

Another distinguished worker in physics—he is better known as Professor of Mathematics at Edinburgh (1879-1911) and as the author of a famous text-book on algebra—was GEORGE CHRYSTAL (1851-1911), who after graduating at Aberdeen became Second Wrangler and Smith's Prizeman. He also holds an uncommon place in the annals of the Royal Society since for his work on the oscillations of the waters of lakes he received a Royal Medal, though never a Fellow. Also awarded a Royal Medal for theoretical physics while he was Professor of Mathematics—in this case at Aberdeen—was HECTOR MACDONALD (1865-1935). He had already been elected to the Royal Society in 1901; after graduating at Aberdeen and being placed Fourth Wrangler at Cambridge he had remained as Fellow of Clare College for fourteen years. His early work in mathematical physics was mainly concerned with the recently discovered 'Hertzian' waves.

Zoology

Although never receiving the customary marks of recognition from his colleagues as an authority in a particular field of discovery (though with an expert knowledge of the *Alcyonaria*), (Sir) JOHN ARTHUR THOMSON (1861-1933) will be remembered as one of the great naturalists of the first half of the twentieth century; it is to be hoped that the *genus* will not be exterminated by the change of environment likely to be characteristic of the second half. The titles of many of his works were household words, as were those written in collaboration with that other remarkable man, Sir Patrick Geddes. Almost as well known at least in Scotland was Thomson's successor JAMES RITCHIE (1882-1958) who, if he left no distinctive mark on zoological science, studied with great assiduity and communicated with charm the influence of man on the salmon river and the farm. Born, nurtured and educated in the North-East, he left a living memorial in the movement to found the Aberdeen Regional Museum, a feature of the Municipal Art Gallery and Museum. He was President of the Royal Society of Edinburgh 1954-8. Graduating at Aberdeen in 1884, (Sir) P. CHALMERS MITCHELL, F.R.S. (1864-1945) will be remembered as the Secretary of the Zoological Society of London mainly responsible for the development of the zoological park at Whipsnade.

Medical Sciences

Of the many eminent men who have lent their distinction to these subjects it is possible to mention only four—representative of Anatomy, Pathology and Physiology—three of whom virtually created their respective disciplines in Aberdeen.

Of Sir JOHN STRUTHERS (1823-1899) it is only necessary to say to anyone entering the Anatomy Building *Si monumentum requiris circumspice*—even to the magnificent museum of comparative anatomy, especially the Selachians, prepared with his own hands and those of his devoted assistant, Robert Gibb.

DAVID J. HAMILTON, F.R.S. (1849-1909), first Professor of Pathology (one of the scientific advances Struthers had fought for), gained world-wide reputation as pioneer in the aetiology of diphtheria and typhoid fever in man and as the discoverer of the organisms responsible for braxy and ' louping ill ' in sheep. His text-book (1889-94) set a standard in English works on Pathology.

J. A. MacWILLIAM, F.R.S. (1857-1937), was not the first Professor of Physiology. Nevertheless, since after graduating at Aberdeen he became a pupil of Ludwig at Leipzig and of (Sir) Edward Sharpey-Schäfer in London, he was well fitted on appointment to the Chair in 1886 to introduce the spirit of the ' new ' physiology—that of experimental biology. His own work—on cardiac muscle—mirrored this spirit; it was comparative; it was pursued down to the histological units; and it employed chemical and electrical means of stimulation.

With whom could we better end this necessarily sketchy account of Science in the North-East of Scotland than with JOHN J. R. MACLEOD, F.R.S. (1876-1935), the only scientist of North-Eastern stock and culture to have received (with Sir John Banting) a Nobel award? Although born at Cluny in Perthshire he was educated at Aberdeen Grammar School and the University. His fundamental researches on carbohydrate metabolism were the bridge between the discovery in 1889 by von Mering and Minkowski of the essential part played by the pancreas in *diabetes mellitus* and the isolation by Banting and Best* in his own laboratory in Toronto of the hormone insulin.

   * Professor E. W. H. Cruickshank, Macleod's successor in the Chair of Physiology, has recently reminded us of a remarkable demonstration by two Aberdeen workers, T. FRASER and J. RENNIE, of the presence of an essential factor in the islet tissue of the pancreas seventeen years before the dramatic isolation of this 'factor' by Banting and Best.

INDEX

Streets and local names within Aberdeen City not indexed.

Aberchirder, 195
Aberdeen, 23, 33, 35, 60, 79, 81-5, 127-8, 134-5, 137-8, 140-52, 159-71, 173-5, 179-81, 185-94, 196, 206-7, 209-14, 224, 226-36
Aberlour, 195
Alford basin, 22, 29, 89
Alltcailleach, 121, 125
Anderson, Alexander, 241
Anguston, 88
Ardoe, 72
Assich, 121
Auchindoir, 83
Aultmore, 21, 93, 121

Bain, Alexander, 248
Ballater, 95, 97
Ballindalloch, 125
Ballochbuie, 58, 118, 121
Balmoral, 49
Banchory, 68, 195, 214
Banff, 35, 81, 209, 214, 237
Balmedie, 23, 40
Ben Avon, 9
Ben Macdhui, 17, 27, 32, 35, 47, 55
Bennachie, 8, 9, 17, 20, 29, 75, 93, 121
Ben Rinnes, 8
Bin, The, 121, 126
Blackall, 121
Boyndie, 39
Braemar, 6, 29, 35, 48-9, 55
Braeriach, 32
Brimmond Hills, 17, 24
Brown, Robert, 245
Buckie, 138, 143, 150, 152, 183
Bucksburn, 221-3
Bullers o' Buchan, 25
Bulloch, William, 248

Cabrach, 28, 89
Cairngorms, 17, 20, 28, 32, 49, 54-6, 185
Cairnie, 94
Cargill, James, 241

Carnelley, Thomas, 249
Catterline, 25
Cawdor, 119, 125
Cheyne, James, 240
Chrystal, George, 250
Clark, James, 246
Clark, Thomas, 245
Clarke, George A., 250
Clashindarroch, 44, 121, 126
Clatt, 94
Clinterty, 24
Clova, 77
Coilacreich, 94
Correen Hills, 17, 29, 93
Cothal, 174
Covesea, 25
Craibstone, 38, 109, 221
Crathes, 85
Cromar, 21-2
Cruden Bay, 79, 97
Cruickshank, William, 245
Culbin, 47, 121, 123, 126
Culblean, 82
Cullen, 25, 81, 83, 97
Cullen, Bin of, 6, 30, 43
Culter, 21, 24, 176-9
Cuminestown, 96
Cushnie, 121

Dallas, 95
Darnaway, 118-9, 125
Dava, 21, 24
Davan, Loch, 24, 62
Davidson, William, 242
Daviot, 73, 89
Dee, River, 24, 28, 33, 55, 62, 138
Deer, Abbey of, 76-7, 79
Deer, Forest of, 121, 126
Delgaty, 121
Deskford, 83
Deveron, River, 28, 62, 89
Dickie, George, 248
Dinnet, 24

Don, Bridge of, 23
Don, River, 21, 24, 28-9, 62, 173-5
Drumtochty, 121, 126
Dufftown, 95
Duffus, 80
Dun, Patrick, 241
Dunnideer, 75
Dunnottar, 25, 84-5
Dunphail, 125
Durn Hill, 6
Durris, 24, 121, 125-6
Dyce, 33-4, 180

Edzell, 31
Elchies, 121, 126
Elgin, 10, 176, 183, 195, 209, 236-7
Ellon, 81
Elphinstone, Bishop, 83
Esk, North, River, 28, 31, 62, 138
Esk, South, River, 28, 138
Etchachan, Loch, 55

Ferguson, James, 243
Ferness, 121
Ferrier, Sir David, 247
Fetterangus, 173
Fetteresso, 121, 126
Feugh, 21
Fichlie, 80
Fiddich, 28
Fife Hills, 23
Findhorn, River, 31, 48
Findon, 93
Fochabers, 95, 97, 183-4
Forbes, James D., 246
Fordyce, George, 244-5
Fordyce, Sir William, 244
Forres, 236-7
Forsyth, Alexander J., 244
Forvie, 26, 47-8, 63
Foudland Hills, 7, 21, 29
Foveran, 92
Fowlsheugh, 63
Fraser, T., 252
Fraserburgh, 133, 137-8, 150, 152, 170-2,
    181-3, 213
Fyvie, 85

Gairn River, 17
Gardenstown, 97

Garioch, 21, 67, 94
Garron Point, 25
Gill, Sir David, 247
Glen Avon, 22, 118, 121
Glen Clova, 22
Glen Cluny, 6, 28
Glen Derry, 24, 28, 35
Glendye, 125
Glen Ey, 28
Glen Grant, 157-8
Glenlivet, 35, 121, 126, 154, 157-8
Glenmore, 24, 185
Glen Muick, 28
Glentanar, 49, 58, 118, 121
Gordon, Alexander, 244-5
Gordon Castle, 125
Gourdon, 70
Grandholm Mills, 174-5
Grantown-on-Spey, 49, 95
' Gregories, Academic ', 240-5

Hamilton, David J., 251
Harlaw, 82
Hill of Fare, 8, 17, 29
Hill of Fisherie, 10
Huntly, 84, 97-8, 175

Inchmarlo, 125
Inchrory, 48
Inglismaldie, 121
Insch, 8, 69, 89, 94
Inverbervie, 195
Invernochty, 80
Inverurie, 80-1, 98, 172, 177-8, 214
Isla River, 89

Japp, Francis R., 249

Keith, 96, 175-6
Kemnay, 9, 121, 160-1
Kildrummy, 81
Kilravoch, 121
Kincardine O'Neil, 79, 98
King, Sir George, 249
Kingussie, 238-9
Kinkell, 83
Kinloss, 195
Kinord, Loch, 24, 75
Kintore, 81, 83, 98
Kirkhill, 121

Laiken, 121, 126
Lamont, John, 245
Larig Ghru, 28
Laurencekirk, 95, 195
Ledingham, Sir John C. D., 248
Leys, Loch of, 75
Liddel, Duncan, 241
Lochnagar, 8, 17, 20, 28, 49
Logie Coldstone, 38
Lonmay, 26
Lossie Forest, 121
Lossiemouth, 138, 149-50, 152, 195
Lossie, River, 31
Lumphanan, 21, 80-1
Lumsden, 95

Mar, 49, 58, 118, 121
McCombie, William, 246
Macduff, 150, 152
MacGillivray, William, 246
McGrigor, Sir James, 244
Mackaile, Matthew, 242
Mackie, William, 246
MacLaurin, David, 243
Macleod, John, J. R., 251
MacWilliam, J. A., 251
Malcolm, Alexander, 243
Manson, Sir Patrick, 248
Maxwell, James Clerk, 246-7
Midmar, 121
Miltonduff, 154
Mitchell, Sir P. Chalmers, 251
Monadliath Mtns., 21
Monaughty, 121, 126
Monquhitter, 89, 93-4
Monymusk, 77, 79, 88
Moray, Laich of, 31
Moreson, Thomas, 242
Morison, Robert, 241
Mormond Hill, 6, 17, 30, 43, 93
Mortlach, 77
Mount Battock, 20
Mounth, 20, 22, 28
Mount Keen, 8, 20
Muchalls, 20
Mugiemoss, 177-9
Muick, 8, 62

New Aberdour, 95
Newburgh, 81

New Byth, 96
New Deer, 96
New Leeds, 96
New Pitsligo, 96, 184
Newton, 126
Newtyle, 121
Nicol, James, 245
Nigg, Bay of, 20, 23
Niven, Charles, 250

Ogston, Sir Alexander, 248
Oire, Loch, 62
Old Deer, 96
Old Rayne, 89

Parkmore, 157
Peterculter, see Culter
Peterhead, 8, 133, 137, 150, 152, 160, 170, 175, 181-2, 214, 236
Pitfichie, 121
Port Elphinstone, 98
Port Errol, 97
Portknockie, 25
Prain, Sir David, 249

Quoich, River, 17

Rattray Head, 26
Read, Alexander, 241
Read, Thomas, 241
Relugas, 125
Rennet, David, 247
Rennie, J., 252
Rhynie, 10
Ritchie, James, 251
Rosarie, 121
Roseisle, 121, 126
Rubislaw Quarry, 7, 160, 163-4

St. Cyrus, 47
Schichallion (Schiehallion), 11
Scootmore, 121
Simpson, Sir William J. R., 248
Skene, 92, 97
Skene, Gilbert, 240
Soddy, Frederick, 249-50
Spey, River, 27, 31, 62, 138
Speymouth, 121, 126
Spynie, Loch, 62

Stonehaven, 25, 213
Stoneywood, 177-9
Stracathro, 81
Strathbeg, Loch of, 27, 62
Strathfinella Hill, 17
Strathmore, 11, 31
Strichen, 8, 96
Struthers, Sir John, 251
Stuartfield, 95

Tap o' Noth, 75
Teindland, 121, 126
Thomson, Allen, 246
Thomson, David, 247
Thomson, Sir John Arthur, 250-1
Tillyfourie, 29
Tomintoul, 32, 95, 195
Tornashean, 121
Torphins, 21

Trail, J. W. H., 249
Traill, William, 243
Turriff, 77, 181
Tyrebagger Hill, 17, 24, 35

Ugie, Rivers, 23, 31, 88, 94, 138
University of Aberdeen, 83-4, 209, 215-20, 240-52

Vat Burn, 24

Whitehaugh, 121
Whitehills, 39
Windyheads Hill, 10
Woodend, 125

Ythan, River, 21, 26, 62, 64